WILLIAM CROCKER *was born at Medina, Ohio, January 27, 1874. He received his B.A. degree from the University of Illinois in 1902, and his Ph.D. from the University of Chicago in 1906. He was instructor in biology at the North Illinois State Teachers College from 1903 to 1904. At the University of Chicago, he was associate plant physiologist, 1907-1909; instructor, 1909-1911; assistant and associate professor, 1911-1921. From 1921 until his retirement in 1949, he was managing director of Boyce Thompson Institute for Plant Research, Inc., Yonkers, N. Y. Other positions he has held are: plant physiologist and collaborator, U. S. D. A., 1913-1918; exchange professor, Wisconsin, 1921; chairman of the division of biology and agriculture, National Research Council, 1927-1928; managing director of the Tropical Plant Research Foundation, 1927-1943; and Walker-Ames visiting professor, University of Washington in Seattle, 1943. He received the Gold Medal of the New York Society of Arts and Sciences in 1931, and the Gold Medal of the American Institute in New York in 1938. He was the author of over 100 articles dealing with seed physiology, effects of noxious gases on plants, plant hormones, sulphur fertilizers, and problems in ageing. He died February 11, 1950.*

LELA V. BARTON *was born at Farmington, Arkansas, on November 14, 1901. She received her B.A. degree from the University of Arkansas in June 1922; the M.A. from Columbia University in New York City in August 1927; and the Ph.D. from Columbia University in June 1939. Professional experience includes employment as a biology teacher in Senior High School at Van Buren, Arkansas and Little Rock, Arkansas, from 1922 to 1927. She came to Boyce Thompson Institute for Plant Research, Inc., Yonkers, N. Y. on March 1, 1928. During 24 years of research she has written some 60 articles dealing with various phases of seed physiology.*

• A NEW SERIES OF PLANT SCIENCE BOOKS •

edited by Frans Verdoorn

Volume 29

PHYSIOLOGY

of

SEEDS

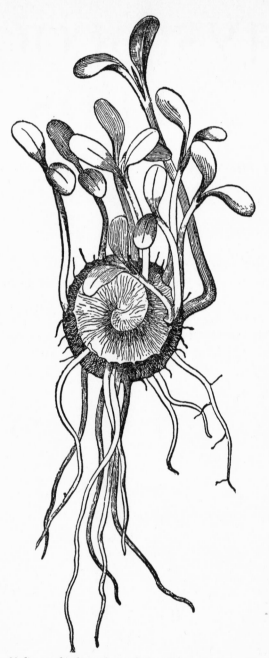

Medicago orbicularis, nine seedlings, all from one fruit.—Wood engraving from LORD AVEBURY's "A Contribution to our Knowledge of Seedlings" (London, 1907), first published in 1892. JOHN LUBBOCK, first Baron AVEBURY (1834-1913), was interested in and wrote about many aspects of natural history, ranging from entomology to plant morphology and from archaeology to anthropology. His love of science kept pace with his multifarious activities in public affairs and he excelled as a writer of popular scientific books, some of which ran into many editions and served a great educational purpose.

PHYSIOLOGY
of SEEDS

An Introduction to the Experimental
Study of Seed and Germination Problems

by the late WILLIAM CROCKER, Ph.D.

formerly Director, Boyce Thompson Institute for Plant Research

and LELA V. BARTON, Ph.D.

Plant Physiologist, Boyce Thompson Institute for Plant Research

SECOND IMPRESSION

1957

WALTHAM, MASS., U.S.A.

Published by the Chronica Botanica Company

Copyright 1953, by the Chronica Botanica Co.

Authorized Agents:—

Printed in the United States of America

Designed by Frans Verdoorn

PREFACE

This is an attempt to give a broad coverage of our present knowledge on seeds and germination in a volume of moderate size. The book, therefore, must be considered an outline rather than a treatise. The classical books in this field, some of them written many years ago before there was a great accumulation of knowledge and others dealing only with certain phases of seed or germination problems, are more voluminous. Amongst the classics in the field are: NOBBE's Handbuch der Samenkunde, 1876, 661 pages; DETMER's Vergleichende Physiologie des Keimungsprocesses der Samen, 1880, 565 pp.; HARZ's Landwirtschaftliche Samenkunde, 1885, 1362 pp.; WITTMACK's Landwirtschaftliche Samenkunde, 1922, 581 pp.; and LEHMANN und AICHELE's Keimungsphysiologie der Gräser, 1931, 678 pp. Of necessity no attempt is made to give a historical development of the several topics treated and only the minimum amount of literature necessary for laying a background for the discussion is cited. Even with this necessary economy in space more than 1100 citations are given in the book. While the book aims at a very broad coverage of basic knowledge on seeds and germination, many topics very worthy of consideration such as seed dispersal, for example, have not received attention because of lack of space.

PEARSON and HARPER in "The World's Hunger," Cornell University Press, 1945, state that seeds (grains), dry weight basis, constitute 80 per cent of the world's food supply and 75 per cent of the food eaten directly by man. The seeds and seed products used as food and in various other industries have an enormous total value, greatly exceeding the value of seeds for seeding purposes. Because of this the economic significance of seeds and seed products is discussed at appropriate points in the book.

The book is written from the viewpoint of the investigator of seed and germination problems. Throughout, the unsolved problems are pointed out and the recent progress made in solving problems emphasized. The relation of these to established knowledge is developed. The book should be of value to all workers with seeds and seed technology who are interested in fundamentals.

Problems in seed physiology that seem simple and settled by past experiments may need a thorough reworking by a combination of good physiological methods and the excellent new biochemical methods that are now being rapidly developed.

Some recent researches on injurious effects of soaking seeds illustrate the point. It is generally assumed that seeds (soy and various other beans) that are very sensitive to soaking are injured by the absence of oxygen during soaking. ALBAUM et al. (Amer. Jour. Bot. 29: 388, 1942) showed that oxygenating oat grains during 24 hours of soaking in contrast to aerating them injured markedly the embryos as shown by later growth. One of the authors of this book has repeated and confirmed these results for oats and some other seeds. With pole beans, oxygenating during 24 hours of soaking did great injury. Aerating during the soaking also showed injury, but treating with nitrogen, hydrogen, or carbon dioxide during the soaking gave successively less injury. In fact treating with carbon dioxide during the soaking seems to be superior to direct sowing in soil. The results with oats did not show this beneficial effect of carbon dioxide.

It is evident from results to date that a real understanding of soaking effects on seeds demands first a thorough physiological restudy of the effect of soaking under a wide range of conditions. When the significant conditions are established the effects of these on various processes and enzyme systems within the seeds should be determined by biochemical methods such as those used by ALBAUM et al. These investigators found that oat grains oxygenated during soaking showed poor digestion and movement of protein constituents from the storage organs to the axis organs of the growing seedling. The changes occurring during germination are numerous and very complex so caution must be shown in interpreting an injurious agent as modifying only a single process or system. An agent that injures the protoplasm of the seed will slow down all vital processes within the germinating seeds. In biochemical work there is danger of interpreting the effect of an injurious or beneficial agent entirely on the basis of its effect on the special process being studied with no consideration of its possible effects on many processes not studied.

There have been attempts at explaining dormancy or delayed germination in seeds as if there were one cause of dormancy in all seeds. Early with the stimulus physiology concept in vogue it was customary to assume that a release stimulus, only, was necessary to overcome dormancy in all seeds except in those with coats impervious to water. At present there is a tendency to explain all seed dormancy on the basis of presence of inhibiting substances. A study of Chapters IX and X will show that there are several types of seed dormancy and that the different types are overcome by a considerable variety of treatments. Some of the treatments take weeks or even months and involve very considerable and easily measured metabolic changes in the embryos and endosperms. This laboratory has worked out ways of after-ripening and germinating a large number of seeds that showed great resistance to germination but have found no single theory that will explain the resistance of all of them.

The authors are very grateful to Mrs. BETTIE M. BROOKS for continuous help in directing the typing of the manuscript, for arranging of chapters, figures, and tables, and for proof reading; to Dr. L. P. MILLER for the critical reading of all chapters dealing with the chemistry and metabolism of seeds; and to Mr. L. P. FLORY and Mr. WILLIAM G. SMITH, Jr. for photographing and arranging plates. The authors are also grateful to the following for permission to reproduce certain figures from original research articles: Dr. R. KOBLET, fig. 4; The Biochemical Journal for fig. 5; Dr. E. H. TOOLE, fig. 6; and Dr. J. VAN OVERBEEK, fig. 7. A detailed acknowledgment is given in the text for each figure. In the text acknowledgments are given for permission to reproduce tables from various publications.

LELA V. BARTON

Summer, 1952

Es war im April 1869, als ein hervorragender Sächsischer Landwirth (Herr Graf zur Lippe-Weissenfeld, gegenwärtig Professor in Rostock) dem Verfasser vier oder fünf Samen-Muster von Handelsgräsern zur botanischen Recognition übersandte. Die Untersuchung führte zu dem befremdlichen Resultat, dass eines dieser Muster, ein "Wiesenschwingel," nur etwa 30 Procente der Species, welche die Etiquette verhiess, wirklich enthielt. Anstatt ein so ungebührliches, vermeintlich isolirtes Vorkommniss sofort öffentlich zu rügen, fassten wir zunächst die z. Th. kostbaren Samen etwas näher ins Auge, welche für die Vegetationsversuche der physiologischen Versuchs-Station Tharand gekauft waren. Auf Grund der an letzteren gemachten Beobachtungen bezogen wir alsdann von den grösseren Handlungsfirmen Deutschlands kleine Posten gangbarer landwirthschaftlicher Samensorten, richteten (im Mai 1869) die erste Samenprüfungs-Station ein, indem wir die Sächsischen Landwirthe zur Einsendung von Durchschnittsproben gekaufter Saatwaaren behufs Untersuchung ihrer Reinheit und Keimfähigkeit aufforderten, und gelangten so in den Besitz eines Materials, dessen Kundgabe im dringenden Interesse der Deutschen Landwirthschaft geboten erschien. (NOBBE, "Handbuch der Samenkunde," 1876.)

Während der letzten Jahre habe ich mich unter anderem mit eingehenderen physiologischen Untersuchungen über den Keimungsprocess der Samen beschäftigt. Die unmittelbaren Beobachtungsresultate dieser Arbeiten, vor allen Dingen aber gewisse allgemeine Gesichtspunkte, welche sich mir bei dem genaueren Studium des Keimungsprocesses allmählich eröffneten, haben zur Entstehung des vorliegenden Buches Veranlassung gegeben. . . . Ich hoffe, dass meine Schrift demjenigen einigen Nutzen gewähren wird, der sich mit Rücksicht auf rein wissenschaftliche Frage oder im Interesse der Praxis mit dem Studium des Keimungsprocesses beschäftigt. (DETMER, "Vergleichende Physiologie des Keimungsprocesses der Samen," 1880.)

Probably few sections of human knowledge contain a larger percentage of contradictory, incorrect and misleading observations than prevail in the works dealing with this subject, and, although such fables as the supposed germination of mummy wheat have long since been exploded, equally erroneous records are still current in botanical physiology. (ALFRED J. EWART, "On the Longevity of Seeds," 1908.)

CONTENTS

Chapter I: Anatomy of Seeds

Chapter II: Seed Production

Chapter III: Chemical Composition of Seeds, I

Chapter IV: Chemical Composition of Seeds, II

Chapter V: Water Relations of Seeds

Chapter VI: Respiration

Chapter VII: Factors affecting Germination, I

Chapter VIII: Factors affecting Germination, II

Chapter IX: Dormancy in Seeds, I

Chapter X: Dormancy in Seeds, II

Chapter XI: Storage and Life Span of Seeds

Chapter XII: Metabolic and Energy
Changes in Seed Development and Germination, I

Chapter XIII: Metabolic and Energy
Changes in Seed Development and Germination, II

Chapter XIV: Metabolic and Energy
Changes in Seed Development and Germination, III

Chapter XV: Vernalization

Chapter XVI: Embryo Culture

Chapter XVII: Seed Transmission of Disease

❀   ❀   ❀

LIST of ILLUSTRATIONS

Vignettes by William G. Smith, Jr.

LIST of TABLES

Handbuch

der

Samenkunde.

Physiologisch=statistische Untersuchungen
über den
wirthschaftlichen Gebrauchswerth
der
land- und forstwirthschaftlichen, sowie gärtnerischen Saatwaaren.

Von

Dr. Friedrich Nobbe,

Professor an der Königl. Akademie, Vorstand der physiol. Versuchs- und Samencontrol-Station zu Tharand,
Redacteur der „Landwirthsch. Versuchsstationen".

Mit 339 in den Text gedruckten Holzschnitten.

Berlin.
Verlag von Wiegandt, Hempel & Parey.
Verlagsbuchhandlung für Landwirthschaft, Gartenbau und Forstwesen.
1876.

TITLE PAGE OF NOBBE'S CLASSIC TREATISE ON SEEDS AND THEIR
PROBLEMS (*cf.* p. vii & ix) IN WHICH HE REPORTS ABOUT THE
RESULTS OF THE WORK ACCOMPLISHED IN HIS PIONEER SEED TEST-
ING STATION WHICH HAD BEEN ESTABLISHED AT THARANDT IN 1869.

Chapter I

ANATOMY OF SEEDS

THE seed habit in plants has developed over a long period of time and represents the highest type of plant development. With the establishment of this habit, the reproduction of the individual plant and the continuance of the species as well as its multiplication and distribution is assured. The technicalities of the evolution of the seed habit together with a critical review of the literature on the subject is to be found in an article by R. B. Thomson (1927).

Following pollination and fertilization of the egg nucleus in the embryo sac which is within the ovule a series of changes is initiated. The result of these changes is seed formation. A seed is a ripened ovule, consisting of the embryo and its coats. This is the simplest definition which can be given to the rather complex reproductive body of the seed plants. In many seeds an additional structure, the endosperm containing most of the stored food, is present. Brink and Cooper (1947) have written an extensive review entitled "The endosperm in seed development." Nucellar tissue with reserve food may also form part of the seed. In the absence of endosperm and perisperm the food reserves are stored in the cotyledons of the embryo.

The embryo in angiosperms consists of a hypocotyl, one or two (rarely three or more) cotyledons, and an epicotyl or plumule. The growing point of the hypocotyl may be developed as a definite primary root, sometimes called the radicle, in which the root-forming tissues and the root cap are already determined, or it may be nothing more than a meristematic mass of cells which will grow and differentiate as germination progresses. The degree of differentiation of the epicotyl before germination is variable. One or more leaf primordia may be developed above the cotyledons or the growing point may be simply a mass of meristematic cells.

In dicotyledonous plants where two cotyledons are typical of the embryos, there sometimes appear embryos with single cotyledons. This may be due to an abortion or suppression of one of the cotyledons, or to a fusion of two. An interesting physiological study has been made of the embryo of *Ceratozamia*, a genus of cycads of the American tropics (Dorety 1908). This embryo has only one cotyledon. In the course of anatomical studies Dorety noted the lateral position of this cotyledon and that there were no external traces of another cotyledon but certain characteristics of the vascular system indicated that the second cotyledon had been suppressed. In every case the cotyledon developed on the under side of the seed. This led her to believe that gravity might be responsible for the monocotyledonous condition. She, therefore, placed fresh ovules covered with sphagnum in pots upon clinostats. The embryos which developed on the clinostat had two cotyledons while those developing from plantings in the greenhouse had only one. She concluded that gravity is the main factor in causing the inequality reported in the cotyledons of other gymnosperms and possibly may be responsible for the monocotyledonous condition found in some dicotyledons and even for the condition of true monocotyledons.

The extreme variability of the degree of development of the embryo in seeds has been pointed out by Coulter and Chamberlain (1903). In *Gramineae*, *Impatiens*, *Cucurbita*, and *Trapa*, for example, a plumule with several leaves and even lateral roots are formed, while in some parasites and saprophytes, such as *Monotropa* and *Pyrola*, the embryo is just a mass of undifferentiated cells. Undifferentiated embryos are also characteristic of the seeds of *Orchidaceae*. At the time the berries of the American holly fall from the tree, the size of the endosperm is approximately 5 mm. $\times$ 1 mm., and the volume of the embryo is not more than 0.00004 that of the endosperm. The tissues of the embryo are somewhat differentiated at that time, however, showing the beginnings of cotyledons, but no hypocotyl or plumule (Ives 1923). These embryos are arrested in development until the germination or after-ripening processes begin at which time they resume growth. *Ginkgo* embryos are very immature at the time the seeds fall from the tree but in this case development continues in the seed without special treatment until the embryo is fully mature.

At germination, the epicotyl gives rise to the shoot of the young seedling and the growing tip of the hypocotyl or the radicle forms the root. The cotyledons which are seed leaves attached laterally to the axis of the embryo serve as food storage or food digestion and absorption organs. They may or may not come above the surface of the soil in germination. If above ground they usually turn green and may carry on photosynthesis for a while. The hypocotyl connects the radicle and the epicotyl and represents the transition from root to stem structure.

Fertilization of the egg which gives rise to the embryo of angiosperms is the same fundamental process which takes place in other plants and animals but the endosperm development represents a unique form of fertilization and development. The second male nucleus from the pollen tube which has penetrated the ovule conjugates with a polar nucleus formed by the fusion of an antipodal polar and a micropylar polar nucleus to form the primary endosperm nucleus. The primary endosperm nucleus thus consists of three nuclei, two polar nuclei and a sperm nucleus. Development into triploid endosperm tissue follows this fusion. This phenomenon has given rise to much speculation as to the morphological nature of the endosperm tissue and as to the physiological function of the male nucleus in the triple fusion. Recent studies (Brink and Cooper 1940) have led to the interpretation that the second male nucleus introduces the advantages of heterosis to the endosperm. Brink and Cooper (1940) present new evidence that this added stimulus to growth may be essential to the development of the seed. This double fertilization occurs in practically all angiosperms. Even in groups such as the orchids where the endosperm fails to develop, conjugation of the second male nucleus with the polar fusion nucleus sometimes takes place. However, the resulting endosperm is not always present in the mature seeds. In many cases it may be used up by the embryo in its development as happens in most of the legumes. This description of endosperm formation applies to the angiosperms. In the gymnosperms the endosperm tissue is gametophytic, being produced by the ovule itself by cell division.   Also in gymnospermous forms the ovules are not enclosed in an ovary.   However, the seeds possess hardened integuments or seed coats.

Fertilization as described above usually results in seeds which are complete with embryo and endosperm as characteristic of the particular species. There are cases, however, where the endosperm is formed and the seed appears plump and normal but no embryos are found.   Such a state is known to exist in *Ginkgo*, wheat, rye, barley, corn, rice, castor-oil plant, and certain umbelliferous seeds.   The phenomenon is ascribed to various causes.   Double fertilization may occur and the fertilized egg cell fail to develop entirely or develop very little and the resulting tissues disintegrate.   Some authors have reported single fertilization with resulting development in the seed of embryo or endosperm but not both.   The former seeds do not appear in cleaned seed material since they are light and are discarded in the cleaning process, while seeds with well developed endosperm but without embryos have a normal weight.   Embryolessness will be discussed further in a chapter on seed production.

Although seed formation is usually preceded by fertilization and the subsequent development of the fertilized egg and the fusion nucleus, other parts of the ovary normally considered as purely vegetative may produce good seeds containing both embryo and endosperm.   The dandelion, *Taraxacum officinale*, illustrates seed production from certain regions of the nucellus.   Such development of seeds without fertilization is known as apomixis.   This also will be discussed in greater detail in the chapter on seed production.

Many fruits because they are dry and indehiscent are called seeds. These are the caryopsis or grain, the akene, the schizocarp and the nut. The grain develops from a single carpel and contains a single seed.   The akene which is characteristic of the *Ranunculaceae* and the *Compositae* is also one-seeded but differs from the grain in that the pericarp can be removed from the mature seed.   The fruit of the *Umbelliferae* and the *Geraniaceae* is a schizocarp which is composed of two or more carpels which separate at maturity, each part indehiscent and resembling an akene.   If the carpel wall is winged, as in the maple, the fruit is a samara or key.   The structure of the nut also resembles an akene but the dry pericarp becomes thick and hard.

Detailed descriptions of the anatomy of the seeds of certain economic plants are given by Hayward (1938).

By far the most extensive study on the internal anatomy of seeds has been made by Martin (1946).   He points out that information on the internal anatomy of seeds as presented in botanical literature is inaccurate and inadequate.   Using the seed collection of the Fish and Wildlife Service from the Economic Investigations Laboratory at Bowie, Maryland, Martin made a survey of seed types as revealed by the gross internal structure of the seeds of 1274 genera representing two-thirds of the plant families of the world.   As a result he developed a system of seed classification based on five major divisions and thirteen seed types, and used his findings to make an outline of seed phylogeny.   Since this piece of work is unique it may be worth while to consider some of its salient features. First of all some criteria of evaluation were established. A quantitative classification of embryo size in proportion to albumen (a term used to designate all storage tissue exclusive of the embryo) was used. This consisted of five size designations for the embryo representing one-fourth minus, one-fourth plus, one-half plus, three-fourths plus, or all of the seed. These embryos were called respectively small (and minute), quarter, half, dominant, or total. The five major divisions and the thirteen seed types described together with the plant families representative of each are presented below.

I. RUDIMENTARY DIVISION—Embryos relatively small and basal in seeds that are usually medium to large; in some of the Broad type seeds are small.
    A. SMALL—Embryo small, globular to short-axile; albumen generally non-starchy; cotyledons frequently evident making embryos appear like miniatures of Axile or Foliate divisions. The group not entirely clear-cut since most of the families have some genera that merge into the Linear type and a few incline toward the Broad. *Aquifoliaceae, Araliaceae, Magnoliaceae, Ranunculaceae, Papaveraceae.*
    B. BROAD—Embryo wider than high, peripheral or nearly so; albumen starchy. *Saururaceae, Nymphaeaceae, Eriocaulaceae, Xyridaceae, Juncaceae, Mayacaceae.*
II. PERIPHERAL DIVISION—Embryo small (in some grasses and sedges) to large or total, contiguous in part at least to the testa and often curved; albumen conspicuously starchy; central or lateral. Two types in the division are Monocots and two Dicots.
    A. CAPITATE—Embryo expanded above into head-like form; this type confined to Monocots and to starchy albumen. *Cyperaceae, Commelinaceae.*
    B. PLANE—Embryo basal or diagonally lateral and usually expanded in the plane of the periphery; small to half. This type includes only the *Gramineae.*
    C. CYLINDRIC—Embryo more or less cylindric or terete, cotyledons not expanded appreciably. *Caryophyllaceae, Amaranthaceae, Chenopodiaceae, Portulacaceae, Cactaceae.*
    D. EXPANDED—Cotyledons expanded, extensively in *Nyctaginaceae;* this type similar to cylindric except for expanded cotyledons and differs from the Foliate division in peripheral position and starchy albumen. *Nyctaginaceae, Polygonaceae.*
III. AXILE DIVISION—Embryo small to total, central (axile) straight, curved, or coiled; albumen fleshy or at least not starchy. Well represented in Gymnosperms, Monocots, and Dicots.
    A. LINEAR—The only type. Embryo generally several times longer than broad. *Umbelliferae, Vacciniaceae, Solanaceae, Liliaceae, Pontederiaceae, Amaryllidaceae.*
IV. REDUCED DIVISION—Seeds small to minute with embryos that are stocky or minute; seed coverings generally delicate; and often cellular reticulate; albumen fleshy.
    A. DWARF—Embryo variable in relative size, small to total generally stocky, usually oval to elliptic or oblong, cotyledons inclined to be poorly developed; seeds small, generally 1 mm. to 0.3 mm. long exclusive of testa, often nearly as broad as long. *Scrophulariaceae, Gentianaceae, Campanulaceae, Loganiaceae, Ericaceae.*
    B. MICRO—Seeds minute, usually about 0.2 mm. long exclusive of testa, generally globular and consisting of relatively few cells, approximately 50 to 150 within the testa; embryo minute to total. *Monotropaceae, Pyrolaceae, Orchidaceae, Burmanniaceae.*

V. FOLIATE DIVISION—Embryo generally quarter to total; central rather than peripheral; cotyledons expanded; seeds generally medium to large.
  A. SPATULATE—Embryo erect; cotyledons variable, thin to thick and slightly expanded to broad. *Compositae, Asclepiadaceae, Apocynaceae, Polymoniaceae, Cornaceae, Urticaceae, Rutaceae, Celastraceae, Rosaceae, Euphorbiaceae, Oleaceae, Rubiaceae.*
  B. BENT—Embryo spatulate but bent in jackknife form; cotyledons generally thick. *Cruciferae, Fabaceae, Anacardiaceae.*
  C. FOLDED—Embryo with cotyledons usually thin, expanded and folded in various ways. *Convolvulaceae, Malvaceae.*
  D. INVESTING—Embryo erect and with thick cotyledons expanded over and encasing the somewhat foreshortened stalk. *Fagaceae, Juglandaceae, Lauraceae, Betulaceae, Bignoniaceae, Labiatae, Mimosaceae, Caesalpiniaceae, Lythraceae, Rhamnaceae.*

Although Martin points out that a single line of evidence such as internal anatomy of seeds can not be used as a basis for final plant classification, he believes that certain evolutionary trends in seed phylogeny have been demonstrated. Medium-sized or large seeds having relatively small embryos represent primitive types. As to seed size one line of development (Reduced Division) was toward quantity and another (Foliate Division) toward quality. Albumen development was also along two lines: conspicuous starchy albumen and lateral embryo (Peripheral Division) and central-embryo location with non-starchy albumen (Axile Division). Within the Foliate Division the cotyledons showed developmental trends with progressive enlargement.

Thus it has been demonstrated that not only have plants become highly specialized in the development of a seed habit but the seeds themselves have evolved along certain definite lines to form distinguishing characteristics of certain plant groups. The complexity of structure and development of the seed points to a complexity of physiological behavior. Many physiologic responses have been determined and will be given in the ensuing chapters of this book.

References:—

Brink, R. A., & D. C. Cooper, 1940: Double fertilization and development of the seed in angiosperms (Bot. Gaz. 102:1-25).
————, ————, 1947: The endosperm in seed development (Bot. Review 13:423-477, 479-541).
Coulter, J. M., & C. J. Chamberlain, 1903: Morphology of angiosperms. (Morphology of spermatophytes. Part II) (D. Appleton & Company, New York, pp. 205-210).
Dorety, H. A., 1908: The embryo of *Ceratozamia*: A physiological study (Bot. Gaz. 45:412-416).
Hayward, H. E., 1938: The structure of economic plants (674 pp., The MacMillan Company, New York).
Ives, S. A., 1923: Maturation and germination of seeds of *Ilex opaca* (Bot. Gaz. 76:60-77).
Martin, A. C., 1946: The comparative internal morphology of seeds (Amer. Midland Naturalist 36:513-660).
Thomson, R. B., 1927: Evolution of the seed habit in plants (Roy. Soc. Canada Trans. Third Series 21:229-272).

Chapter II

SEED PRODUCTION

SINCE the production of seeds by plants depends upon the existence of a flower the first requirement is that the conditions for induction of flower formation be met. This in itself is a large subject and one on which much time has been spent. We will, however, for our purposes, omit a detailed discussion of flower induction and its attendant problems and confine our attention to actual seed production from the flower.

Sexual Seed Formation:—The embryo of the seed is usually the result of the fusion of the egg nucleus with a sperm cell. The sperm cell reaches the ovary following pollination in which process the pollen is transferred in some manner to the stigma. Germination of the pollen grain on the surface of the stigma is followed by growth of the pollen tube through the style and into the ovary. Then ensues the fertilization process as described in Chapter I.

FACTORS AFFECTING SEED SET

Flower shape.—Several factors are known to play important parts in the setting of seed. The very shape of the flowers themselves may favor or inhibit pollination. Flowers may be adapted for wind or insect pollination or the reproductive parts may be enclosed in a rigid position within a special structure of the flower.

Such a condition exists, for example, in the flower of alfalfa, *Medicago sativa* L. In order to bring about pollination the tension of the pistil and stamens must be released. This may be done by pressure inside the corolla tube, causing the pistil and stamens to spring forward, thus dusting the pollen on to the stigma. This process has been referred to as "tripping" the flower. It is generally agreed that an alfalfa flower will not set seed unless it has been tripped. Because of the vital economic need for large seed crops of this form, considerable work has been done to ascertain the conditions under which natural tripping takes place and to evolve methods for ensuring adequate pollination. Hadfield and Calder (1936) found that natural tripping may be caused by heat or, more specifically, by a sudden change in temperature. The flowers trip readily on a hot day. Wind is a second factor which may aid in accomplishing pollination. A combination of a hot day and a high wind results in a good set of seeds. Bees visiting the flowers to obtain nectar also trip the flowers. In large bee cages it has been shown that bumblebees are more helpful than honey bees, twelve of the former effecting a higher seed set than four thousand of the latter (Hadfield and Calder 1936). This is not to say that honey bees should not be used for pollination of alfalfa fields, but simply that a large number is required to give a significant increase to the seed yield. In spite of this fact, the method was the only recommendation made by Hadfield and Calder after studying various phases of the problem. They tried to design an implement which would cause tripping when drawn over a field of alfalfa in full flower but were unsuccessful. Even if this could be accomplished it would mean self pollination when cross pollination has been shown to stimulate seed production.

In spite of the demonstration by Hadfield and Calder and others of the importance of insect pollination in the setting of seeds of alfalfa, the subject has continued to be the object of investigation. Emphasis has been placed upon the reasons for the limited geographical locations in which large-scale seed production is possible in contrast to the extensive favorable areas for forage production of this crop.

Knowles (1943) reported detailed studies in which meteorological data of 24-hour periods were compared with the behavior of new alfalfa flowers in blossom during the same period. Careful work considering the character of the plants and the weather conditions led again to the conclusion that the suitability of an area for seed production was due to the insect population, in this particular case to leaf-cutter bees. Publications made as recently as 1946 (Carlson 1946; Tysdal 1946; Vansell and Todd 1946) have described other particular phases of this problem but all have come again to the necessity of beneficial insects to ensure seed production.

Tysdal's tests of the effects of different levels of soil moisture are especially elucidating in view of the claims that only those regions with a relatively dry season mature good seed crops. He demonstrated that a high soil moisture content, in itself, was not the cause of decreased seed production. Whereas, plants spaced eight inches apart produced more seed in soil with low than with high moisture content, seed production of plants spaced 32 inches apart was the same in low and high soil moisture plots. In his discussion of weather effects, Tysdal (1946) stated (p. 533), "While the weather is probably the dominating influence in seed production in the eastern half of the United States, it cannot, in many cases, explain the ups and downs in alfalfa seed production in the western states, especially under irrigated conditions. In 1926, Utah produced over 25,000,000 pounds of alfalfa seed. During the last 10 years, the average production in that state has been about 4,000,000 pounds. In all probability, weather has played a minor role in this change. An increase in harmful insects and a decrease in the abundance of beneficial insects, together with a greater population of plants more attractive than alfalfa to the beneficial insects are probably the determining factors. Under conditions of central and eastern United States, weather has at least a three-fold influence. It influences growth, including stimulating new growth at the wrong time for seed production. It influences the abundance and activity of beneficial insects, and it influences the abundance of harmful insects, such as the potato leaf hopper and others. . . . In addition, the weather can influence insect populations, both beneficial and harmful, from year to year. Thus, the weather may have a carry-over effect which might be a determining factor in seed production the following year even though weather conditions are then favorable."

Lygus bug infestation affects pollination adversely (Carlson 1946). DDT has been used successfully to eliminate *Lygus* and thrips (Vansell and Todd 1946). In the application of any insecticide to control infestation care must be taken not to injure bee pollinators. Sulfur-pyrethrum, for example, has been found to repel bees for two to three days. Vansell and Todd (1946) have pointed out that 500 pounds of seeds per acre require the tripping of 38,000,000 flowers. Beneficial insect populations must be kept at a maximum for the performance of this task.

Viability of pollen from alfalfa flowers has been studied (Sexsmith and Fryer 1943) in an effort to resolve the factors responsible for seasonal variation in the set of seed. No significant differences in pollen viability counts made at intervals throughout the flowering season on individual alfalfa plants were found. There were differences between plants, however.

It is evident then that even when the flowers are tripped, seed production does not always follow. Further analysis of this problem has been made by Cooper *et al.* (1937) who made detailed observations on ten alfalfa plants, five high-seed producers and five low-seed producers, and found that a high percentage of fertile ovules failed to develop into seed due to lack of fertilization. This was associated with growth of the pollen tubes which failed to reach all of the ovules. Much more embryo abortion occurred in low-seed producing than in high-seed producing plants. In a later paper, Cooper and Brink (1940) attributed the low seed set after self pollination in part to restricted pollen tube growth and in part to self-incompatibility. Frequently after selfing the pollen tubes passed directly by the micropyles containing unfertilized eggs.

The desirability of developing a strain of alfalfa which is self-tripped under normal conditions has been recognized. An attempt at this has been made by Southworth (1928) who crossed black medick, *Medicago lupulina* L., which normally has self-tripping flowers with alfalfa and carried the resulting hybrids to the seventh generation. The net results were somewhat disappointing since some of the hybrid alfalfa plants having a high percentage of self-tripping flowers were largely sterile. However, some plants which were partially self-tripping and partially fertile led to the hope that eventually a strain having self-tripping, highly fertile flowers will be evolved.

The alfalfa has been cited as an example of a flower, the morphology of which inhibits seed production. Many other such flowers exist.

Insects.—The seed set in species of the *Yucca* plant is interesting because of its dependence upon a special moth, the *Pronuba*. Riley (1892) stated that the first announcement of such pollination was made by him and Engelmann in 1872.

The female moths deposit their eggs in the ovaries of the *Yucca* flower and then to ensure the development of the ovules to furnish food for the larvae when they hatch, the moths seem deliberately to thrust pollen, previously collected from other flowers, into the stigma. The *Yucca* plant is characterized by anthers much shorter than the styles. Over a twenty-year period, Riley studied other insects associated with the *Yucca* and found that none of them acted as pollinators. These results have been confirmed by other workers (Trelease 1902; Ellis 1913; Czaja 1947). Trelease (1902) pointed out that in the arid table-land of Mexico, the yuccas are known to be dependent upon the rainfall for their blooming, "so that a given species, though usually fairly regular, may bloom in aberrant years at any time between midwinter and midsummer, and the *Pronuba* moth which serves as pollinator appears to show a similar susceptibility to moisture in the soil, and commonly emerges from the pupa state synchronously with the flowering of the yuccas" (p. 85). Only those yuccas which flower when the moth flies produce seeds, though all seem fertile when artificially pollinated. The moths seem uninterested in the nectar glands which are present and which may indicate other modes of pollination in ages past. According to Ellis (1913) about 21 per cent of the total seed production is eaten by the moth larvae.

Another legume, seed production of which depends to a large extent upon the work of insects in pollination, is clover. Dunham (1943) demonstrated that clover plants in cages with honey bees developed seeds at the rate of 16.4 bushels to the acre as compared with 0.11 for those without bees. The seasonal and yearly trends of seeds per head in red clover have been shown to follow closely those of the number of bumblebees for the same period (Bird 1944).

Genetic factors.—The structure and shape of the flower depends upon the variety, *i.e.*, upon inheritance. To a large extent the physiological behavior also depends upon heredity, as for example the self-incompatibility described for alfalfa. Other inherited physiologic qualities influencing seed formation are growth habit and earliness of maturity. The nature of these and other attributes determines the physiologic differences in varieties which affect seed yield. There is, of course, a very close relationship between morphological characters and physiologic responses. In the bush lima bean (Andrews 1936) greater yielding ability has been found to be associated with more active stomata and greater chlorophyll content resulting in greater photosynthetic action. This in turn was followed by increased osmotic pressure of the cell sap, greater carbohydrate content of the leaves and stems and more pods per plant. Early maturing strains of vetch are good seed producers because their flowering and seed formation and maturation periods are over before adverse weather conditions begin (Albrecht 1942). Seeding of wheat depends on variety, date of sowing, and seasonal environmental factors (Boyles and Martin 1931).

Environmental factors.—Next to the morphological construction and the physiological behavior of the flower itself, environmental conditions are of importance in seed production. The most obvious of these factors are those we usually speak of as climatic, including temperature, wetness or dryness of the season, light, and wind. Some of these effects will be discussed further in the chapter on vernalization. It is very difficult, if not impossible, to separate the effects of these several agencies. Cool, wet, cloudy weather is especially favorable for seed-stalk development of beets and, when followed by a cool, dry period, gives an excellent seed yield (Kohls 1937; Chroboczek 1934).

Pecans present a serious problem in orchard management since more profuse blossoming accompanies a highly vegetative state but the filling and maturation of the nuts takes place more satisfactorily with a low degree of vegetativeness of the tree (Finch and Van Horn 1936). The practices and environmental conditions tending to produce low and high vegetativeness have been reported, thus offering to the pecan grower a basis for his orchard treatment. Low vegetativeness during the summer resulting at harvest in well filled nuts with high oil content could be attained by withholding nitrogen fertilization, using soil-robbing cover crops, limiting soil moisture and exposing to full sunlight. Root pruning of pecan has also helped to decrease vegetativeness. A similar practice, that of girdling, has been used to induce seed formation. Pond (1936) made a horizontal knife cut through the bark and cambium of the black ash tree entirely encircling the tree at breast height and found that one-half of such trees produced seed, whereas only three out of 29 trees not girdled bore seed.

Very little is known about the basic causes of the periodicity of the seed crops of certain coniferous trees. In a number of coniferous species the differentiation of reproductive organs takes place the year previous to maturation of the cones and the seeds. Hence the seed crop could be directly affected by adverse weather conditions of two seasons instead of one as is the case for most seeds. Wakeley (1947) reporting on loblolly pine seed production, stated that in coastal or near-coastal locations in Maryland, North Carolina, South Carolina, and Louisiana there were three to six good to heavy seed crops from 1931 to 1941 inclusive. The inland areas produced much less seed. In east Texas there was not one good crop in those eleven years. In central Alabama very few seeds were produced from 1939 through 1945 and only a moderate crop in 1946. The roles of food reserves, weather, and pollination difficulties in these failures have not been ascertained.

Among the environmental factors playing major roles in seed production is light. Photoperiodic effects have been studied extensively in connection with the induction of flowering but comparatively few analyses of the continued influence on seed setting and maturation have been reported. The most satisfactory day length for both flowering and fruiting of potato varieties was found by Clarke and Lombard (1939) to be approximately 16 hours. Both temperature and light conditions greatly affect the number of grains per spike of spring wheat (Nesterova 1939). Constant low temperature (8.5° C. mean daily temperature) as well as low temperature only at night increased the number of grains per spike. Normal daylight was also essential to a good grain yield, which was reduced in plants shaded by two layers of gauze.

Reduced light intensity favored seed production during June, July, and August by guayule plants but shading was less effective during September when the normal light intensity was less (Mitchell *et al.* 1944).

Nutrition effects.—The nutrition of the plant must be considered in seed production. It is not enough simply to provide the essentials for good vegetative growth for we have already seen that good seed yield does not always accompany good vegetative growth. It is desirable, then, to know whether certain food substances will increase or reduce the amount and quality of seed produced.

A lack of nitrogen speeds the initiation of the earing stage in barley, which is a long-day plant, while a lack of phosphorus or of potassium has the opposite effect (Borodina 1931). In the short-day plant, millet, lack of nitrogen and potassium did not affect the formation of the panicle. Lack of phosphorus in these plants delayed the appearance of the panicle by depressing the growth of the plant.

Nitrogenous fertilizer applications increased the total number of seeds produced by beech and sugar maple trees (Chandler 1938). Nitrate of soda fed to Paraguay Bahia grass (Burton 1943) increased the yield of seeds. It has been demonstrated by Claypool (1932) that nitrogen is the chief factor influencing size and yield of seed in lettuce. Also it was the chief limiting factor in soil fertility in the case studied. Phosphorus, the second limiting factor in fertility, also influenced seed development. Addition of potash gave no increased benefits. The author concluded that whatever element is lacking, its addition will have a direct favorable effect in hastening maturity and increasing yield and size of the seed. Fertilizing with phosphorus, potash, and nitrogen has resulted in increased seed production for Red Fescue (Musser 1947). Maximum seed yields of onion followed growing of the plants on high nitrogen for a time, transferring to low nitrogen for two months, then replacing on high nitrogen (Stuart and Griffin 1946). Other combinations of nutrient conditions were inferior.

A more recent inquiry into the requirements for seed production has established the importance of a minor element, zinc, for seed formation of peas, beans, and milo (Reed 1942). Highly purified nutrient salts were used in these trials. It was demonstrated that when no zinc was added, growth proceeded to a certain point but not far enough for seeds to develop. Zinc concentration of 0.02 p.p.m. produced small seedless pods in peas and beans; 0.10 p.p.m. produced best seeds. That zinc is essential for the complete development of many agricultural plants has been known for some time but this work adds emphasis and may explain the failure of seed crops on certain soils.

Clipping Mammoth clover plants did not increase seed production but did reduce vegetative growth so that harvest was facilitated (Megee et al. 1942). Late rolling may cause a complete loss of the seed crop. Burning old sods increased the yields of seed of Bahia grass and Bermuda grass, had no effect on the seed yield of ribbed *Paspalum,* and reduced the yield of carpet grass.

Disease effects.—The effect of disease on seed setting should not be overlooked. Burton (1944) presented evidence that as ergot in Dallis grass increased, the percentage of florets setting seed was lowered. Brewbaker (1942) found a definite and consistent reduction in the quantity of seed per sugar beet plant with increasing infection with mosaic.

Chemical effects.—Plant hormones or growth substances have been used extensively to cause the formation of seedless fruit. There are some instances, however; where they have assisted in seed formation when employed in connection with pollination. Howlett (1942) obtained a marked increase in fruit set in earliest tomato flowers to reach anthesis and no interference with seed formation by applying indolebutyric acid to pollinated flowers. Production of fruit from later flowers was not affected by treatment.

The reduction of bud and flower drop or stimulation in growth following treatment with growth substances has important implications in breeding in making possible hybrid seed development from parent plants normally incompatible or in augmenting seed set in difficult forms or under adverse conditions. Comparatively few trials have been made in this field and the results have been inconclusive or conflicting. Hormone spray treatment of snap beans (Murneek et al. 1944) increased the yield of pods which developed under high temperatures which normally prevent the setting of fruit. Very little increase resulted from treatment when the weather was moderately warm and a decrease followed treatment during a cool summer. It was not possible to make recommendations for general practice from these results. Allen and Fisher (1943) applied dusts and sprays of naphthaleneacetic acid to wax and Refugee beans in an attempt to prevent the dropping of blossoms and small pods, a condition observed to be serious in Wisconsin in certain years. Significant increases in yield were recorded for dust treatment of wax beans only. Spray treatments were ineffective and Refugee beans failed to give any increase with dust or spray treatments. The larger yield from dust-treated wax beans was due to a larger number of small pods rather than to an increased size of pods.

In an effort to prevent premature dropping of the fruit of the squirrel variety of pecan (*Carya illinoensis* K. Koch) α-naphthaleneacetic acid and α-naphthaleneacetamide in water solutions at concentrations of 0.001 and 0.005 per cent and indole-3-

butyric acid at 0.005 per cent by weight have been used (Smith 1944). The solutions were applied after the stigmas had dried, indicating that any dropping due to poorly developed flowers had already occurred. Instead of preventing fruit drop the growth substance treatments caused greater drops than exhibited by the untreated controls. It was pointed out that growth substances have also failed to prevent early drop of blossoms or fruit in the apple but reduced the drop just before harvest. This suggested that the substances may be effective only on definite types of abscission, since it has been shown that the mode of abscission of blossoms and young fruit of the apple is different from that of older fruit. Some such phenomenon may be present in pecan nuts.

Sometimes a secondary effect of some chemicals applied to plants for other reasons involves the delay of flowering and fruiting. This has been found true for plants sprayed with solutions of 2,4-dichlorophenoxyacetic acid for weed control. Flowering of beans has been markedly delayed by such treatment (Stromme and Hamner 1948) while timothy showed injurious effects early in the season but developed normal seed stalks and seed heads (Marth et al. 1947).

Exactly the opposite effect has been noted for 2,4-dichlorophenoxyacetic and naphthaleneacetic acids by van Overbeek (1945) who found that they induced flowering in pineapple plants which normally would have remained vegetative for another year or more. One ounce of either of these acids was sufficient to cause 113,000 plants to flower. With increased knowledge of the varied effects of growth-regulating substances has come the realization of their versatility in the production of biological effects. Concentration, method and time of application, and the test object are all of prime importance in determining the results obtained.

Eyster (1941) found that self-sterile plants of Golden Rose petunia could be made self-fertile by spraying the flowering plants with a solution composed of ten parts of naphthaleneacetamide dissolved in one million parts of water. Self-sterility in these plants is imposed by slow growth of the pollen tubes and the formation of an abscission layer which causes the style to drop from the ovary before pollen tubes enter. The growth substance treatment corrected these difficulties. Spraying with α-naphthaleneacetamide failed to increase flower or seed-ball production in the potato (Clarke et al. 1941).

Rodriguez (1932) treated pineapple plants in the field with smoke formed by the slow combustion of dry husk of the coconut fruit combined with green bud scales of the coconut palm and effected a general flowering of all plants and the early formation of large fruits. Ethylene treatment also caused flowering six months earlier than the controls though the fruits obtained from the ethylene-treated plants were smaller than normal size. From his results, Rodriguez concluded that one or more constituents in the smoke, rather than the temperature, were responsible for the hastening of flowering.

Blakeslee (1941) used colchicine to make sterile hybrids of Datura and Anagallis species fertile. Györffy and Melchers (1938) were able to produce a fertile amphidiploid species hybrid between Hyoscyamus niger and H. albus by the use of this same chemical. Doubling the chromosome number by colchicine treatment has been accompanied by a change to self-compatibility in fertilization and seed formation in plants of Petunia axillaris (Lam.) B.S.P. (Stout and Chandler 1941). Practical significance of such effects are emphasized by the report of Langham (1942) that seed size in colchicine-induced tetraploids of Sesame show an increase of 56 per cent over that of the normal plant. At the same time there was no reduction in the number of seeds per pod or in the number of pods per branch. Since sesame oil is obtained from seed, increased seed size might be of commercial importance.

There are some records indicating larger seed yield from plants produced from seeds which have been pretreated in some way. Chief among these are vernalization and growth substance treatments, both of which will be discussed later.

In some cases a breeding program is impossible or has been seriously hampered by the inability to induce flowering and seed set. The sweet potato is a case in point. Miller (1937) was able to make definite controlled crosses in 1936, and stated that as far as he had determined this was the first time such crosses had been made in the continental United States. He induced blooming and seed set by building up the carbohydrate reserves in the vines through a series of light, water, and fertilizer treatments.

HYBRID SEEDS

In any discussion of seed production the importance of hybrid seeds, especially in the flower and vegetable markets, should not be overlooked. To keep a supply of such seeds, pollinations must be made year after year under controlled conditions for the commercial crop must be grown from hybrid seeds each year. This requires emasculation of the seed plants if the flowers are perfect unless some other method can be devised. In certain cases male sterile plants have been developed. Since these can not be self-pollinated all the seeds produced on the plants must be hybrids. Such male sterile lines have been developed in onion (Jones and Clarke 1943) and furnish a means for producing hybrid onion seeds on a large scale by crossing with other selected lines.

Not only must precautions be taken against pollination from undesirable strains in hybrid seed production, but crossing with other related plants must be avoided. For example, all varieties of garden cabbage, kale, Brussels sprouts, cauliflower, and kohlrabi will cross readily with each other (Myers and Fisher 1944). A field of any one of these grown for seed production must be isolated from all the others, and since pollination may be effected by wind and insects, a considerable distance between fields is required.

The value of hybrid seed corn has become a classic example of the practical advantage of research which was purely theoretical in the beginning. A short review of the history of hybrid corn is given in the Year-Book of Agriculture for 1943-1947 (Moore). Corn breeding was begun about 1870 by Beal. The production of inbred lines in studies of theoretical genetics by Shull and East and the recognition by Shull of the practical possibilities of the detasseling method for hybrid seed production marked the beginnings of a spectacular revolution in corn-growing in the United States. Moore (1943-1947) states (p. 14): "The spread of hybrid corn is probably the greatest food-production story of the century. Like a prairie fire it swept across the central part of the country. In 1933 only one acre of corn out of a thousand in the United States was planted to hybrids. Ten years later the percentage of land planted to hybrids was a little more than 51. Since that time it has jumped to 67.5 per cent." Double cross hybrids are now more commonly used for seeds (Crabb 1947).

Controlled seeding.—Most of the research on seed production has been directed at greater yields and high quality seeds. The result has made possible recommendations for improvement in many commercial forms. So successful have some of the practices based on these recommendations been that in one instance, at least, there has arisen some fear that the fruit crop may be excessive. Reference is made to the apple and its tendency to become biennial with large crop production. The principal method recommended for inducing more regular bearing in the apple is provision for more insects, especially bees, for cross pollination. Howlett (1940) presents quantitative evidence that exposure of flowers of different varieties of apples to insect visits for an equal period of time does not induce an equal amount of fruit development. Varieties of apples differ in fertility of egg cells and pollen produced, and this must be considered before cross pollination is restricted.

A thining method which apparently has given much more uniform results is chemical in nature. A number of reports on the use of growth-regulating substances have indicated their value for this purpose. In one of these (Hoffman 1947), the method of thinning Wealthy apples at blossom time with sprays of dinitro-o-cresol or its salts is described. Such treatment has caused the trees to bear commercial crops annually, in contrast to the characteristic biennial bearing of fruit. An additional advantage is the elimination of the laborious hand thinning which has been necessary for Wealthy apple trees which are bearing fruit.

Other cases in which it is desirable to restrict seed production are those of plants like celery and beets which are normally biennial in habit but which may develop flowering shoots and seeds the first year. Such premature seeding, which ruins the marketable parts of these plants, is to be avoided. Investigations have shown that seeding of both of these forms the first year is mainly due to long exposures of the seedlings to temperatures of 60° F. or below. Premature seeding or "bolting" of early celery, a serious problem for the grower, has been prevented by spraying the young plants with 100 p.p.m. of α-o-chlorophenoxypropionic acid (Wittwer et al. 1947). Seedstalk development was obvious on the control plants receiving cold-frame exposure one month after early spring planting. By July 13, two and one-half months later, 80 per cent of the plants had bolted and 100 per cent were seeding by August 21. Treated plants remained strictly vegetative throughout.

Asexual Seed Formation:—We have spoken of seed formation in what is considered the normal manner, that is, by sexual production. Seeds may be produced without the fertilization of the ovule by the male nucleus from the pollen grain. An asexual reproductive process which does not involve nuclear or cellular fusion is substituted for sexual reproduction. Such a process is called apomixis. A review of apomixis in the angiosperms has been made by Stebbins (1941). He describes two main types, vegetative apomixis and agamospermy, or apomixis through seed production. Not all vegetative reproduction is apomictic but only those methods which are substitutes for the sexual process. These are effected principally through vegetative buds or proliferations which develop instead of flowers.

A familiar seed, some of the embryos of which are produced apomictically, is that of the *Citrus*. Here adventitious embryonic development or apogamy takes place. Viable embryos having no direct relation to the egg cell and fertilization are formed within the seed. Certain cells or groups of cells in the nucellus of the maternal plant become active and divide more rapidly than those around them. The resulting mass of meristematic tissue pushes out into the embryo sac and differentiates to form an embryo which can not be distinguished in appearance or germination behavior from the sexual type present in the same seed. Polyembryony or the development of more than one embryo in the seed is characteristic of *Citrus*. Of the several embryos which may be present in one seed obviously only one may be sexual and the rest apogamic. This one sexual embryo may fail to develop or be crowded out by the development of the others so that only asexual embryos remain. This presents a special problem in connection with hybridization studies.

Since apogamic embryos originate from the somatic tissue of the mother plant and are not preceded by reduction division in the formation of germ cells and subsequent union of these cells, they possess the identical diploid chromosome complement and hence the same characteristics as the mother type. Seedlings produced by these embryos thus form a vegetative clone and provide a stable genetic stock for propagation. Studies relating to the economic advantages of propagation of *Citrus* by apogamic seeds have been made and reported (Frost 1938; Hodgson and Cameron 1938; Webber 1932). Often seedlings can be grown more cheaply than budding or grafting can be accomplished. Furthermore, once a desirable clonal variety has been established and its existence continued by budding or grafting, there is a tendency for the individuals to exhibit less vegetative vigor with increasing clonal age from seed. There is some evidence indicating vegetative rejuvenation, called neophyosis by Swingle (1928), of such declining clones by reproduction by nucellar embryony. The work in this connection has involved a comparison of trees of established varieties from old and young clones, the clones having been produced from apogamous embryos. Certain characteristics such as thorniness and vegetative vigor are typical juvenile attributes in *Citrus*. Frost (1938) and Hodgson and Cameron (1938) found these juvenile characters much more pronounced as a result of propagation by asexually-produced seeds, *i.e.*, in new clones, than in old clones of the same variety. The age of the trees compared was identical and the growth conditions essentially uniform. However, with twice the top volume, the young clone produced only half as much fruit as the old clone (Hodgson and Cameron 1938). Also the latter came into bearing two years earlier. There was a striking difference in the seed content of the fruit. For the old clone the highest number of seeds per fruit was 27 and none of the fruits were seedless. The highest for the young clone was 8 and 41 fruits were seedless. These findings have practical horticultural implications in the reduction of the seed content of the fruit and the prevention of premature decline of certain commercial varieties due to decrease or loss of scion vigor by propagation with apomictic seeds. This would be feasible, however, only when a high percentage of the seeds produced are apomictic and when there are few or no irregularities in cell division. It should probably be pointed out that the sexually formed embryo is equally capable of imparting vegetative rejuvenation, but it is not superior in this regard to the apogamous embryo and has the disadvantage of producing atypical seedlings.

Although pollen does not function directly in the production of apo‑ gamic embryonic seeds, there is some indication that the stimulation of pollination is necessary for the development of such seeds (Wong 1940).

Another economically important crop, many seeds of which are formed apomictically, is that of the Kentucky blue grass, *Poa pratensis* L. (Brittingham 1943; Engelbert 1940; Tinney and Aamodt 1940). The predominance of embryo development in this form is from maternal tissues without previous fertilization of the egg nucleus by a sperm from the pollen. However, breeding experiments and pollen tube studies have revealed that the pollen tube enters the stigma and stimulates the apomictic embryo sac to develop, a condition referred to as pseudogamy (Engelbert 1940; Tinney and Aamodt 1940). The chances are that the progeny will have the morphological and physiological characters of the mother plant. The extent to which apomictic embryo development has superseded the sexual type can be determined by growing populations and ascertaining the nature and extent of variation in the plants. Atypical plants appearing are the results of gametic union or of mutations due to chromosomal irregularities. The progeny of the apomictic types are clones and only one selection of an economically useful variety need be made. On the other hand, the high percentage of apomictic embryos makes any improvement in type by hybridization extremely difficult.

Parthenogenesis and polyembryony characterize seeds of *Alnus rugosa* (Du Roi) Spreng. (Woodworth 1929). Morphologically imperfect pollen is formed in this case due to irregularities in microsporogenesis. No pollen tubes were seen in thousands of ovaries at various stages of development from the 2 to 3 per cent good pollen which may be produced. Furthermore, when seed-producing catkins were bagged so that pollination could not be accomplished, embryos were formed as under normal conditions. In this case, then, pollen seems to be totally unnecessary in the setting of an abundance of viable seed.

Similarly pollination is not necessary for the set of seed in the dandelion, *Taraxacum officinale* Weber. This makes its seed production independent of weather conditions suitable for pollination and becomes a factor in its successful establishment and distribution (Roberts 1936).

Apomixis is also exhibited by seeds of *Trillium*, in which the pollen tubes usually do not penetrate the ovary. In the rare cases when they do, no fertilization is effected according to Jeffrey and Haertl (1939). They claim that in spite of this both the egg and the endosperm begin to develop. The young embryo produced by the egg soon aborts but the endosperm continues to grow and a diploid embryo is formed from the endosperm tissue. This embryo functions in a normal way in reproducing the plant. In 1947, Swamy presented evidence which he believed invalidated the conclusions of Jeffrey and Haertl. He maintains that double fertilization takes place normally and that adventive embryony is present in only 19 per cent of the ovules; furthermore, that these embryos almost always originated from the nucellar layer of cells adjoining the chalazal end of the embryo sac. In *Trillium*, seeds may form and appear normal but contain no embryo.

Genetic evidence (Flory 1939) indicates that some form of apomixis occurs in some genera of *Zephyrantheae*.

Kobel (1927) reported cases of apparent apogamy in the apple, a view supported by cytological studies.

The significance of asexual embryo production from both the scientific and the economic points of view can not be overlooked. It is possible that the phenomenon exists but is not yet known in many other forms. Stebbins (1941) points out that apomicts are splendid "opportunists" due to their polymorphism and frequent hybrid vigor. Hence at the time of their appearance they are unusually adaptable to their environment and become well established.

With such a variety of conditions and treatments bringing about or concerned in flowering, fruiting, and seed production, the question arises as to the internal requirements of the plant which must be met before these phases of development can occur. The problem is extremely complex and very little fundamental information is available. It is known, however, that carbon and nitrogen relations in the plant definitely influence its response in regard to vegetative growth and reproduction. This relationship of the carbon and nitrogen content of the plant is known as the carbon/nitrogen ratio. The value of this ratio varies in the different stages of the growth of the plant. The vegetative phase up to the seed production period is characterized by a carbohydrate content which is relatively low in proportion to the nitrogen. As the seed production period approaches, the carbohydrate reserve is built up so that when actual reproduction takes place the carbon/nitrogen ratio is high. Kraus and Kraybill (1918) were the first to associate fruitfulness with a condition of balance between nitrates and carbohydrates rather than with the highest nitrate or highest carbohydrate content. These facts have been demonstrated for many plants among which are those of wheat (Hicks 1928), and the same conditions may exist in other forms. In that case, the requirements for building up a reserve of carbohydrates in the plant would be those which would bring about seed production. Obviously these would vary according to the inheritance and environmental conditions of the variety and the individual.

Arthur et al. (1930) found no relation between carbohydrate and nitrogen content and flowering in either long day plants (radish and lettuce), a short day plant (salvia), or an everblooming type (buckwheat). The amount and quality of light and the time of day affected the amount of carbohydrates present in tomato leaves and hence caused variations in the carbohydrate/nitrogen ratio since the total nitrogen remained practically the same. Also, the percentages of both carbohydrate and nitrogen could be changed by varying light intensity, length of day, and in some cases by changing the nutrient supply when the plants were grown in sand instead of soil.

Although the facts concerning the carbon/nitrogen ratio may have helped to explain many established practices, it is still necessary to attack each seed production problem separately to find its solution.

Embryolessness:—It is not unusual to find seeds which are entirely devoid of contents or contain aborted or shriveled material. Other cases where the firm white endosperm gives the appearance of a good seed but where no embryo is present are more rare. However, recent tests made by Flemion and Uhlmann (1946) indicate that they may be more prevalent than formerly supposed especially in the *Umbelliferae*. Two hundred different lots of seeds of anise, caraway, carrot, celery, coriander, dill, Florence or sweet fennel, parsley, and parsnip were examined for the presence of embryos by splitting the seeds longitudinally after soaking in water. The extent of embryolessness in these forms is shown in Table I. It will be noted that the average per cent of embryoless seeds runs from 8 per cent in celery and parsnips to 34 per cent in fennel. This is in sufficient amounts to be serious in the commercial production of crops from the seeds.

The injury to alfalfa flowers by *Lygus* bugs and the subsequent reduction in seed set has been noted above. Corroboration of this injury is to be found in the work of Pederson (1948) who was able to increase the yield of alfalfa and clover seed by using insecticides. Formulations of DDT, benzene hexachloride, and chlordane alone or in combination favored seed production. It was suggested that the dust should be applied when the flowers are in the bud stage. No applications should be made when the flowers are in bloom, because of the toxicity to pollination insects. Also

TABLE I: *Summary of Extent of Embryolessness and Embryo Immaturity found in nine Species of Umbelliferae:—*

| SPECIES | EMBRYOLESSNESS PER CENT | | | | IMMATURE EMBRYOS PER CENT | | | |
| | NUMBER OF LOTS EXAMINED | WITHOUT EMBRYOS | | | NUMBER OF LOTS EXAMINED | | | |
		Av.	Maxi-mum	Mini-mum		Av.	Maxi-mum	Mini-mum
Carrot (*Daucus carota* L.)	54	16	37	3	44	4	17	0
Celery (*Apium graveolens* L.)	40	8	20	2	36	14	48	1
Dill (*Anethum graveolens* L.)	39	24	62	4	0	—	—	—
Parsley (*Petroselinum hortense* Hoff.)	31	20	36	2	8	4	5	2
Parsnip (*Pastinaca sativa* L.)	15	8	19	0	0	—	—	—
Fennel (*Foeniculum dulce* Mill.)	12	34	58	6	0	—	—	—
Caraway (*Carum carvi* L.)	5	11	25	0	0	—	—	—
Coriander (*Coriandrum sativum* L.)	3	2	3	1	0	—	—	—
Anise (*Pimpinella anisum* L.)	1	6	—	—	0	—	—	—
For all species	200	17	62	0	88	8	48	0

— Indicates percentage not determined.

treated plants can not be used for forage since there is a possibility of poisoning live stock. Flemion *et al.* (1949) found that embryoless dill seeds occurred on the plants or individual umbels which had been caged with *Lygus oblineatus* Say, while very few embryoless seeds were produced in the insect-free plants or those caged with other insects.

Brink (1948) has attributed the collapse of seed from fertile crosses between different species, or between diploids and their respective autotetraploids to an imbalance set up in the different parts of the seed as a result of double fertilization by foreign sperm. The primary changes bringing about this collapse may occur in the endosperm, but death of the embryos appeared to be a result of the embryo genotype.

Seedless peppers are said to be due to a single Mendelian recessive character (Curtis and Scarchuk 1948). The ovules in the seedless fruits were elongated while those in the normal fruits were almost round. Approximately 90 per cent of all the flowers on the seedless plants formed parthenocarpic fruits in spite of the demonstrated ability of the pollen of those plants to effect fertilization.

References:—

Albrecht, H. R., 1942: Earliness of maturity as a factor influencing seed production in vetch (Amer. Soc. Agron. Jour. 34:662-667).

Allen, T. C., & E. Fisher, 1943: Increase yield of wax beans with "hormone" insecticide dusts (Canner 96(22):12-13; *abstr. in* Exp. Sta. Rec. 89:310, 1943).

Andrews, F. S., 1936: Physiological factors associated with the fruiting habits of the bush lima bean (Proc. Amer. Soc. Hort. Sci. 33(1935):473-476).

Arthur, J. M., J. D. Guthrie, & J. M. Newell, 1930: Some effects of artificial climates on the growth and chemical composition of plants (Amer. Jour. Bot. 17:416-482; *also in* Contrib. Boyce Thompson Inst. 2:445-511, 1930).

Bird, J. N., 1944: Seed setting in red clover (Amer. Soc. Agron. Jour. 36:346-357).

Blakeslee, A. F., 1941: Effect of induced polyploidy in plants (Amer. Nat. 75:117-135).

Borodina, I. N., 1931: The influence of nitrogenous and mineral nutrition on the time of heading in barley and millet under the conditions of different day length (Bull. Appl. Bot., Genet., & Pl. Breed. 27:171-195; in Russian, English summary p. 194-195).

Boyles, B. B., & J. F. Martin, 1931: Growth habit and yield in wheat as influenced by time of seeding (Jour. Agr. Res. 42:483-500).

Brewbaker, H. E., 1942: Mosaic and seed production (Amer. Soc. Sugar-Beet Tech. Ann., 5 pp.).

Brink, R. A., 1948: The angiosperm seed as a genetic mosaic (Science 107:458-459).

Brittingham, W. H., 1943: The type of seed formation as indicated by the nature and extent of variation in Kentucky bluegrass, and its practical implications (Jour. Agric. Res. 67:225-264).

Burton, G. W., 1943: Factors influencing seed setting in several southern grasses (Amer. Soc. Agron. Jour. 35:465-474).

————, 1944: Seed production of several southern grasses as influenced by burning and fertilization (Amer. Soc. Agron. Jour. 36:523-529).

Carlson, J. W., 1946: Pollination, Lygus infestation, genotype, and size of plants as affecting seed setting and seed production in alfalfa (Amer. Soc. Agron. Jour. 38:502-514).

Chandler, R. F., Jr., 1938: The influence of nitrogenous fertilizer applications upon seed production of certain deciduous forest trees (Jour. Forestry 36:761-766).

Chroboczek, E., 1934: A study of some ecological factors influencing seed stalk development in beets (*Beta vulgaris* L.) (N. Y. Agric. Exp. Sta. [Ithaca] Mem. 154, 84 pp.).

Clarke, A. E., W. C. Edmundson & P. M. Lombard, 1941: Seed-setting in potatoes as affected by spraying with α-naphthaleneacetamide and by light (Amer. Potato Jour. 18:273-279).

Clarke, A. E., & P. M. Lombard, 1939: Relation of length of day to flower and seed production in potato varieties (Amer. Potato Jour. 16:236-244).

Claypool, L. L., 1932: Influence of fertilizer treatment on lettuce head and seed production (Proc. Amer. Soc. Hort. Sci. 29:438-441).

Cooper, D. C., & R. A. Brink, 1940: Partial self-incompatibility and the collapse of fertile ovules as factors affecting seed formation in alfalfa (Jour. Agric. Res. 60:453-472).

Cooper, D. C., R. A. Brink & H. R. Albrecht, 1937: Embryo mortality in relation to seed formation in alfalfa (*Medicago sativa*) (Amer. Jour. Bot. 24:203-213).

Crabb, A. R., 1947: Hybrid-corn makers; prophets of plenty (Rutgers University Press, New Brunswick, 331 pp.).

Curtis, L. C., & J. Scarchuk, 1948: Seedless peppers. A single Mendelian recessive character (Jour. Hered. 39:159-160).

Czaja, A. T., 1947: Untersuchungen über die Samenproduktion der gebauten Yuccapflanzen (Planta 35:117-131).

Dunham, W. E., 1943: Honeybees increase clover seed production 15 times (Amer. Bee Jour. 83:310-311; *abstr. in* Biol. Abstr. 18:357, 1944).

Ellis, M. M., 1913: Seed production in *Yucca glauca* (Bot. Gaz. 56:72-78).

Engelbert, V., 1940: Reproduction in some *Poa* species (Canad. Jour. Res. Sec. C, 18:518-521).

Eyster, W. H., 1941: The induction of fertility in genetically self-sterile plants (Science 94:144-145).

Finch, A. H., & C. W. Van Horn, 1936: The physiology and control of pecan nut filling and maturity (Ariz. Agric. Exp. Sta. Tech. Bull. 62:420-472).

Flemion, F., H. Poole & J. Olson, 1949: Relation of *Lygus* bugs to embryoless seeds in dill (Contrib. Boyce Thompson Inst. 15:299-310).

Flemion, F. & G. Uhlmann, 1946: Further studies of embryoless seeds in the Umbelliferae (Contrib. Boyce Thompson Inst. 14:283-293).

Flory, W. S., Jr., 1939: Parthenogenesis in Zephyrantheae (Herbertia 6:196-202; *abstr. in* Tex. Agric. Exp. Sta. Circ. 93:18, 1941).

Frost, H. B., 1938: Nucellar embryony and juvenile characters in clonal varieties of citrus (Jour. Hered. 29:423-432).

Györffy, B., & G. Melchers, 1938: Die Herstellung eines fertilen, amphidiploiden Artbastardes *Hyoscamus niger* X *H. albus* durch Behandlung mit Kolchizinlösungen (Naturwiss. 26:547).

Hadfield, J. W., & R. A. Calder, 1936: Lucerne. Pollination and seed production (New Zeal. Jour. Agric. 53:28-33).

Hicks, P. A., 1928: The carbohydrate/nitrogen ratio in the wheat plant (New Phytol. 27:1-46).

Hodgson, R. W., & S. H. Cameron, 1938: Effects of reproduction by nucellar embryony on clonal characteristics in citrus (Jour. Hered. 29:417-419).

Hoffman, M. B., 1947: Further experience with the chemical thinning of Wealthy apples during bloom and its influence on annual production and fruit size (Proc. Amer. Soc. Hort. Sci. 49:21-25).

Howlett, F. S., 1940: Fruit set in the apple following daily exposure of flowers to insect visits (Ohio Agric. Exp. Sta. Bimonth. Bull. 25:44-50).

————, 1942: Fruit set and development from pollinated tomato flowers treated with indolebutyric acid (Proc. Amer. Soc. Hort. Sci. 41:277-281).

Jeffrey, E. C., & E. J. Haertl, 1939: The production of unfertilized seeds in *Trillium* (Science 90:81-82).

Jones, H. A., & A. E. Clarke, 1943: Inheritance of male sterility in the onion and production of hybrid seed (Proc. Amer. Soc. Hort. Sci. 43:189-194).

Knowles, R. P., 1943: The role of insects, weather conditions, and plant character in seed setting of alfalfa (Sci. Agric. 24(1):29-50).

Kobel, F., 1927: Zytologische Untersuchungen an Prunoideen und Pomoideen. Mit 17 Abbildungen im Text (Archiv der Julius Klaus-Stiftung für Vererbungsforschung, Sozialanthropologie und Rassenhygiene, Zürich, 3(1):1-84).

Kohls, H. L., 1937: The influence of some climatological factors on seed-stalk development and seed yield of space-isolated mother beets (Amer. Soc. Agron. Jour. 29:280-285).

Kraus, E. J., & H. R. Kraybill, 1918: Vegetation and reproduction with special reference to the tomato (Oregon Agric. Coll. Exp. Sta. Bull. 149, 90 pp.).

Langham, D. G., 1942: Fertile tetraploids of sesame, *Sesamum indicum* Loew, induced by colchicine (Science 95:204).

Marth, P. C., V. K. Toole & E. H. Toole, 1947: Influence of 2,4-D spray applications on vegetative growth and seed development in Timothy (Amer. Soc. Agron. Jour. 39:780-783).

Megee, C. R., M. G. Frakes & I. T. Larsen, 1942: The influence of clipping treatment and rolling on the yield of clover seeds (Amer. Soc. Agron. Jour. 34:841-843).

Miller, J. C., 1937: Inducing the sweet potato to bloom and set seed (Jour. Hered. 28:347-349).

Mitchell, J. W., A. G. Whiting & H. M. Benedict, 1944: Effect of light intensity and nutrient supply on growth and production of rubber and seeds by guayule (Bot. Gaz. 106:83-95).

Moore, E. G., 1943-1947: Men who went before (Science in Farming. Year-Book of Agriculture, p. 1-16).

Murneek, A. E., S. H. Wittmer & D. D. Hemphill, 1944: "Hormone" sprays for snap beans (Proc. Amer. Soc. Hort. Sci. 44:428-432).

Musser, H. B., 1947: The effect of burning and various fertilizer treatments on seed production of Red Fescue, Festuca rubra L. (Amer. Soc. Agron. Jour. 39:335-340).

Myers, C. H., & W. I. Fisher, 1944: Experimental methods in cabbage breeding and seed production (N. Y. [Ithaca] Agr. Exp. Sta. Memoir 259, 29 pp.).

Nesterova, E. I., 1939: Number of grains in a spring wheat ear as dependent upon temperature and light conditions (Compt. Rend. Acad. Sci. U.R.S.S. 24:812-816).

Pederson, C. E., 1948: Insecticides increase legume seeds (Seed World 62(8):10, 12, 38).

Pond, J. D., 1936: Girdling for seed production (Jour. For. 34:78-79).

Reed, H. S., 1942: The relation of zinc to seed production (Jour. Agric. Res. 64:635-644).

Riley, C. V., 1892: The yucca moth and yucca pollination (Mo. Bot. Gard. Third Ann. Report, pp. 99-158).

Roberts, H. F., 1936: Seed reproduction in the dandelion (Sci. Agric. 17:235-242).

Rodriguez, A. G., 1932: Influence of smoke and ethylene on the fruiting of the pineapple (Ananas sativus Shult) (Jour. Dept. Agric. Porto Rico 16:5-18).

Sexsmith, J. J., & J. R. Fryer, 1943: Studies relating to fertility in alfalfa (Medicago sativa L.). I. Pollen viability as affected by seasonal age of the plant (Sci. Agric. 24:95-100).

Smith, C. L., 1944: Effects of some growth chemicals on premature dropping and development of pecan nuts (Proc. Amer. Soc. Hort. Sci. 44:119-122).

Southworth, W., 1928: Influences which tend to affect seed production in alfalfa and an attempt to raise a high seed-producing strain by hybridization (Sci. Agric. 9:1-29).

Stebbins, G. L., Jr., 1941: Apomixis in the angiosperms (Bot. Rev. 7:507-542).

Stout, A. B., & C. Chandler, 1941: Change from self-incompatibility to self-compatibility accompanying change from diploidy to tetraploidy (Science 94:118).

Stromme, E. R., & C. L. Hamner, 1948: Delayed maturity of bean plants sprayed with solutions of 2,4-dichlorophenoxyacetic acid of nonherbicidal concentrations (Science 107:170-171).

Stuart, N. W., & D. M. Griffin, 1946: The influence of nitrogen nutrition on onion seed production in the greenhouse (Proc. Amer. Soc. Hort. Sci. 48:398-402).

Swamy, B. G. L., 1947: Post-fertilization development of Trillium undulatum (Amer. Jour. Bot. 34:590).

Swingle, C. F., 1928: Vegetative propagation of the apple by seed (Science 67:296).

Tinney, F. W., & O. S. Aamodt, 1940: The progeny test as a measure of the types of seed development in Poa pratensis L. (Jour. Hered. 31:456-464).

Trelease, W., 1902: The Yucceae (Mo. Bot. Garden 13th Ann. Rept., pp. 27-133).

Tysdal, H. M., 1946: Influence of tripping, soil moisture, plant spacing, and lodging on alfalfa seed production (Amer. Soc. Agron. Jour. 38:515-535).

van Overbeek, J., 1945: Flower formation in the pineapple plant as controlled by 2,4-D and naphthaleneacetic acid (Science 102:621).

Vansell, G. H., & F. E. Todd, 1946: Alfalfa tripping by insects (Amer. Soc. Agron. Jour. 38:470-488).

Wakeley, P. C., 1947: Loblolly pine seed production (Jour. For. 45:676-677).

Webber, H. J., 1932: The economic importance of apogamy in Citrus and Mangifera (Proc. Amer. Soc. Hort. Sci. 28(1931):57-61).

Wittwer, S. H., L. L. Coulter & R. L. Carolus, 1947: A chemical control of seedstalk development in celery (Science 106:590).

Wong, C.-Y., 1940: The influence of pollination on seed development in certain varieties of Citrus (Proc. Amer. Soc. Hort. Sci. 37(1939):161-164).

Woodworth, R. H., 1929: Parthenogenesis and polyembryony in Alnus rugosa (Du Roi) Spreng. (Science 70:192-193).

Chapter III

CHEMICAL COMPOSITION OF SEEDS, I

MAN is interested in seeds as a large source of nutrients and accessory nutrients for himself * and other animals, and plant physiologists are interested in the materials stored in seeds as a source of nutrient material and energy for early development of the seedling. Table II shows the average chemical composition of six dry roughages and many agricultural seeds and fruits. These data were selected from the very extensive table in "Feeds and Feeding" and are published with the kind permission of the author and publisher, Professor F. B. Morrison (1936, p. 953-993). Table III shows the chemical composition of various nuts as reported by Wainio and Forbes (1941) and is published with the permission of the authors.

Table IV is selected from Melville's (1947) tables omitting all species already reported upon in Tables II and III.

The chemical composition of seeds and grains given in Table II is the average composition based mostly on several and in some cases on hundreds of analyses. It must not be forgotten, however, that the composition of any given crop of seeds may vary considerably from the average composition and that two sets of factors determine this variation—genetic and environmental. The latter includes soil and climatic conditions. There are many researches showing the effect of genetic constitution and environment on the chemical composition of seeds.

The selection of high and low protein and high and low oil corn at the University of Illinois (Smith 1908) shows how much the genetic constitu-

TABLE II: *Average Chemical Composition of Seeds and Roughages* (Morrison 1936):—

FEEDING STUFF	% TOTAL DRY MATTER	PRO- TEIN	FAT	FIBER	N-FREE EXTRACT	MINERAL MATTER	NO. OF ANAL.
			Average total composition, %				
Dry Roughages:—							
Alfalfa hay, all analyses	90.4	14.7	2.0	29.0	36.4	8.3	632
Bromegrass hay, all analyses	88.1	9.9	2.1	28.4	39.5	8.2	74
Buffalo grass hay (*Bulbilis dactyloides*)	88.7	6.8	1.8	23.8	46.2	10.1	15
Clover hay, bur	92.1	18.4	2.9	22.9	37.8	10.1	14
Clover leaves, sweet	92.2	26.6	3.2	9.5	41.9	11.0	10
Johnson grass hay	90.1	6.5	2.1	30.4	43.7	7.4	37

* Pearson and Harper (1945) state that grains represent 80 per cent of the world's food production on the dry weight basis and that seeds constitute about 75 per cent of the food eaten directly by man on the dry weight basis.

TABLE II (*continued*)

FEEDING STUFF	% TOTAL DRY MATTER	Average total composition, %					
		PRO- TEIN	FAT	FIBER	N-FREE EXTRACT	MINERAL MATTER	NO. OF ANAL.
Concentrates:—							
Acorn, whole (red oak)	50.0	3.2	10.7	9.9	25.0	1.2	1
Acorn, whole (white and post oaks)	62.4	3.3	3.4	11.3	43.0	1.4	3
Barley, Pacific Coast states	89.9	8.7	1.9	5.7	71.0	2.6	78
Barley, light weight	89.8	12.3	2.3	8.5	63.7	3.0	18
Barley, hull-less or bald	90.2	11.6	2.0	2.4	72.1	2.1	6
Beans, Adzuki (*Phaseolus angularis*)	86.0	21.0	0.7	4.0	56.7	3.6	2
Beans, field	88.2	22.9	1.4	3.5	56.1	4.3	14
Beans, mat	90.3	23.0	0.7	4.2	58.1	4.3	6
Beans, pinto	90.9	22.7	1.2	4.5	58.0	4.5	5
Beans, tepary	90.5	22.2	1.4	3.4	59.3	4.2	1
Beechnuts	91.4	15.0	30.6	15.0	27.5	3.3	1
Broom corn seed	88.6	10.8	3.5	8.4	62.7	3.2	5
Buckwheat, common	90.4	11.9	2.4	10.3	63.8	2.0	31
Buckwheat kernels, without hulls	89.4	11.2	2.4	0.7	73.6	1.5	4
Carob bean seeds	88.5	16.7	2.6	7.6	58.4	3.2	5
Chick-peas	90.0	20.3	4.3	8.5	54.0	2.9	—
Corn, flint	88.5	9.8	4.3	1.9	71.0	1.5	450
Corn, pop	90.6	12.1	5.2	2.0	69.7	1.6	7
Corn, sweet, mature	90.7	11.5	7.9	2.3	67.2	1.8	68
Cottonseed kernel, without hull, Texas	93.6	39.0	33.2	2.2	14.8	4.4	70
Darso grain	89.9	10.6	3.3	2.8	71.7	1.5	10
Durra grain	89.8	10.3	3.5	1.6	72.4	2.0	7
Feterita grain	89.6	13.0	2.9	2.2	69.8	1.7	60
Flaxseed	93.6	23.5	36.4	5.9	24.2	3.6	10
Hegari grain	90.0	9.7	2.5	2.3	73.7	1.8	12
Horse beans	87.5	25.7	1.4	8.2	48.8	3.4	5
Kafir grain	88.6	11.2	3.0	2.3	70.3	1.7	230
Millet seed, foxtail	89.1	12.1	4.1	8.6	60.7	3.6	32
Millet seed, hog, or proso	90.7	11.7	3.3	8.1	64.2	3.4	61
Millet seed, Japanese	89.8	10.7	4.7	16.0	52.8	5.6	3
Milo grain	89.4	11.2	2.9	2.2	71.2	1.9	784
Oats, except Pacific Coast states	91.1	12.0	4.7	10.6	60.2	3.6	960
Oats, winter, Pacific Coast states	91.1	9.6	7.2	8.7	62.2	3.4	16
Oat kernels, without hulls	91.7	16.2	6.4	1.9	65.3	1.9	133
Pea seed, field	90.5	23.8	1.2	6.2	56.2	3.1	11
Pea seed, garden	89.2	25.3	1.7	5.7	53.6	2.9	12
Peanut kernels, without hulls	94.7	30.5	47.7	2.5	11.7	2.3	104
Pigeon-grass seed	89.3	14.4	5.4	17.2	45.7	6.6	3
Pumpkin seed, not dried	55.0	17.6	20.6	10.8	4.1	1.9	2
Rice grain, or rough rice	88.6	8.3	1.8	8.8	64.7	5.0	12
Rice, brown	90.2	8.9	2.0	1.0	77.2	1.1	2
Rice, polished	87.8	7.4	0.4	0.4	79.1	0.5	39
Rye grain	90.0	12.3	1.7	2.3	71.7	2.0	58
Schrock sorghum grain	89.1	10.2	3.0	3.4	70.8	1.7	3
Shallu grain	89.8	13.4	3.7	1.9	68.9	1.9	19
Soybeans	90.2	36.9	17.2	4.5	26.3	5.3	161
Sunflower seed	93.4	15.9	25.1	28.1	21.2	3.1	11
Sunflower seed, without hulls	95.5	27.7	41.4	6.3	16.3	3.8	6
Velvet bean, seed only	90.0	23.4	5.7	6.4	51.5	3.0	10
Wheat, Minn., N.D., S.D., Nebr., Kan.	89.6	13.5	2.1	2.4	69.8	1.8	190
Wheat, Rocky Mountain states	91.5	13.3	2.2	2.1	71.9	2.0	193
Wheat, Pacific Coast states	89.1	9.9	2.0	2.7	72.6	1.9	57
Yeast, dried	92.0	45.0	3.0	1.0	36.0	7.0	—

tion can alter the chemical composition of grains. After 10 years of selection the high protein strain bore 14.26 per cent and the low protein strain 8.64 per cent protein and the high and low oil strains bore 7.37 and 2.66 per cent oil respectively. Ivanov (1933) mentions an extreme case. Chick peas (*Cicer arietium*) grown in some regions bore only 12.5 per cent proteins while those grown in other regions contained as high as 31.5 per cent. Extremely low protein content was generally related to absence of the proper nodule-forming organisms in the soil. The yield of seeds per acre was often equal in two localities, although the protein content varied widely. Ivanov *et al.* (1931) found that flax seed varied considerably in oil content as well as iodine number of the oil with the locality in which it was grown. Lower temperatures and high moisture during the growth of the crop led to higher oil content and iodine number. Ivanov gives other data on the effect of geographical location of the crop on oil content of oil-bearing seeds.

TABLE III: *Chemical Composition of Nuts (dry basis;* Wainio and Forbes 1941):—

COMMON NAME	C.P.*	E.E.	C.F.	N-FREE EXTRACT	A.P.	L.	C.	T.	T.A.	Ca	Mg	P₂O₅
Buckeye, fetid	12.63	6.13	2.48	73.95	11.44	1.42	3.21	—	4.81	0.11	0.16	0.52
Chestnut, Italian	6.88	3.34	2.42	84.31	5.69	0.38	3.69	0.19	3.05	—	0.07	0.15
Hazelnut	26.50	61.40	2.16	7.18	23.88	1.22	3.91	—	2.76	0.29	0.17	0.40
Hickory, shell bark	13.31	74.36	1.51	8.81	12.13	0.74	2.63	0.48	2.01	**	0.16	0.37
Oak, red	6.56	20.81	3.10	67.11	6.13	2.99	4.14	9.77	2.42	**	0.07	0.14
Oak, rock	6.94	5.05	2.62	83.17	6.25	2.50	3.53	10.43	2.22	**	0.09	0.15
Oak, scrub	10.25	19.99	3.00	64.64	9.56	4.00	3.76	11.28	2.12	**	0.14	0.19
Oak, scrub	7.63	6.30	2.42	81.67	6.88	6.56	3.19	4.43	1.98	0.07	0.08	0.15
Oak, white	6.25	6.32	2.47	82.32	6.00	2.64	3.24	5.58	2.64	**	0.10	0.16
Walnut, black	29.25	60.23	1.03	6.73	27.06	0.87	2.01	0.25	2.76	**	0.27	0.59

* C.P. = Crude protein; E.E. = ether extract; C.F. = crude fiber; A.P. = available protein; L. = lignin; C. = cellulose; T. = tannin; T.A. = total ash.
** Trace.

Now let us examine Tables II, III, and IV for the purpose of considering some of the wider variations in the composition of different kinds of seeds. One striking thing in Table II is the low mineral content of seeds in contrast to dry roughages. It is well known that leaves are the best source of minerals for animal nutrition but some seeds are much richer in minerals than others. Amongst those with higher mineral content are various beans, cotton, sunflower, and soybean. Wheat is low, while oats with hulls are high.

The soil and fertilizer treatments modify the mineral content of grains. Snook (1939) found Western Australian wheats low in minerals, bearing about one-half as much phosphorus as English and American wheats. His results show that the ash of these wheats is considerably lower than the average mineral content of wheat reported in Table II. Greaves and Hirst (1929) found that the ash content of wheat varies little with variety, but the ash content of wheat, oats, and barley varies greatly with the amount of irrigation water furnished the crops in rich calcareous soils of Utah. The basic elements (Ca, Mg, and K) varied even more widely than the total ash, but acid-

TABLE IV: *Composition of Nuts (moisture free basis;* Melville 1947):—

NUT	NAME	STARCH etc., %	FAT, %	PROTEIN, %
Lotus	*Nelumbo nucifera*	56.5	2.6	18.2
Ginkgo	*Ginkgo biloba*	79.7	2.8	13.0
Tiger nut	*Cyperus esculentus*	51.2	32.3	3.6
Yeheb	*Cordeauxia edulis*	67.3	11.9	14.5
Bambara groundnut	*Voandzeia subterranea*	63.1	6.6	23.3
	Juglandaceae			
Walnut	*Juglans regia*	16.5	65.0	17.0
Butternut	*J. cinerea*	3.6	64.1	29.2
Pecan	*Carya pecan*	10.7	74.4	11.4
	Rosaceae			
Almond	*Prunus amygdalus*	15.0	57.7	22.0
Apricot	*P. armeniaca*	12.2	55.8	32.8
Peach	*P. persica*	—	45.5	26.0
Plum	*P. domestica*	—	41.2	26.2
Cherry	*P. avium*	—	41.3	29.9
	Corylaceae			
Barcelona	*Corylus maxima*	5.5	67.8	13.7
Cob	*C. avellana*	11.5	61.2	16.3
	Anacardiaceae			
Cashew	*Anacardium occidentale*	18.0	46.7	12.8
Pistachio	*Pistacio vera*	17.0	56.4	23.3
	Cucurbitaceae			
Oysternut	*Telfairia pedata*	—	68.5	28.0
Marrow	*Cucurbita pepo*	7.4	37.5	31.8
Watermelon	*Citrullus vulgaris*	5.2	47.8	37.9
Melon	*Cucumis melo*	—	34.4	—
	Pinaceae			
Arolla pine	*Pinus cembra*	17.2	59.4	19.4
Korean pine	*P. koraiensis*	3.7	78.9	14.8
Nut pine	*P. cembroides* v. *edulis*	17.9	64.1	15.1
Stone pine	*P. pinea*	6.4	47.9	33.9
Digger pine	*P. sabiniana*	8.8	56.6	29.6
	Burseraceae			
Pili	*Canarium pachyphyllum*	7.2	76.4	12.3
Pili	*C. polyphyllum*	7.7	73.6	14.6
Java almond	*C. commune*	7.0	72.0	13.0
	Caryocaraceae			
Swarri	*Caryocar nuciferum*	—	67.7	17.2
	Proteaceae			
Queensland	*Macadamia ternifolia*	15.9	68.0	9.1
	Lecythidaceae			
Brazil	*Bertholletia excelsa*	6.0	68.2	18.3
Paradise	*Lecythis zabucajo*	10.4	64.1	22.7
	Palmae			
Coconut	*Cocos nucifera*	15.8	64.5	7.6
Oil palm	*Elaeis guineensis*	29.3	53.2	9.2
Ivory nut	*Phytelephas macrocarpa*	84.8	1.3	5.2
Date stones	*Phoenix dactylifera*	57.5	9.7	5.6

forming elements (P and S) were also affected by the amount of irrigation water supplied.

It will be noted also that seeds in contrast to the roughages are relatively low in fiber. The exceptions to this are seeds or grains that are covered with massive non-living fibrous structures as in the case of oats or barley with hulls or of various seeds or fruits such as pumpkin and sunflower. Note the low percentage of fiber in hulled oats or the sunflower seed without the coats in contrast to those with glumes or hulls on.

As is seen from the examination of the tables, the cereals and grass grains in general are rich in carbohydrates (N-free extracts), low in fats, and rather low in proteins. The peas and beans, except soy, are moderately high in carbohydrates, high in proteins, but low in fats. The chestnut, buckeye, and acorns of the several oaks are rich in carbohydrates, poor in proteins and fats, except for red and scrub oak acorns, which are rather high in fats. In cereals and in many other seeds the main storage carbohydrate is starch with some soluble sugars present. The cotyledons of *Lupinus luteus* contain too little starch to give an iodine reaction. In many seeds, the button and other palms, iris, etc., the endosperm is hemicellulosic. Reserve hemicelluloses, when hydrolyzed, produce various hexoses and pentoses. Table IV mentions several other seeds and fruits that are rich in starch.

It will be noted that a number of the seeds reported in Tables II, III, and IV are high in proteins. This is true of seeds of all legumes, as might be expected, for most members of this family have nitrogen fixing *Rhizobium* tubercles on the roots. There are several non-leguminous seeds reported in the tables that are high in protein: cotton, peanut, flax, pumpkin and other cucurbits, sunflower, hazelnut, black walnut, two species of *Pinus,* and several species of *Prunus.* This is more evident for sunflower if one examines the analysis with the hulls removed and for the pumpkin if it is calculated on the dry weight basis rather than with 45 per cent moisture as shown in Table II.

An examination of Table II shows that beechnut and peanut, and seeds of flax, cotton, sunflower, and soybean bear 30.6, 47.7, 36.4, 34.6, 41.4, and 17.2 per cent fat, respectively, on the air-dry basis and pumpkin seeds, if figured on the dry weight basis, bear almost 40 per cent fat. Table III (ether extract) shows the hazelnut, hickorynut, and black walnut embryos even higher in fat than any mentioned above and the red and scrub oak embryos moderately rich in fats. Table IV shows many other seeds that are rich in oils. The pecan, hickory, Korean pine, two species of pili nuts, and Java almond bear more than 70 per cent oil.

The gross analyses in these tables leave out of consideration many important organic compounds existing in seeds, generally in small amounts. The seed fraction soluble in ether or various other fat solvents bears several compounds besides the triglycerides, or true fats, that need consideration. These will be considered in more detail later under seed fats and oils and related substances. Waxes are present in many seeds, more commonly in the coats. They contain mixtures of several esters of higher alcohols and higher acids. Commonly mixed with these esters are higher alcohols, acids or their salts, and hydrocarbons. The waxes are more difficult to hydrolyze than the glycerides.

Many other chemical substances are found in seeds or seed coverings. Only a few of these can be mentioned. Many seeds contain alkaloids; the coffee bean bears caffein, the cacao bean, theobromine, and the calabar bean, physostigmine. Many seeds contain saponins or other glycosides. *Ginkgo* seeds are rich in saponin and are sometimes used as soap and *Aesculus* seeds are rich in saponin. While poisonous glucosides and those used in therapeutics, as in the case of *Digitalis,* are largely in vegetative portions of plants, some are found in seeds. The meal of tung oil seeds bears a saponin and some other toxic substance that makes it toxic to animals (Emmel 1945). Autoclaving the meal for two hours under 25 pounds' pressure seems to make it safe for animal food (McKinney 1944). Seeds of conifers, especially the coat structures, are rich in oleoresins consisting of resin acids dissolved in essential oils. Mucilage is abundant in or on the seeds of various *Plantago* species, flax, etc. The much folded cotyledons of cotton seeds bear black glands that contain the poisonous phenolic compound, gossypol. The glands must be removed from the seed meal by flotation or otherwise removed or rendered innocuous before the seed meal, an excellent protein source, can be fed to animals. Tannins are also common in seeds, especially in the coat structures. Various seeds contain substances that have anthelmintic or vesicant action or both. Amongst these are pumpkin, *Cleome,* and mustard. Space will not permit the discussion of many other substances that exist in seeds in small amounts.

Carbohydrates Stored in Seeds:—Starch and hemicellulose are the common storage forms of carbohydrates in seeds where a high percentage of carbohydrate is present; there are, however, a number of carbohydrates stored in seeds in smaller percentages. Sucrose is rather common, also other soluble sugars appear in low percentages. In many plant organs as well as germinating seeds sucrose is the more common soluble sugar.

In dormant sugar maple (*Acer saccharum*) seeds Jones (1920) found only 0.06 per cent of reducing sugars, 6.40 per cent of sucrose, 5.21 per cent of other easily hydrolyzable carbohydrates, but no starch. Sucrose fell off considerably with after-ripening in stratification and still more during very early stages of germination, but increased with later stages. In numerous analyses of cereal grains representing many varieties of summer and winter types grown during different years and in different locations, Scheibe and Staffeld (1931) found that oat grains contained 1 to 2 per cent, wheat and barley 2 to 3 per cent, and rye 6 to 7 per cent of sucrose and that there was a correlation between sucrose content of the grain and vigor of the resulting seedling, as well as the minimum germination temperature. James (1940) found a trace of raffinose in barley grains. Like the sucrose it disappeared rapidly with germination, but unlike sucrose there was no reappearance in the later stages of germination. Kretovich (1934) showed that sucrose was most concentrated in the embryo of the wheat grain with slightly lower concentration in the inner layer of the endosperm, a very much lower concentration in the outer layer of the endosperm, and none in the aleurone. The sunflower seed (Miller 1910) contains about 4 per cent soluble sugar, practically all sucrose, and no starch. The sugars disappear rapidly with germination. *Ricinus* seeds (Houget 1942) bear about 0.1 per cent reducing and 1 per cent non-reducing sugars. These sugars increase markedly during the first five days of germination. Curl and Nelson (1944) state that the seeds of *Daubentonia drummondii,* a leguminous shrub growing in southern United States, contain about 16 per cent of a water-soluble fraction consisting mainly of a polysaccharide. Upon hydrolysis this fraction yields about 43 per cent mannose. The seed is suggested as a possible source of mannose. Kretovich and Petrova (1948) find that rye, unlike most cereal grains, contains considerable mucilaginous pentosans of high or low molecular weight. These vary in amount during ripening and germination of the grain. There are many other records of low percentages of carbohydrates other than starch and hemicellulose in seeds.

Starch:—As is seen in Tables II, III, and IV a number of seeds are rich in N-free extract. This is mainly starch which is hydrolyzed to glucose before extraction. A part of the N-free extract is soluble sugars of various sorts and hemicelluloses that are hydrolyzed by weak acids. If in the determination the soluble sugars are first extracted and the starches hydrolyzed with

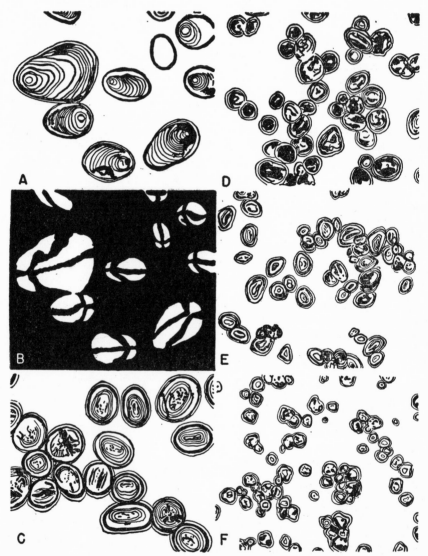

FIGURE 1.—Starch grains (× ca. 300) from potato tuber in natural light (A), and polarized light (B), and from seeds (in natural light) of bean (C), *Ginkgo* (D), oak (E), and buckwheat (F).

amylase this N-free extract will more nearly represent the starch. In any case the N-free extract reported in these tables is predominantly starch.

Starch is the chief reserve carbohydrate of seeds as well as plants in general. It will be noted that all the grains (wheat, corn, rice, etc.) are high in N-free extract. These furnish a large part of the food for man and animals, consequently starch is very important as food. Other seeds reported in these tables are also high in starch, some of the nuts are even higher than the grains, while several of the beans are somewhat lower. While seeds are the main source of starch, roots and stems including tubers, such as tapioca, potato, sago, arrowroot, and sweet potato produce much starch.

Kerr (1944) and 14 co-authors have summarized our knowledge on starch and discussed its uses as food and in the industries. Seventy-two to 75 per cent of the bread we eat is starch. Rice, oatmeal, and other cereal products are likewise very high in starch. In making biscuits and crackers, specially prepared starch is added to the grain flour. Starches are used in salad dressing and starch or modified starch (dextrin or glucose) is used in making candies.

For industrial uses starches are often modified by controlled treatment with amylases, alkalies, and acids followed sometimes by further treatments with formaldehyde, urea, borax, etc. These modified products are used as adhesives for many purposes, as sizing or adhesives for paper, yarns, and spun fabrics and as constituents of printing pastes. Cereal starch after hydrolysis with amylase has been long used in the ethyl alcohol industry. Shortage of blackstrap molasses as a cheap sugar source is likely to lead to the use of cereal starch in several other growing fermentation industries (butanol, acetone, butyl glycol, and citric, gluconic, and itaconic acids). Christensen (Kerr 1944) mentions the rapid progress that is being made in the efficiency of the fermentation industries which will make cereal starch more valuable in the fermentation industries. Cereals have been inefficiently used the world over both as animal and human food because they are poor in proteins and have not been supplemented by some rich protein source. Jones and co-workers (Anon. 1946) point out that the increasing industrial use of cereal starches will improve nutrition in America by giving as a by-product the protein-rich embryo and aleurone layer that can be used to balance the nutritive value of cereals used directly for food by man and animals and will aid in the future expansion of American agriculture by increasing the demand for cereals.

Starch grains.—The starch exists in the form of grains in the cells of seeds. The deposit occurs within living plastids of living cells during the development of seeds. Figure 1 shows the size, shape, and markings of various starch grains.

There is a great variation in the size of starch grains in different plant organs as well as a range of size within a single seed or plant organ. The starch grains of the potato tuber, long diameter, run from 25 to 100μ, those of corn endosperm from 5 to 25μ, wheat 2 to 35μ, barley 2 to 35μ, and rice 3 to 8μ. There is also a considerable range in shape of starch grains; the larger grains of the potato tuber are egg-shaped, those of horny endosperm of corn polygonal, and those of the floury endosperm spherical. Many starch grains show a hilum, a point around which the grain is supposed to develop. The hilum is often more definitely located by the crossing of the double refraction lines under polarized light.

The crystalline structure that produces the dark refraction lines +-shaped in globular, and almost V-shaped in greatly elongated starch grains, disappears when the grains are greatly swollen, crushed, or thoroughly dried. The bi-refringence also appears in crystallized amylose. The X-ray diffraction patterns of starch grains, crystallized amylose, etc., also indicate a crystalline structure. Some starch grains show striations arranged concentrically around the hilum. When potato starch grains are crushed under the cover glass the cleavage lines do not coincide with the striations. The striations may be surface rather than internal structural features. The structural features mentioned above are illustrated in Figure 1.

Chemistry of starch.—In 1906 Maquenne and Roux found that starch consisted of two essentially different constituents, amylose (amylocellulose) and amylopectin. The former, they believed, constitutes the greater part of the starch grain. In solution it stains blue with iodine and is transformed entirely to maltose by malt extract. Amylopectin is the mucilaginous substance which does not stain blue with iodine and dissolves in malt extract without formation of reducing sugar.

According to French (Kerr 1944, Chap. VII), the terms amylose and amylopectin probably apply to the two extreme types of starch molecules as to length and branching of chains and size of molecule; amylose designates the smaller molecules with unbranched chains, and amylopectin larger molecules with branched chains. Glycogen seems to consist of very large branched chain molecules. Kerr's recent book on starch indicates that the French authors are in error in the estimated percentage of amylose and amylopectin in the starch grain. While starches more generally contain 20 to 25 per cent amylose and 75 to 80 per cent amylopectin, waxy starches contain so little amylose that they fail to give the iodine reaction. Hilbert and MacMasters (1946) found starches of certain wrinkled peas that were very difficult to gelatinize with hot water and contained 60 to 70 per cent amylose. Whistler and Weatherwax (1948) found little variation in amylose percentages in 39 varieties of maize, which ran from 22.2 to 28.3 per cent of the starch with an average of 24.25 per cent. Schoch (1947) mentions that normal starches contain 15 to 30 per cent of amylose while waxy or glutinous cereals have starches entirely lacking in amylose and a certain wrinkled pea contains 75 per cent of the starch as amylose. He suggests that the proportion of the two starches in a seed may depend upon the proportion of two synthesizing enzymes present, one forming amylose and the other amylopectin.

It is now evident that this does not give even an approximately quantitative separation. Later it was discovered that the alcohols, butanol, or pentanol, cause a selective precipitation of the amylose from starch paste leaving the amylopectin in solution. It was also shown that cotton or filter paper absorbs selectively the amylose constituent of starch mixtures. By the use of the latter method it is possible to prepare amylopectin practically free from amylose.

On the basis of later work French characterizes amylose and amylopectin as follows:

Amylose.—(1) Nearly 100 per cent digestible by β-amylase; (2) relatively low molecular weight (approximately 200 glucose molecules with only one non-reducing end-group per molecule) (Kerr, p. 122); (3) pure blue color with iodine; (4) absorption of large amounts of iodine isopotentially in potentiometric titration; (5) practically complete crystallizability with butanol or other crystallizing agents; (6) complete absorption on cellulose; (7) high intrinsic viscosity and low solution stability at ordinary concentrations in water.

Amylopectin.—(1) About 50 per cent digestibility in β-amylase; (2) high molecular weight (about 1000 glucose residues with one non-reducing end-group for every 20 to 30 glucose residues) (Kerr, p. 122); (3) purplish-red color with iodine; (4) does not absorb iodine isopotentially; (5) does not form crystalline complex with butanol; (6) unabsorbed by cellulose; (7) fairly high solution stability, low tendency to retrograde.

Starches have been synthesized *in vitro.* Synthetic starch prepared from Cori ester (α-glycopyranose 1-phosphate) by potato phosphorylase is practically pure amylose while potato starch (synthesized *in vivo*) is less than one-fourth amylose, muscle phosphorylase synthesizes amylose *in vitro* and glycogen *in vivo.* Phosphorylase from heart, liver, and brain synthesizes glycogen both *in vitro* and *in vivo.*

In order to explain the reaction between amylose and iodine the amylose molecule is assumed to be a helix or spiral and the iodine is thought to be tightly bound and oriented within the amylose helix. This also explains the dichroism of the amylose-iodine solutions during flow. Amylose absorbs iodine isopotentially up to 18.7 per cent of the amylose or 1 molecule of iodine to 8 glucose residues. After that amylose seems to absorb iodine much as does amylopectin. Potentiometric titration of starch mixtures is a means of estimating the percentages of amylose and amylopectin in the starch.

The amylose molecule is assumed to consist of 300 to 400 (Kerr, p. 127) glucose residues and the amylopectin molecule is thought to be 1000 (Kerr, p. 127) times as large. Cole estimated the average molecular weight of potato amylose and amylopectin at 185,000 and 1,000,000 respectively. The high viscosity of starch solutions indicates that starch molecules are highly asymmetrical. Formation of helical coils by amylose reduces the asymmetry. Sodium chloride solutions reduce the viscosity of amylose solutions perhaps by tightening the helical coils.

Starches are hydrolyzed by dilute acids almost completely to glucose. They are split by diastases to maltose with yields of about 80 per cent, the balance consists of materials of higher molecular weight which can be split to glucose by dilute acid and α-glucosidases. The unbranched starch molecules are supposed to be made up of a ring form of glucose residues, glucopyranose, linked through oxygen atoms in the 1,4 positions and branched chained molecules are similarly made up with periodic branching in the 3,6 positions.

Hemicelluloses:—Some seeds have the carbohydrate reserves stored as hemicelluloses in the tertiary much thickened layer of the cell walls of the endosperms of cotyledons instead of in the interior of the cells as starch is stored. Perhaps the most striking seed of this kind is the ivory nut, the seed of the South American ivory nut palm (*Phytelephas macrocarpa*). This seed is about the size of a hen's egg and consists almost entirely of the ivory-like endosperm bearing a small embryo. The seed is used extensively for carving and button-making. Several organic chemists, including Emil Fischer, who have studied the sugar, mannose, obtained this sugar by hydrolysis of these nuts. The mannans in the endosperm exist in two forms: (Wehmer 1929) hemicellulose and mannose-cellulose. The nuts give more than 40 per cent of their dry weight in mannose. Hydrolysis also gives dextrose, levulose, and pentoses. The Polynesian ivory nut (*Collococcus arnicarum*) is similar to the South American ivory nut and is used for similar purposes. The industrial value of vegetable ivory is a few million dollars a year, in contrast with the great value of the starches in the endosperm of cereals.

We are, of course, all acquainted with the seed of the date palm which consists of a small cylindrical embryo embedded in a sizable horny endosperm of hemicellulose. Probably many of us have germinated these seeds and have seen how the foot of the embryo enlarges as the seedling grows and with the secreted cytase digests the endosperm from the inside outward until the seed becomes a mere shell.

Mitchell (1930) has reviewed the literature on the subject and studied the color and solubility reactions and optical properties of the following hemicelluloses: endosperms of (1) *Phoenix dactylifera*, (2) *Coffea arabica*, (3) *Strychnos nux-vomica*, (4) *Iris pallida*, (5) *Diospyros virginiana*, (6) *Asparagus sprengeri*; and cotyledons of (7) *Impatiens balsamina*, (8) *Lupinus hirsutus*, (9) *Tropaeolum majus*, and (10) *Primula officinalis*. These tests showed a great range in the chemical characteristics of the several storage hemicelluloses of the ten seeds. Various investigators have identified six sugars in the hydrolytic products of these hemicelluloses: mannose, glucose, fructose, galactose, arabinose, and xylose. These exist in the seeds themselves in the form of polysaccharides: mannans, galactans, arabans, and xylans. The hemicelluloses are dissolved when heated with 1 per cent HCl while the celluloses are not.

Hemicellulose of the cotyledons of *Tropaeolum* only was colored blue with I$_2$KI. Hemicelluloses of cotyledons of *Tropaeolum*, *Primula*, and *Impatiens* became violet with I$_2$KI and 26 per cent H$_2$SO$_4$ treatment indicating "amyloid." Hemicelluloses of endosperms of *Diosypros*, *Phoenix*, *Strychnos*, *Coffea*, and cotyledons of *Lupinus* became blue with I$_2$KI and 50 per cent H$_2$SO$_4$ like some celluloses, but not with lower concentrations of H$_2$SO$_4$. Hemicelluloses of the endosperm of *Iris* and *Asparagus* in the natural state are not stained blue by I$_2$KI and H$_2$SO$_4$ of any concentration.

The staining of the several hemicelluloses with the reagent, chlorzinc-iodid, also varied; the hemicelluloses of the endosperms of *Iris*, *Asparagus*, and *Diospyros* and the cotyledons of *Primula* and *Impatiens* failed to stain, and the hemicelluloses of the endosperm of *Coffea*, *Phoenix*, and *Strychnos* and the cotyledons of *Lupinus* and *Tropaeolum* stained blue. Only the colored walls of *Lupinus* were pleochroic. All the hemicelluloses studied except those of *Asparagus* and *Diospyros* became violet when heated with phloroglucinol or orcinol and concentrated HCl indicating pentosans. These two became gold in color indicating hexosans.

All ten hemicelluloses studied dissolved in agents classed as cellulose and hemicellulose solvents. The tertiary or thickened storage wall dissolved completely in cuprammonium indicating cellulose or hemicellulose. It is the pectic-like continuous phase (Farr 1936) rather than cellulose particles that dissolves. The secondary walls dissolved less readily in cellulose and hemicellulose solvents. Boiling in glycerinol for half an hour dissolved all tertiary walls except those of *Diospyros* and *Strychnos*. All hemicelluloses except those of *Coffea* and *Strychnos* were dissolved in from 1 to 26 days in Javelle water, a lignin solvent. This reagent does not distinguish between hemicellulose and lignin. Hemicelluloses of the tertiary walls of several of the seeds dissolved in H$_2$O$_2$ in 2 to 10 days, a pectin and perhaps lignin reagent. This reagent does not distinguish between hemicellulose and pectic substances.

The tertiary walls showed double refraction. Mitchell interpreted this as indicating anisotropic crystalline structure rather than strain in colloids due to tension or compression. The tertiary walls in *Asparagus*, *Iris*, *Phoenix*, and *Tropaeolum* show cylindrical pits which extend to the secondary walls. Surrounding the pits there is an area of high interference color which gradually fades out in spaces between the pits. Dark crosses are visible whose centers are the pits. The author concludes that the tertiary walls may be composed of crystal aggregates and that the biaxial crystals forming these aggregates radiate from the pits.

Many seeds contain glucosides or other glycosides. No doubt the sugars and perhaps some of the aglycons serve in nourishing the growing seedlings. There is some evidence (Miller 1940) that formation of glycosides is a means of removing toxic materials, aglycons, from action on the living cells. Many seeds and seedlings bear HCN as part of the aglycon of glycosides.

Proteins:—Proteins are the main form of nitrogen storage in seeds. A protein (Anderson 1946) is a substance of large molecular size, the greater part of which ultimately yields amino acids upon hydrolysis. The non-amino acid group in any protein is known as the prosthetic group. Even some of the simple proteins are known to bear prosthetic groups: in casein it is thought to be phosphoric acid, in egg albumin and serum, a carbohydrate, and in some if not all catalases, hematin (Sumner and Somers 1947). Unlike starches and fats, proteins have relatively few technical applications except as human or animal food. They are used to some extent in plastics and have promise as raw material for artificial fabrics.

Protein and nitrogen storage in seeds.—Proteins give a very usable form of storage for the growing seedling. With hydrolysis of the proteins to amino acids followed by de-amination the amino group becomes available for formation of new amino acids or other organic nitrogen compounds and the carbon chains can be oxidized as energy sources or built into new nitrogen or carbon compounds. As was said above, green plants have great capacity for building amino acids, proteins, and other organic nitrogen compounds. All the amino acids can be manufactured by green plants. On this basis we have previously been led to assume that the seed embryo, while growing and maturing in the developing seed as well as in the early stages of germination, has power to synthesize all amino acids; that is, it is autotrophic rather than heterotrophic so far as amino acids are concerned.

This assumption is proving wrong. Jacquot and Harding (1947) have shown that the growing axis (embryo with the two cotyledons removed) of the embryo of *Phaseolus multiflorus* is incapable of synthesizing the amino acid, tryptophane. When the intact embryo germinates, the increase of tryptophane in the axis is entirely due to tryptophane withdrawn from the cotyledons. This inability of the axis organs of the embryo to synthesize tryptophane persists even if photosynthesis occurs and nicotinic acid is added.

It is possible that Kent and Brink's (1947) "embryo factor" involves essential amino acids. They have shown that when very immature embryos from barley are cultured they can get the embryos to mature much as they do right on the plant if, besides the sugar and mineral nutrients, they add vitamin-free hydrolysates of casein or other proteins. Tomato juice also contains the "embryo factor." The addition of sodium nucleate from yeast also helped the growth of the immature embryo. Apparently in the absence of the "embryo factor" germination occurs without normal growth and maturing of the embryo previous to germination and a weak spindling seedling results. Of 19 amino acids tried (Spoerl 1948), arginine was the only one as effective as NH_4NO_3 as a nitrogen source for immature orchid embryos in pure culture. Aspartic acid proved to be a good nitrogen source for mature orchid embryos. The nutrient factors required in the development and germination of embryos is fully discussed under embryo culture. Mention is made of the subject also under vitamins, hormones, and chemical changes during after-ripening of seeds.

Benecke and Jost (1923) speak of seven groups of organisms that require or prefer different types of N-compounds: (1) Nitrogen-organisms (using free N_2 of the air); (2) nitrate-organisms; (3) nitrite-organisms; (4) ammonia-organisms; (5) amido-organisms (growing better on asparagine than on NH_3); (6) peptone-organisms (growing much better on peptone than on asparagine or NH_3); and (7) protein-organisms (such as the gonorrhea or tuberculosis organisms which do not grow on peptone or simpler N-sources). A big literature is accumulating on the nutrient requirements of fungi and bacteria that may modify some of the Benecke-Jost classification. This is especially true when the N-needs come to be considered on the basis of necessary amino acids or perhaps peptides rather than on the basis of peptones or proteins. It is of great interest, however, to know that the N-requirements of lower organisms can be modified by conditions that cause mutations. Wild strains of *Neurospora sitophila* and *N. crassa* (Ascomycetes) can use inorganic nitrogen sources if they are supplied with biotin, sugar and various inorganic salts. Doermann (1944) finds that strain #4545 of *N. crassa* needs the amino acid, lysine, in addition to other nutrient requirements of the wild strains. By use of X-ray and ultraviolet Beadle and Tatum (1945) produced strains of the above mentioned species of *Neurospora* that had various requirements as to amino acids, vitamins, etc., and Bonner (1946) has produced similar mutations in *Penicillium notatum* (another Ascomycete).

Amino acids.—There is an enormous literature on amino acids, the building stones of the proteins. Much of this work has been done on animal proteins and on plant proteins in relation to animal nutrition. The literature on the subject was recently summarized by several specialists in a 1290-page book and addendum (Schmidt 1938, 1943).

TABLE V: *Names and Structural Formulas of the accepted Amino Acids* (Merck 1940):—

1. Alanine	$CH_3CH(NH_2)COOH$	α-aminopropionic acid
2. Arginine	$NH_2C(:NH)NHCH_2CH_2CH_2CH(NH_2)COOH$	α-amino-δ-guanidinovaleric acid
3. Aspartic acid	$HOOCCH_2CH(NH_2)COOH$	aminosuccinic acid
4. Cystine	$HOOCCH(NH_2)CH_2S-SCH_2CH(NH_2)COOH$	di-α-amino-β-thiopropionic acid
5. Glutamic acid	$HOOCCH_2CH_2CH(NH_2)COOH$	α-aminoglutaric acid
6. Glycine	NH_2CH_2COOH	aminoacetic acid
7. Histidine	$\overset{\displaystyle\lceil\qquad\quad\rceil}{NH\cdot CH:N\cdot CH:C\cdot CH_2CH(NH_2)COOH}$	α-amino-β-imidazolepropionic acid
8. Hydroxyglutamic acid	$HOOCCH_2CH(OH)CH(NH_2)COOH$	α-amino-hydroxyglutaric acid
9. Hydroxyproline	$\overset{\displaystyle\lceil\qquad\qquad\rceil}{NH\cdot CH_2\cdot CH(OH)\cdot CH_2CH\cdot COOH}$	γ-hydroxypyrrolidine-α-carboxylic acid
10. Iodogorgoic acid	$\overset{\displaystyle\lceil\qquad\qquad\quad\rceil}{CH\cdot Cl:C(OH)\cdot Cl:CH\cdot C\cdot CH_2CH(NH_2)COOH}$	3,5-diiodotyrosine
11. Isoleucine	$CH_3CH_2CH(CH_3)CH(NH_2)COOH$	α-amino-β-methylvaleric acid
12. Leucine	$CH_3CH(CH_3)CH_2CH(NH_2)COOH$	α-aminoisocaproic acid
13. Lysine	$NH_2CH_2CH_2CH_2CH_2CH(NH_2)COOH$	α-amino-ϵ-aminocaproic acid
14. Methionine	$CH_3SCH_2CH_2CH(NH_2)COOH_2$	α-amino-γ-methylthiolbutyric acid
15. Norleucine	$CH_3CH_2CH_2CH_2CH(NH_2)COOH$	α-aminocaproic acid
16. Phenylalanine	$C_6H_5\cdot CH_2CH(NH_2)COOH$	α-amino-β-phenylpropionic acid
17. Proline	$\overset{\displaystyle\lceil\qquad\qquad\rceil}{NH\cdot CH_2\cdot CH_2\cdot CH_2\cdot CH\cdot COOH}$	pyrrolidine-α-carboxylic acid
18. Serine	$HOCH_2CH(NH_2)COOH$	α-amino-β-hydroxypropionic acid
19. Threonine	$CH_3CH(OH)CH(NH_2)COOH$	α-amino-β-hydroxybutyric acid
20. Thyroxine	$\overset{\displaystyle\lceil\qquad\rceil\quad\lceil\qquad\qquad\rceil}{CH:Cl\cdot C(OH):Cl\cdot CH:C\cdot O\cdot CH:Cl\cdot C:Cl\cdot CH:C}$ $-CH_2CH(NH_2)COOH$	β-[3,5-diiodo-4-(3′,5′-diiodo-4′-hydroxyphenoxy)phenyl]-α-aminopropionic acid
21. Tryptophane	$\overset{\displaystyle\lceil\qquad\qquad\rceil}{HC:CH\cdot CH:CH\cdot C:C\cdot NH\cdot CH:C}$ $-CH_2CH(NH_2)COOH$	α-amino-β-indolepropionic acid
22. Tyrosine	$p\text{-}HO\cdot C_6H_4\cdot CH_2CH(NH_2)COOH$	α-amino-β-(p-hydroxyphenyl)-propionic acid
23. Valine	$CH_3\cdot CH(CH_3)CH(NH_2)COOH$	α-aminoisovaleric acid

In mammalian nutrition the proteins have their importance in furnishing amino acids, for the protein needs of higher animals can be entirely supplied by hydrolysates of proteins or by proper mixtures of amino acids.

The story of amino acids (Merck & Co., p. 10, 1940) gives the names and structural formulas of 23 generally accepted amino acids (Table V). In order to be "accepted" the amino acid must have been isolated from a protein hydrolysate, also it must have been synthesized. Another table in this booklet lists the accepted amino acids along with the dates of isolation and synthesis and the investigators by whom each was accomplished. Glycine and leucine were the first isolated from hydrolysates of proteins by Braconnot in 1820. The first was synthesized by Perkin, Duppa in 1858 and the second by Limpricht 1855. The later discovered ones are methionine isolated by Mueller 1922 and threonine isolated by Schryver, Buston 1926. Methionine was synthesized by Barger, Coyne 1928 and threonine by Carter 1936. These facts indicate the newness of some of our knowledge on amino acids. It is likely that other amino acids will be added to the "accepted" list in the future for in the analyses of protein hydrolysates only about 70 per cent of the protein is recovered as amino acids.

Woods (1945) on the basis of earlier work by Rose *et al.* states that the following ten amino acids are essential for growth of the rat: lysine, tryptophane, histidine, phenylalanine, leucine, isoleucine, threonine, methionine, valine, and arginine. Rose (Anon. 1949) states that histidine and arginine are not necessary for maintaining the nitrogen balance in humans. This leaves eight amino acids essential for this purpose. Methionine was unique in that the *D* and *L* forms were equally effective in maintaining the nitrogen balance and with the others the *L* form was required or preferable.

Some seeds that are rich in proteins do not furnish all the essential amino acids in the right proportion for animal nutrition. Animal proteins such as casein of milk, white of egg, and lean meat are good protein sources because of the high content and proper proportions of essential amino acids. Soybeans are nearest to these in giving proper protein quality for animal nutrition. Zucker and Zucker (1943) find soybean meal somewhat superior to peanut or cottonseed meal as a protein source for supplementing wheat flour and recommend the use of a mixture of all three because, besides proteins, cottonseed meal is rich in riboflavin and peanut meal in niacin. Briggs *et al.* (1946) confirm the high nutrient value of the proteins of the seeds of soybean, peanut, and of cottonseed meal but so far as proteins are concerned find no advantage in combining them rather than using them singly. Jaffé (1949), in 13 legume seeds studied, found methionine was the only limiting essential amino acid for the nutrition of the white rat except for pigeon pea where tryptophane as well as methionine was deficient. The embryos (Anon. 1946) of the grains are a good protein or amino acid source. Amongst the essential amino acids methionine (Heinz Nutritional Observatory 1947) is of special importance to animals as a therapeutic and nutritional factor. It protects animals against liver injuries by chloroform, industrial halogenated fumes, and protein deficient diets and prevents the great loss of body nitrogen in the case of fractures, burns, and surgical operations. The effectiveness of casein in some of these cases is entirely determined by the methionine content of the casein. Methionine, like choline (du Vigneaud 1947, 1948), is also a source of the essential labile methyl group ($-CH_3$) for animal nutrition. This and other findings on the importance of methionine and other essential amino acids is of course leading agriculturalists to give great attention to the amino acid content of various seeds used as food. Methionine (Anon. 1948) and other essential amino acids are being synthesized in quantities from cheap abundant materials like coal tar. Such amino acids are racemic and their value depends on whether both *D* and *L* forms can be used. Aside from cystine, methionine is the only S-containing amino acid known unless djenkolic acid, closely related to cystine and claimed to have been isolated from the djenkol beans, qualifies as such. Block and Bolling (1945) list on pages 304-306 the percentage of various amino acids in a number of plant proteins. Amongst the essential amino acids tryptophane makes up 1.3 per cent of corn germ proteins, 4.8 per cent of yellow enzyme, 0.1 per cent of zein, and 0.4 per cent of ricin; methionine 5.5 per cent of gluten of corn, 4.8 per cent of zein residue, 3.8 per cent of linseed meal proteins, and 2.3 per cent of cottonseed globulin; while leucine is much higher, 24.7 per cent of gluten, 23.7 per cent of zein, and 21.5 per cent of whole protein of corn, 8 per cent of whole protein of oats, and 7.5 per cent of whole flax meal proteins.

Sheldon *et al.* (1948) got a marked increase in the percentage of nine of the ten essential amino acids in the forage from alfalfa and *Lespedeza* by adding major or trace fertilizer elements to the soil. Even the trace elements (manganese and boron in combination with copper, zinc, and cobalt) in meager amounts increased the protein constituents from 25 to 100 per cent. If these results hold up under practical production they may contribute much to the production of essential foods. With the ever-growing population of the world, seed proteins must become more and more important as the primary source of essential amino acids for man.

Protein changes in seeds during storage.—Grains and legumes to be used as food remain in storage for a year or two in connection with the U. S. Government price support. In this connection Jones *et al.* (1939, 1941, 1942, 1943) have studied the changes occurring in the proteins of such seeds and seed meals during open and sealed storage at 30° and 76° F. for various periods. During storage the proteins become less soluble and break down showing an increase in amino acids. The change is more rapid in open than sealed storage, in meals than in intact seeds, and at 76° than at 30° F. Mori (1944) found that in cereals and legume and cotton seeds during storage the globulin fraction decreases, increasing the non-protein content. There is an increase in glutelins. The *p*H falls from 6.5 to 4 and the SH radical falls, the SH probably changing to S—S. The changes are partly due to oxygen absorption and partly to enzyme action. Plant physiologists who are used to seeds remaining fully viable for some years under good storage conditions will be surprised at the rate of protein degeneration found by Jones *et al.* in seeds stored at 30° F. It is to be regretted that moisture content of these seeds was not recorded. It is possible that extensive protein changes can occur without changing the germination capacity.

Linkage in the protein molecule.—Glycine, CH_2NH_2COOH, aminoacetic acid is the simplest amino acid. It, like all amino acids, is amphoteric, that is, has both basic —NH_2 and acid —$COOH$ groups and is capable of ionizing both as a base and an acid. The amino acids react with each other through the basic and acidic groups as follows:

$$NH_2CHCOOH + (NH_2)CHCOOH \rightarrow NH_2CHCONHCHCOOH$$
$$\quad | \qquad\qquad | \qquad\qquad\qquad | \qquad\quad |$$
$$\quad R \qquad\qquad R \qquad\qquad\qquad R \qquad\quad R$$

The new linkage, CONH, is known as the peptide linkage.

After two amino acids are tied together by this linkage, the dipeptid still has at least one free basic and one acidic group so that other amino acids may be tied on to form other polypeptides. Many amino acid molecules have been tied together by this linkage to form large molecules that give various protein reactions. Simple proteins may possibly be polypeptides resulting from the tying together of many amino acids through the peptide linkage. Other linkages such as hydrogen bondage may exist. Laine (1944) suggests linkage through the —S—S— bond of cystine. For a full consideration of protein linkages the reader is referred to Schmidt (1943). Some amino acids such as lysine, arginine, cystine, and histidine have more than one basic group while others, aspartic, cystine, glutamic, hydroxyglutamic acids, have two acidic groups each. When these are tied into polypeptides there will be extra free basic or acidic groups within the molecules.

Storage proteins in seeds.—Osborne (1924) points out that most of our knowledge of vegetable proteins comes from the study of storage proteins in seeds because there is so little protoplasmic protein that it is difficult to get enough purified products to study. More recently (Vickery 1945), extensive studies have been made on leaf proteins by Chibnall and others including both chloroplastic and cytoplastic proteins. Leaf proteins are more difficult to handle than seed proteins because they exist in low concentration in the leaf and are tied up with lipids and other prosthetic groups. Attempts to purify lead to very low yields.

Table VI from Osborne's (1924) "The Vegetable Proteins" shows the percentage of the several classes of proteins found in wheat. The author states that part of the globulin, albumin, and proteose is from the embryo. The reserve proteins of the grains are more stable than the protoplasmic proteins and in this respect resemble the animal albuminoids, collagen of connective tissue and keratin of hair and nails. Unlike the albuminoids reserve seed proteins can be brought into solution readily and later separated by fractional precipitation. As a consequence of these characteristics several seed reserve proteins have been crystallized. Like albuminoids of animals seed reserve proteins are likely to be rich in one or two amino acids; silk fibroin contains 36 per cent glycine and 21 per cent alanine while gliadin of wheat and hordein of barley yield more than 40 per cent of glutamic acid. Osborne states there is almost an infinite number of seed proteins. Only a few of these have been separated individually. The purity of a protein can be partly judged by its physical and chemical characters such as solubility and amino acids formed by hydrolysis. Anaphylaxis aids in identifying proteins. Proteins from different species of seeds, although showing like chemical and physical properties, fail to act anaphylactically with one another while those from closely related seeds and apparently identical chemically and physically do react.

Classification of proteins.—If one reads the chapters on prolamins, glutelins and water- and salt-soluble proteins of wheat (Bailey 1944) he will be convinced that attempts at classification of seed proteins has been very unsatisfactory to date and will

TABLE VI: *Proteins of Wheat* (Osborne 1924):—

	SPRING WHEAT, %	WINTER WHEAT, %
Glutenin	4.68	4.17
Gliadin	3.96	3.90
Globulin	0.62	0.63
Albumin	0.39	0.36
"Proteose"	0.21	0.43

remain so until many of the seed proteins have been purified and then physical and chemical characters fully determined. In general proteins are classified as *simple, conjugate,* or *derived.* The simple proteins found in seeds according to Osborne are albumins, globulins, glutelins, and prolamins. The following definitions are taken from Osborne and over-simplified to save space.

Seed *albumins* are soluble in water at neutral or slightly acid reaction and are coagulated by heat. Leucosin of grains, legumelin of various pulse seeds, and ricin of rice are seed albumins. Seed *globulins* are proteins that are soluble in saline solutions but not in water. They are generally more difficult to coagulate with heat than animal globulins, also their solubility is modified by the combined acids and concentration of saline solutions. Legumin, vignin, glycinin, vicilin, and arachin are seed globulins. Seed *glutelins* are proteins not dissolved by aqueous or saline solutions or ethyl alcohol; glutenin of wheat and oryzenin of rice are examples. *Prolamines* are soluble in 70 to 90 per cent ethyl alcohol but insoluble in water. The salts with acids and bases are soluble in water. They are found only in cereal grains. Gliadin of wheat and rye and zein of maize are examples. Upon hydrolysis they yield much proline, glutamic acid, and ammonia. Glutelins and prolamines are not found in animals and the animal proteins, albuminoids, histones, and protamines are not found in plants.

The following conjugate proteins exist in animal tissues: nucleoproteins, glycoproteins, phosphoproteins, chromoproteins, and lecithoproteins. Conjugate proteins are also common in plants. Vickery (1945) mentions nucleoproteins, lipo-proteins, and speaks of chlorophyll as a prosthetic group in conjugate proteins. The carotenoids may also be prosthetic groups in conjugate proteins. Stanley (1939) classified viruses as nucleoproteins. The protein molecule tied up with chlorophyll is much larger than the protein molecule of hemaglobin, and tobacco virus molecule is very large compared with the molecules of most storage and protoplasmic proteins of seeds. Schmidt (1938, p. 775) emphasizes the fact that amino acids and proteins can combine with a great variety of elements and compounds and that large protein complexes may play important roles in biological phenomena.

Proteoses, peptones, and peptides are derived from proteins by partial hydrolysis. *Proteoses* are secondary proteins that are not coagulated by heat, are soluble in water, but precipitated out by half saturation with zinc sulfate. *Peptones* are secondary proteins that are not coagulated by heat, are soluble in water, and are not precipitated even by saturating their solution with ammonium sulfate. *Peptides* are secondary proteins consisting of two or more amino acids linked through the amino group of one and the carboxyl group of the other. Glutathione is a tripeptide consisting of cysteine, glycine, and glutamic acid. It functions biocatalytically through the sulfhydryl (SH) group of the cysteine.

TABLE VII: *Protein Color Reactions:—*

	REAGENT	COLOR	BASIS OF REACTION
1. Millon reaction	Mercury in fuming nitric acid plus water, heated with protein	Brick red	Tyrosine of protein molecules
2. Xanthoproteic	Nitric acid followed by sodium hydroxide	Yellow followed by orange	Phenyl groups, phenyl alanine, tyrosine, etc.
3. Hopkins-Cole	Glyoxylic acid and protein mixture stratified with conc. sulfuric acid.	Purple ring between layers	Tryptophane
4. Ninhydrin	Ninhydrin	Blue to violet or red	Free alpha amino groups or substances containing such groups
5. Biuret	Strong K or NaOH followed by dilute soln. copper sulfate	Purple or pinkish violet	Peptide linkage

Color reactions of proteins.—A number of color reactions of proteins are of general interest. For details on these reactions and for several color tests not shown in the table the reader should examine Schmidt (1938, p. 183-188) and Malisoff (1943) under names of several reactions. Table VII shows the general facts about the five color tests. Some of the reagents serve for quantitative determination of the particular groups with which they react.

Chromatography.—Within recent years, scores of papers have appeared describing the use of paper chromatograms for making qualitative analyses of the chemical content of various materials. Among these, Brown *et al.* (1951) have used the method to study the nature of the stimulant involved in the germination of *Orobanche minor* Sm. seeds.

Chromatography is a valuable tool which no doubt will be used extensively in future determinations of the chemical composition of seeds.

Some physiological effects of proteins.—Some of the seed proteins show interesting physiological effects. We have already spoken of the anaphylaxis which plant proteins show in common with animal proteins. A number of seeds contain small amounts of proteins that are very toxic to animals

—toxalbumins. The following have been studied: ricin from seeds of *Ricinus communis*, curcin from seeds of *Jatropha curcas*, and crotin from seeds of *Croton tiglium*.

There is a powerful allergenic protein in castor bean meal (Spies *et al*. 1943, 1944) in addition to the slightly toxic alkaloid, ricinin, and the very toxic ricin. Even the dust from apparently clean bags in which the meal has been stored will induce dangerous allergy in the handlers. The many uses that can be made of the versatile castor oil is leading to a great increase in castor bean production in United States and elsewhere and to a great increase in the by-product, castor bean cake (Jones 1947). This means that caution must be observed in using the meal as a N-fertilizer or for other purposes, such as glutamic acid source.

References:—

Anderson, J. A., editor, 1946: Enzymes and their role in wheat technology (371 pp., Interscience Publishers, Inc., New York).

Bailey, C. H., 1944: The constituents of wheat and wheat products (332 pp., Reinhold Publishing Corp., New York).

Beadle, G. W., & E. L. Tatum, 1945: *Neurospora*. II. Methods of producing and detecting mutations concerned with nutritional requirements (Amer. Jour. Bot. 32:678-686).

Benecke, W., & L. Jost, 1923: Pflanzenphysiologie. Bd. I (441 pp., Gustav Fischer, Jena).

Block, R. J., & D. Bolling, 1945: The amino acid composition of proteins and foods. Analytical methods and results (396 pp., Charles C. Thomas, Springfield, Ill.).

Bonner, D., 1946: Production of biochemical mutations in *Penicillium* (Amer. Jour. Bot. 33:788-791).

Briggs, H. M., W. D. Gallup & A. E. Darlow, 1946: The nutritive value of cottonseed meal, soybean meal, and peanut meal when used separately and together to supplement the protein of prairie hay in experiments with steers (Jour. Agric. Res. 73:167-176).

Brown, R., A. D. Greenwood, A. W. Johnson, A. G. Long, and G. J. Tyler, 1951: The stimulant involved in the germination of *Orobanche minor* Sm. II. Chromatographic purification of crude concentrates. (Biochem. Jour. 48:564-568).

Curl, A. L., & E. K. Nelson, 1944: A water-soluble Mannan from the seeds of *Daubentonia drummondii* (Jour. Amer. Chem. Soc. 66:1227).

Doermann, A. H., 1944: A lysineless mutant of *Neurospora* and its inhibition by arginine (Arch. Biochem. 5:373-384).

du Vigneaud, V., 1947: The migration of the methyl group in the body (Science 106:630).

————, 1948: Migration of the methyl group in the body (Proc. Amer. Phil. Soc. 92:127-135).

Emmel, M. W., 1945: The toxic principle of the tung tree (Proc. Amer. Tung Oil Assoc., p. 38-42; *abstr. in* Chem. Abstr. 39:4165).

Farr, W. K., 1936: Disintegration of cellulose membranes (Amer. Chem. Soc. Div. of Cellulose Chem., Absts. of Papers 92nd Meeting, Pittsburgh, Pa., p. 3).

Greaves, J. E., & C. T. Hirst, 1929: The mineral content of grains (Utah Agric. Exp. Sta. Bull. 210, 38 pp.).

Heinz Nutritional Research Division, 1947: New developments regarding methionine (Nutritional Observatory 8(1):9-12). (Mellon Institute, Pittsburgh, Pa.)

Hilbert, G. E., & M. M. MacMasters, 1946: Pea starch, a starch of high amylose content (Jour. Biol. Chem. 162:229-238).

Houget, J., 1942: Sur la formation des glucides au cours de la germination du ricin (Compt. Rend. Acad. Sci. [Paris] 215:387-388).

Ivanov, N. N., 1933: Cause of the chemical variation of chickpea seeds (Bull. Appl. Bot., Genet., Plant-Breeding [Leningrad] Ser. III(1):3-11; *abstr. in* Chem. Abstr. 27:5370, 1933).

Ivanov, N. N., M. N. Lavrova & M. P. Gapochko, 1931: Die chemische Zusammensetzung der Samen der Ölpflanzen in den geographischen Versuchen (Trudy Prikl. Bot. 25:1-86 [Engl. summ. p. 87-102]; *abstr. in* Chem. Abstr. 26:756, 1932).

Jacquot, R., & F. Harding, 1947: Les variations du tryptophane au cours de la germination de *Phaseolus multiflorus* (Compt. Rend. Acad. Sci. [Paris] 224:1576-1578).

Jaffé, W. G., 1949: Limiting essential amino acids of some legume seeds (Proc. Soc. Exp. Biol. & Med. 71:398-399).

James, A. L., 1940: The carbohydrate metabolism of germinating barley (New Phytol. 39:133-144).

Jones, D. B., 1947: Proteins of the castor bean—their preparation, properties and utilization (Jour. Amer. Oil Chemists' Soc. 24:247-251).

Jones, D. B., J. P. Divine & C. E. F. Gersdorff, 1942: The effect of storage of corn on the chemical properties of its proteins and on its growth-promoting value (Cereal Chem. 19:819-830).

Jones, D. B., G. S. Fraps, B. H. Thomas & L. Zeleny, 1943: The effect of storage of grains on their nutritive value (Natl. Res. Counc. Reprint & Circ. Ser., #116, 14 pp.).

Jones, D. B., & C. E. F. Gersdorff, 1939: The effect of storage on the proteins of seeds and their flours. Soy beans and wheat (Jour. Biol. Chem. 128:xlix-l).

————, ————, 1941: The effect of storage on protein of wheat, white flour, and whole wheat flour (Cereal Chem. 18:417-434).

Jones, H. A., 1920: Physiological study of maple seeds (Bot. Gaz. 69:127-152).

Kent, N., & R. A. Brink, 1947: Growth *in vitro* of immature *Hordeum* embryos (Science 106:547-548).

Kerr, R. W., editor, 1944: Chemistry and industry of starch; starch sugars and related compounds (472 pp., Academic Press Inc., New York).

Kretovich, V., 1934: The distribution of sugar and nitrogen compounds in wheat grain (Sci. Inst. Cereal Res. [Moscow] 13:70-73; *abstr. in* Chem. Abstr. 29:490, 1935).

Kretovich, V. L., & I. S. Petrova, 1948: Transformation of slime (soluble pentosans) during germination and ripening of rye seed (Doklady Akad. Nauk. SSSR 59:281-283; *abstr. in* Chem. Abstr. 42:6418-6419, 1948).

Laine, T. A., 1944: Investigations of the structure and enzymic splitting of the seed protein zein (Ann. Acad. Sci. Fennicae Ser. A II, Chemica No. 11:7-97; *abstr. in* Chem. Abstr. 40:3781, 1946).

McKinney, R. S., 1944: Miscellaneous studies at the Gainesville tung-oil laboratory (Proc. 10th Ann. Convention, Amer. Tung Oil Assoc. and United Tung Growers Assoc., p. 59-63; *abstr. in* Chem. Abstr. 39:2890, 1945).

Malisoff, W. M., editor, 1943: Dictionary of bio-chemistry and related subjects (579 pp., Philosophical Library, New York).

Melville, R., 1947: The nutritive value of nuts (Chem. & Indus. 1947(22):304-306).

Merck and Co. Inc., 1940: The story of the amino acids (p. 1-40, Rahway, N. J.).

Miller, E. C., 1910: A physiological study of the germination of *Helianthus annuus* (Ann. Bot. 24:693-726).

Miller, L. P., 1940; Formation of β-o-chlorophenyl-gentiobioside in gladiolus corms from absorbed o-chlorophenol (Contrib. Boyce Thompson Inst. 11:271-279).

Mitchell, E. M., 1930: A microchemical study of hemicelluloses of endosperms and cotyledons (Amer. Jour. Bot. 17:117-138).

Mori, S., 1944: Changes in seed globulin (Jour. Agric. Chem. Soc. Japan 20:265-268; *abstr. in* Chem. Abstr. 42:3098, 1948).

Morrison, F. B., 1936: Feeds and feeding. A handbook for the student and stockman. (20th ed., 1050 pp., Morrison Publ. Co., Ithaca, N. Y.).

Osborne, T. B., 1924: Monographs on biochemistry. The vegetable proteins (154 pp., Longmans, Green and Co., London).

Pearson, F. A., & F. A. Harper, 1945: The world's hunger (90 pp., Cornell Univ. Press, Ithaca, New York).

Scheibe, A., & U. Staffeld, 1931: Der Rohrzuckergehalt der Samen als ein Hinweis für den physiologisch-ökologischem Charakter der Getreidearten und -sorten (Fortschr. d. Landw. 6:364-369).

Schmidt, C. L. A., editor, 1938: The chemistry of the amino acids and proteins (1031 pp., Charles C. Thomas, Springfield, Ill.; abstr. in Exp. Sta. Rec. 80:438-439, 1939).

————, 1943: Addendum to "The chemistry of the amino acids and proteins" inclusive of some of the advances since 1937 (pp. 1035-1290, Charles C. Thomas, Springfield, Ill.).

Schoch, T. J., 1947: A decade of starch research (Bakers Digest 21:1-4; abstr. in Biol. Abstr. 21:18263, 1947).

Sheldon, V. L., W. G. Blue & W. A. Albrecht, 1948: Diversity of amino acids in leguminosae according to soil fertility (Amer. Jour. Bot. 35:812).

Smith, L. H., 1908: Ten generations of corn breeding (Illinois Agric. Exp. Sta. Bull. 128:457-488).

Snook, L. C., 1939: The composition of wheat and oat grain grown in western Australia (Jour. West. Australia Dept. Agric. 16:283-287).

Spies, J. R., & E. J. Coulson, 1943: The chemistry of allergens. VIII. Isolation and properties of an active protein-polysaccharidic fraction, CB-1A, from castor beans (Jour. Amer. Chem. Soc. 65:1720-1725).

Spies, J. R., E. J. Coulson, D. C. Chambers, H. S. Bernton & H. Stevens, 1944: The chemistry of allergens. IX. Isolation and properties of an active, carbohydrate-free protein from castor beans (Jour. Amer. Chem. Soc. 66:748-753).

Spoerl, E., 1948: Amino acids as sources of nitrogen for orchid embryos (Amer. Jour. Bot. 35:88-95).

Stanley, W. M., 1939: The architecture of viruses (Physiol. Reviews 19:524-556).

Sumner, J. B., & G. F. Somers, 1947: Chemistry and methods of enzymes (415 pp., Academic Press Inc., New York).

Vickery, H. B., 1945: The proteins of plants (Physiol. Reviews 25:347-376).

Wainio, W. W., & E. B. Forbes, 1941: The chemical composition of forest fruits and nuts from Pennsylvania (Jour. Agric. Res. 62:627-635).

Wehmer, C., 1929: Die Pflanzenstoffe (2nd ed., Vol. I; 640 pp., Gustav Fischer, Jena).

Whistler, R. L., & P. Weatherwax, 1948: Amylose content of Indian corn starches from north, central, and south American corns (Cereal Chem. 25:71-75).

Woods, R., 1945: The amino acids in nutrition (Borden's Rev. of Nutrition Res. 6(1):1-10).

Zucker, T. F., & L. Zucker, 1943: Nutritive value of cotton, peanut, and soy seeds (Indus. & Eng. Chem. 35:868-872).

Anon., 1946: Grains supply protein (Science News Letter 50:239).

Anon., 1948: The amino acids and the world food supply (Down to Earth 3(4):6-7).

Anon., 1949: Rose reports human amino acid requirements (Chem. & Eng. News 27:1364-1365).

Chapter IV

CHEMICAL COMPOSITION OF SEEDS, II

Oily Seeds:—Table IV lists many species of seeds representing 11 different families that contain a high percentage of oil. To these, Table III adds hazelnut (*Betulaceae*) and red and scrub oak (*Fagaceae*). Table II lists, in addition, cotton (*Malvaceae*), flax (*Linaceae*), and sunflower (*Compositae*). The very important commercial oil seeds, tung and castor (*Euphorbiaceae*), and oiticica (*Rosaceae*) are not mentioned in these tables. In fact, there are hundreds of species of seeds that have been analyzed and found rich in oils. The continuous search for new commercial oils is extending greatly our knowledge of oily seeds. Examination of a standard text like Hilditch (1947) or Jamieson (1943) will give the reader some idea of the great number and systematic range of oil seeds that have been studied. In a number of seeds (soybean, peanut, cotton, pumpkin, etc.) high oil is associated with high protein as storage materials. In many beans and peas high oils are associated with high carbohydrates.

In consideration of seed fats and oils, their chemical constitution, their use in industry including food for man and animals, and their use by germinating seedlings, the reader will find the following publications valuable: books by Hilditch (1947), Jamieson (1943), Kirschenbauer (1944), Sherman (1941, Chap. III), Miller (1938, Chap. X), and an article by Woods (1947a). Seed fats and oils in analyses, such as those shown in Tables II, III, and IV, include all materials extracted from bone dry seed material by ether, petrol ether, or other fat solvents. The oils are also removed by hydraulic pressure. The seed fats or oils obtained by these methods consist mainly of triglycerides, that is, esters of the trihydric alcohol, glycerol, and various fatty acids. The fat fraction of seeds also contains smaller quantities of other physiologically very important lipoids such as phospholipids and phytosterols.

There is one known exception to seed oils consisting mainly of triglycerides. Jojoba (*Simmondsia californica*) (Green et al. 1936) seeds yield 25 to 30 per cent of a fatty oil under hydraulic pressure and the extraction of the meats with fat solvents gives as high as 48 per cent of oils. This oil is a marked exception to the usual fatty material in seed endosperms and embryos. There is also a marked difference in the component acids and alcohols. This oil consists of a mixture of wax esters and not of glycerides. The acid portion of the esters is composed largely of a 20-carbon atom unsaturated fatty acid with perhaps a small fraction of a 22-carbon atom fatty acid and very little if any oleic and palmitic acids. A mixture of 20- and 22-carbon atom unsaturated alcohols instead of glycerol form the alcohol or alkyl portion of the esters. It has been suggested that this oil may have considerable commercial value because of its resemblance to sperm oils on one hand and to the valuable carnauba wax on the other. Seeds of other members of the family *Buxaceae* ought to be examined for wax esters as storage fats. These nuts are consumed by rodents, eaten with relish by humans, and evidently have food value.

TRIGLYCERIDES

The triglycerides have the general formula in which R_1, R_2, and R_3 are fatty acid radicals. The characteristics of triglycerides are determined by the constituent fatty acids: the length of chain, the degree of unsaturation, and the existence of OH groups. Table VIII shows the principle fatty acids found in vegetable fats and oils.

$$
\begin{array}{c}
\text{H} \quad\quad \text{O} \\
| \quad\quad\quad \| \\
\text{H—C—O—C—}R_1 \\
| \\
\text{O} \\
\| \\
\text{H—C—O—C—}R_2 \\
| \\
\text{O} \\
\| \\
\text{H—C—O—C—}R_3 \\
| \\
\text{H}
\end{array}
$$

Special tests for oils.—There are certain numbers, values or tests for fats, oil, and waxes that are of great value in characterizing the fatty acids of these substances (Malisoff 1943).

Iodine number is the number of milligrams of iodine absorbed by one gram of fat or oil under specific conditions; it indicates the degree of unsaturation of the fatty acids present. Several different methods are in use for this determination, such as Wijs, Hanus, Hübl. In general a high iodine number in an oil indicates high drying qualities. Eisenschiml and Eisenschiml (1945), however, find an oil with I number of 260 that is poor drying oil. Van Nostrand's (1947) Scientific Encyclopedia gives the following as the range of iodine numbers for various drying oils: linseed, 170-190; tung oil, 150-175; perilla oil, 187-200; walnut oil, 142-146; and soybean, 128-135. Values given by individual workers show wider variations; Painter and Nesbitt (1943*b*) find linseed oil varying from 128-203 in I number.

Thiocyanogen value (Painter 1943) is the number of milligrams of $S_2C_2N_2$ absorbed by one gram of oil. This reagent is absorbed by the double bonds as is iodine, but the saturation of the double bonds is not complete. Values have been determined for linoleic and linolenic acids. In combination with the iodine number and various other methods it is of value in the quantitative estimation of the percentage of various unsaturated acids in oils.

Reichert-Meissl number is the number of milliliters of 0.1 N KOH required to neutralize the fatty acids of a steam distillate obtained, under specific conditions, from five grams of hydrolyzed oil. It is a measure of the short chain fatty acids such as butyric in the oil. For most oils the number is small, about 0.5, but in the case of butter because of high butyric acid content it is high, 20-40. Coconut oil gives a value of 6.5 to 7.5; palm kernel oil 5 to 7; and palm oil 1 to 2.

Saponification number is the number of milligrams of KOH needed to saponify one gram of fat or oil; it is an estimation of the average length of the component fatty acids of the fat or oil. Van Nostrand's (1947) Standard Encyclopedia gives the following values for various oils and fats: linseed, 188-195; tung oil, 190-195; soybean, 185-195; and butter fat, 216-240.

Acid number is the number of milligrams of KOH needed to neutralize the free fatty acids in one gram of fat, oil, or wax. Karon and Altschul (1944) find that high moisture content of cotton seeds in storage leads to the hydrolysis of oils and an increase in acidity. The most rapid increase in acidity occurs when the moisture rises from 15 per cent to 18 per cent. Hoffpauir *et al.* (1947) find that cotton seeds that have been exposed to high moisture in the field or to high moisture and temperature in storage show a marked correlation between the percentage of free fatty acid in the seed and the vitality. All seeds whose non-germ end contained more than 5 per cent free fatty acid were dead and few of those containing less than 1 per cent free fatty acid were dead. The loss of vitality in the latter was from some other cause than acidity. Painter and Nesbitt (1943a) found that flax seeds stored in the dark for two to seven years, no doubt in the dry atmosphere of North Dakota, showed little lowering of the iodine number. Seeds with intact coats showed little change and those with broken coats a rapid change.

TABLE VIII: *Partial List of Fatty Acids found in Plants or produced by Plant Metabolism mostly found as Triglycerides or other Esters in Seeds or Fruits:—*

NAME	CARBON ATOMS	FORMULA	NAME	FORMULA
I. *The saturated fatty acids,* acetic acid series, $C_nH_{2n}O_2, C_nH_{2n+1}COOH$ (only those in which n is an even number are found in natural fats):—			Oleic	$C_{18}H_{34}O_2$
			Erucic	$C_{22}H_{42}O_2$
			2. Linoleic or linolic acid series*	
				$C_nH_{2n-3}COOH$
Acetic	2	$C_2H_4O_2$	Linoleic	$C_{18}H_{32}O_2$
Butyric	4	$C_4H_8O_2$	Tariric	$C_{18}H_{32}O_2$
Caproic	6	$C_6H_{12}O_2$	Elomargaric	$C_{18}H_{32}O_2$
Caprylic	8	$C_8H_{16}O_2$	3. Linolenic acid series**	
Capric	10	$C_{10}H_{20}O_2$		$C_nH_{2n-5}COOH$
Lauric	12	$C_{12}H_{24}O_2$	Linolenic	$C_{18}H_{30}O_2$
Myristic	14	$C_{14}H_{28}O_2$	III. Unsaturated monohydroxy acids	
Palmitic	16	$C_{16}H_{32}O_2$		$C_nH_{2n-2}O_3$
Stearic	18	$C_{18}H_{36}O_2$	Ricinoleic	$C_{18}H_{34}O_3$
Arachidic	20	$C_{20}H_{40}O_2$	IV. Saturated dihydroxy	
Behenic	22	$C_{22}H_{44}O_2$	acids	$C_nH_{2n}O_4$
Lignoceric	24	$C_{24}H_{48}O_2$	Dihydroxystearic	$C_{18}H_{36}O_4$
Carnaübic	24	$C_{24}H_{48}O_2$	V. Saturated dibasic acids	$C_nH_{2n-2}O_4$
Cerotic	26	$C_{26}H_{52}O_2$	Japanic	$C_{22}H_{42}O_4$
II. *The unsaturated fatty acids:*—			VI. Chaulmoogric series	
1. Acrylic or oleic acid series			Cyclic acids with one	
		$C_nH_{2n-1}COOH$	double bond	
Tiglic		$C_5H_8O_2$	Hydnocarpic	$C_{16}H_{28}O_2$
Hypogeic		$C_{16}H_{30}O_2$	Chaulmoogric	$C_{18}H_{32}O_2$

* Acids with two double bonds; only the C_{18} acids occur in nature.
** Acids with three double bonds; only the C_{18} acids occur in nature.

Other values given in tabulated data on fats and oils are melting points, solidification point, specific gravity, index of refraction, and titer test (re-solidification temperature of the alkali hydrolized fatty acids of fats or oils).

Classes of triglycerides.—The triglycerides are classified as simple or mixed. In the simple ones the three fatty acids in the molecule are all the same as in tristearin, tripalmitin, and triolein in which the fatty acids are stearic, palmitic, and oleic, respectively. In mixed triglycerides each fat molecule bears two or three different kinds of fatty acids. Sherman points out the fact that with ten different fatty acids only ten different simple fats are possible, while with the same number of fatty acids 540 different mixed triglycerides are possible. It is evident that a very great number of different fats are possible when one considers all the fatty acids mentioned in Table

VIII. The constitution of the fatty acids in various plant and animal fats has recently been worked out by Hilditch and co-workers and others. Cocoa butter contains stearodiolein, oliopalmitostearin, oleodistearin, palmitodiolein, and oleodipalmitin. In the unsaturated fatty acids the position of the double bond in the carbon chain is determined and designated by the sign for the double bond, $\triangle$, along with the numbers of the carbon atoms between which the double bond or bonds occur: oleic acid is $\triangle$ 9:10; linoleic, $\triangle$ 9:10, 12:13; and linolenic, $\triangle$ 9:10, 12:13, 15:16. According to Jamieson licanic α-acid of oiticica oil, an 18-carbon atom keto acid with three double bonds, has the following constitution: 4 keto $\triangle$ 9:10, 11:12, 13:14. The constitution of this acid can also be expressed as follows: CH_3—$(CH_2)_3$—$(CH=CH)_3$—$(CH_2)_4$—$CO(CH_2)_2COOH$. It is largely due to the high content of this acid, more than 70 per cent, that oiticica oil has such marked drying qualities. Elaeostearic acid of tung oil has a similar arrangement of the three double bonds which may account for some of the similarities in behavior between oiticica and tung oil. The position of the double bonds in the acid chain as well as the number determine the character of the oil.

In general it may be said the longer the fatty acid chains allowing for equal unsaturation, the higher the melting points of the simple triglyceride and the more unsaturated the fatty chains allowing for equal fatty acid chain length, the lower the melting point of triglycerides. Melting points of simple triglycerides are rendered complex by the fact that those with long chain acids have three different polymorphic forms, each with a different melting point (Ralston 1948). In mixed triglycerides there are other complications, but on the whole fatty acid chain length and degree of unsaturation of the fatty acids determine the melting points of seed fats. The unsaturated acids affect other characteristics than the melting point of the oils; the highly unsaturated oils are drying oils and can be used in paints, varnishes, manufacture of linoleum, etc., while the more saturated ones are available for food, soap-making, etc. Certain plant oils are treated with hydrogen in the presence of the catalyst, nickel. In this way the double bonds are partially saturated with hydrogen and the melting point raised. Such partially saturated plant oils are used in cooking instead of lard. The more complete the saturation the higher the melting point. The degree of saturation is adjusted to meet the need for which the hydrogenated oil is to be used.

In the case of castor oil in which the fatty acid is dominantly ricinoleic, either acid or the oil can be rendered more unsaturated. This acid already has one double bond as well as an OH group. By dehydration the OH group along with an H atom on an adjoining carbon atom can be removed as water, giving a second double bond. Dehydrated castor oil becomes a drying oil and can be used in making linoleum. Recent work on castor oil by Munzel Chemical Works of Switzerland (Jamieson 1943) showed that purified dehydrated castor oil "dienol" treated with hypochlorous acid, with later removal of introduced chlorine and hydroxyl groups, formed "trienol" with triple-conjugated double bonds. While unsaturated fats have long been saturated commercially by hydrogenation it is only recently that fats and fatty acids have been rendered more unsaturated. This advance is of great interest to those industries using drying oils.

Uses of seed oils and fats.—Plant oils and fats have hundreds of uses. Gregory (1939, 1944) "Uses and applications of chemicals and related materials" uses three double-column pages to enumerate the uses of castor oil, dehydrated castor oil, and the fatty acids from castor oil; nearly two such pages for the uses of linseed oil; one-half page for the use of the more recently commercialized oiticica oil; and one and three-fourths pages for coconut oil and its constituents.

Three big uses of oils and fats, so far as tonnage is concerned, are for foods, soap, and paint and varnishes. The uses in or for medicine are of course important but of minor significance so far as amount is concerned. Castor oil and chaulmoogra are two important oils used as medicine. Coconut oil and others are used in medical preparations.

Use as foods.—Woods (1947b) states that on the average each person in the United States eats 100 pounds of fat a year, which amounts to one-third of the caloric intake of the diet. About half of this is "invisible" fat naturally contained chiefly in meats and dairy products other than butter. The remainder is "visible" fat such as butter, lard, peanut butter, margarines, and various cooking fats and oils. Of course only a portion of these are directly of seed origin.

Plant oils and fats are highly digestible and readily utilized by animals. The ready utilization seems to fall with rise in melting point, especially above 50° C. This may not be due mainly to the melting point as such but to the constitution of the triglycerides. High melting point is generally accompanied by high stearic acid content. The 18-carbon atom unsaturated fatty acids, oleic or linoleic, are more readily available for animal nutrition than stearic acid. Ivanow (1912) noted that in germination of fatty seeds the iodine number fell with progress in germination and interpreted this as meaning that the unsaturated fatty acids are more readily available for nourishing the growing seedling. Over-hydrogenation of plant oils, as in cooking fats, renders them less nutritious. Apparently some fatty acid or acids are essential (Woods 1948) for animal nutrition in the same sense that certain amino acids are essential. The animal cannot synthesize such acids at all or at least not rapidly enough to take care of its needs. Unsaturated fatty acids are found commonly in seed oils or other oils from plants as well as in animal fats. The ultimate main source of essential fatty acids for man and animals is seeds.

Schoenheimer (1946) concludes, on the basis of work he and associates have done with tagged atoms, that there is a continuous exchange between fatty acids of fats and phosphatides in fat storage depots of animals and fatty acids of the nutritional fats taken into the body. The acids are temporarily liberated by rupture of the ester linkages with a continuous interchange between the nutritional and storage fats. These changes include modification in length of the fatty acid chains. These complex reactions are so balanced that the total amount and structure of the fat mixture in storage depot, blood and organs, remains constant. It would be interesting to have a similar study of fats in plants especially where there is repeated storage in certain organs or cells. In seeds one would hardly expect a similar situation for the fat storage is very temporary; it is rather rapidly built up in the developing seed after which the seed is dried with the metabolism at a minimum followed by absorption of water and germination with the rapid removal of the storage fats, perhaps as carbohydrates, to the growing seedling. This tagged atom work in animals gives a picture of fat metabolism that the botanist should have in mind.

Paints and varnishes.—A very large amount of oils, mainly seed oils, are used in paints and varnishes. According to the 1937 census, paints, varnishes, and related products produced in United States had a factory value of 552 million dollars. Konen (1944) states that in 1942, 77 per cent of all oils used as protective coatings was linseed oil.

United States is a large importer of flax seed and a rather low producer except when prices are high as in World War II. During times of depression or in periods when international trade is not interfered with, drying oils are likely to sell below cost of production in United States. It is a question whether an oversupply of such oils as linseed, perilla, tung, and oiticica will not exist in the near future following the shortage during and a few years after the war.

Oils used in paints and varnishes must be mainly drying oils which means they must have a high I number, that is, contain many fatty acids with two or three double bonds in the chain. Oxygen is absorbed at the double bonds to form a permanent dry film as oxidation products. These films should be tough, hard, and durable. Oils receive various additions or treatments to improve or hasten the film formation; driers, compounds of manganese, cobalt and lead may be added; blown oils are formed by heating to 125° C. while air is blown through or by this treatment in addition to driers; polymerization is brought about by heating oils to 200° C. in absence of air.

Drying oils are meeting a competitor in the form of the newer plastic films. Up to date high grade varnishes and paints seem to hold their own against the plastics for many purposes.

Soaps.—Soaps are salts of fatty acids with metal ions. They are made mainly by heating or boiling lyes with fats thus forming salts and releasing glycerol as a by-product. Fatty acids are also treated with lyes to form the soaps. Hard soaps are sodium salts of fatty acids, liquid soaps are potassium salts of fatty acids. Other metals form insoluble soaps. Aluminum soaps are used in waterproofing compositions, and lead, zinc, iron, and nickel, cobalt, and chromium soaps are used as paint and varnish driers. Palmitic, stearic, and oleic are the desirable acids for soap-making, consequently non-drying oils and fats are mainly used. Organic bases such as guanidine (Poliakoff and Smith 1948) as well as metallic bases form soaps with fatty acids.

In soaps, unlike paints, animal fats such as tallow and waste greases are used extensively. The particular oils and fats used for soap-making will depend upon the price of the various fats and the quality or nature of the soap to be produced. The latest report available on the soap industry, showing the amounts of different materials used in making soaps and the amounts of the different soaps made, is "Canadian Soap Industry" published in Soap and Sanitary Chemicals, Vol. 10, No. 10, October 1947, p. 46-49 covering the years 1944 and 1945. The principal plant oils used were coconut oil and palm oil, the former being the main seed oil. Smaller amounts of the following seed oils were also used: corn, foots of cotton and other seed oils, linseed, palm kernel, peanut, and soybean oils. There were nearly twice as many pounds of tallow and waste fats used as all plant oils, including palm and olive oils as well as the seed oils. Various other detergents, Dreft, Drene, Gardinol, have come to displace soaps. They have the advantage of not being precipitated by the calcium, magnesium, and iron salts in hard water as are the soaps, rendering much of the soap useless and producing dirt of it.

Rancidity.—One of the big drawbacks in the industrial use of fats and oils is the fact that they or the products in which they are used become rancid during storage. Rancidity has been ascribed to three different types of changes. As we have already seen even in intact seeds lypolytic hydrolysis of oils occurs when the moisture and temperature of the seeds are high. Seed oils are also likely to contain some lipase from the seeds or microorganisms that produce lipase. Hilditch speaks of the oxidation of fatty acids to ketones (β-oxidation). The more common oxidation of fatty acids is at the double bonds with the formation of various aldehydes and other compounds that give undesirable odors or flavors. Storage of oils in dark cool places and in full vessels that exclude air prevents these oxidations. Fats in stored seeds may show oxidative as well as hydrolytic changes under bad storage conditions including broken seed coats. Rancid fats used as food are not only undesirable because of the taste and odor, but the rancidity leads to the destruction of the fat-soluble vitamins (Woods 1948) A, E, K, and D.

While oxidation of the fatty acid chain occurs at the double bond, some highly unsaturated oils are very stable while some non-drying oils become rancid very readily. This may be due to natural antioxidants in the oils. Refined oils are likely to become rancid because of the removal of natural antioxidants during refining. Many antioxidants have been found to prevent rancidity but only a few of these are safe to use in fats that are to be used for foods. Gum guaiac, lecithin, and tocopherols (Heftmann 1947) are safe. Guaiac protects even when the fats are in the baked goods. Lecithin bears choline which is a good source of the CH_3 group in liver and kidney functions. The tocopherols, especially alpha, have vitamin E activity. The tocopherols are thought to be the most abundant antioxidants in vegetable oils. Wheat germ oil is rich in tocopherols. Oat flour and other cereal flours and their extracts are used to retard rancidity. There are many antioxidants that can be used to prevent rancidity in oils that are not used as food. Much research is still being done on fat antioxidants.

Effect of climate and taxonomic relationship of plants on nature of fats and oils.—Jamieson summarizes S. Ivanow's extensive work on the effect of climate on the nature of plant fats under three conclusions: (1) Plants bearing fats having acids with two or three double bonds are more sensitive to variations in climate than plants with fats in which the fatty acids bear only one double bond. (2) The climate of southern lands (in Europe) favors the formation of oleic acid and that of northern lands favors the formation of linolenic acid. (3) The variation in the iodine number depends upon climate. It is more striking in the case of those fats that bear the larger quantity of acids with two or three double bonds. The farther north flaxseed and soybean seed are grown the higher the iodine number of the oils.

Jamieson also states that certain plant families or smaller groups produce fats in which a given acid or acids predominate: lauric acid predominates in the kernel fats of *Palmae;* myristic acid in *Myristicaceae;* erucic acid in *Cruciferae;* petroselinic acid in *Umbelliferae;* and chaulmoogric acid in *Flacourtiaceae.* Hilditch states that the fatty acid components of seeds are specific and closely related to the families in which the parent plants have been grouped by botanists. He speaks of it as no exaggeration to say that the component acids of seed fats could be made the basis of a system of plant classification.

Phospholipids in seeds.—There are two groups of phospholipids common in seeds, lecithins and cephalins. They are substituted fats in which one fatty acid is displaced by phosphoric acid to which a nitrogenous base is attached. In lecithins the base is choline and in cephalins it is amino ethyl alcohol. The formula of α-lecithin is:

$$H_2C-O-CO-R_1$$
$$H-C-O-CO-R_2$$
$$H_2C-O-\overset{\displaystyle O}{\underset{\displaystyle OH}{P}}-OCH_2CH_2N(CH_3)_3OH$$

In β-lecithins the phosphoric acid is attached through the middle carbon-atom of the glycerol chain.

The phospholipids are soluble in alcohol, benzene, ether, chloroform, and insoluble in acetone, ethyl acetate, and other similar esters. Lecithins are soluble in water forming a colloid. Cephalins are insoluble in alcohol but soluble in water. Hilditch states that seeds are often very low in phospholipids running more generally 0.1 to 0.2 per cent and a bigger proportion appears in light petrol extract than in expressed oils. Lischkevitsch (1939) found 1.7 per cent of phospholipids in cotton seeds with the percentage of lecithins and cephalins about equal. Rewald (1942) found that only about one-half of the phospholipids was expressed from seed meals by hydraulic pressure. The other half was held rather tenaciously in the cake meals. He found the following proportions of lecithins and cephalins in the phospholipids of the five seeds mentioned below:

	LECITHINS, %	CEPHALINS, %
Peanut	35.7	64.3
Sesame	52.2	40.6*
Cotton	28.8	71.2
Linseed	36.2	63.8
Sunflower	38.5	61.5

* 7.2 per cent soluble in hot, insoluble in cold, alcohol.

The phospholipids have had much more attention in animals than in plants. Sherman (1941) states that in animals they are more prevalent in active cells than in adipose tissue. Protoplasm always contains lipids as well as proteins. Phospholipids are hard to remove completely from animal tissues with solvents and may be so highly dispersed that they are not microscopically visible nor stained with fat stains. Rewald believes that the phospholipids retained in the cake meal when the oils are expressed are physically attached to the carbohydrates. They also seem to be closely associated with proteins. They are essential both to the structure and function of protoplasm. They probably aid in the digestion and movement of fats in plants and animals by emulsifying the fats and thereby suspending them in small particles. They have also been suggested as intermediary products in fat metabolism. As has already been mentioned, the choline is a source of essential methyl groups.

The phospholipids in seeds seem to differ in fatty acid content from the oils in the corresponding seeds. In both plants and animals the phospholipids contain a larger proportion of saturated fatty acids than the fats and oils of the same organisms. The saturated fatty acid in seed phospholipids is dominantly palmitic and in animal phospholipids, stearic. According to Hilditch and Zaky (1942) the phospholipids of seeds, unlike the oils, contain a small amount (3 to 6 per cent) of highly unsaturated C_{20} and C_{22} fatty acids. All acids found in the oils of given seeds are also found in the phospholipids of the corresponding seeds. Linoleic acid is the dominant unsaturated acid in the phospholipids of seeds though not generally higher than in the corresponding oils while oleic acid is more general in animal phospholipids.

Olcott (1944) found that phospholipids of cotton seed have antioxidant activity of high order. They have already been mentioned as safe agents for preventing rancidity in oils and fats. Jamieson mentions that soybean or vegetable lecithins are on the market under various trade names. They bear 30 to 35 per cent lecithins and more cephalins. They are emulsifying, wetting, and stabilizing agents and are used with leathers and textiles and in margarines, shortening, certain candies, and pharmaceuticals.

Unsaponifiable fraction of seed fats and oils.—There is always an unsaponifiable fraction in seed oils, whether the oils are pressed out or extracted with solvents. This fraction amounts to a fraction of a per cent to a few per cent of the oil.

A number of different compounds have been isolated and identified from this fraction (Bhargava 1946) and more are being found all the time. Amongst those found to date are sterols; glucosides of sterols; hydrocarbons such as carotene, squalene, etc., xanthophyll; tocopherols (vitamin E). Tocopherols avoid reproductive failure and prevent a type of male sterility. They also seem to have many other functions in the animal body. In one short article Ichiba (1937) mentions the isolation of several substances from the unsaponifiable fraction of wheat germ oil; an oily alcohol, $C_{29}H_{50}O_{2}$ with a M. P. of 78-79° C., licosanol, $C_{20}H_{42}O$, M. P. 68° C.; "tritiol," probable formula $C_{22}H_{40}O_{3}$, M. P. 84-85° C.; β-amyrin, $C_{30}H_{50}O$, M. P. 195-196° C.; and a "tritisterol," M. P. 178° C. In a previous short paper he reports a sterol melting at 162-165° and a crystalline substance melting at 74-75° C.

Jamieson defines sterols as polycyclic hydroaromatic secondary alcohols that exist free or as esters in all living matter and play an important but little understood role in life processes. Those in animals are known as zoösterols, in phanerogams as phytos-terols, and in cryptogams as mycosterols. Several phytosterols have been isolated from seed oils, purified and characterized chemically; stigmasterol, $C_{29}H_{48}O$, M. P. 170° C., has been found in many legume seeds; several sitosterols (Malisoff 1943) $C_{29}H_{49}OH$, M. P. 137° C., in seeds from several families of plants. Brassicasterol, M. P. 148° C. (Feinholz and Stavely 1940), has been isolated from rape seed oil. When fully hydrogenated brassicasterol, ergosterol, and yeast mycosterol are identical compounds.

Some other more recent researches on seed phytosterols should be mentioned. Thornton *et al.* (1941) found that the mixed sterol glucosides of cotton seeds had a higher M. P. than those from the cotton plant, and the sterols a lower M. P. The seed sterol glucosides melted at 248-250° C. and the seed sterols at 128-130° C. Soy-bean oil sterol glucoside melted at 267-270° C. and the mixed sterols at 133-134° C. Gloyer and Schuette (1939) isolated three different sitosterols from rye germ oil, also a new doubly unsaturated sterol which is an isomer of stigmasterol. Ott and Ball (1944) determined the percentage of stigmasterol and β-sitosterol present in the com-mon bean and state that other phytosterols are probably present. Beumer (1933) finds that sterol formation proceeds very rapidly during germination and growth of seedlings. Manceau and Bigé (1931) find the percentage of phytosterols in the outer coverings of fruits and seeds much greater than in the interior. In hemp seeds the difference is very marked. One of the functions of the phytosterols is to aid in the formation of a protective layer.

Vitamin E.—The tocopherols are abundant in wheat germ oil and in oils from other seeds. They are also rather widely distributed in the plant kingdom. Leaves of lettuce and alfalfa are good sources. Woods (1945, 1947*b*) recently summarized the later research on tocopherols as vitamin E. There are four natural tocopherols: alpha, beta, gamma, and delta. *a*-Tocopherol is the most active. It is a slightly yellow oil, a phenol, soluble in fat solvents. It is slowly oxidized in air but possesses antioxidant or anti-rancidity properties. It helps to preserve easily oxidizable vitamins in foods. While vitamin E is spoken of as the anti-sterility vitamin, it seems to per-form many other functions in the animal body, perhaps more than any other vitamin. It has been suggested that it regulates the metabolic activity of the cell nucleus, par-ticularly the process of cell maturation and differentiation. It has also been thought to prevent certain faults in nutrition of muscles and nerves. The full dependence on plants, especially seed oils, for vitamin E for clinical use has been removed by a syn-thetic racemic DL-*a*-tocopherol that is more than twice as active as natural *a*-tocopherol. Repeatedly in this chapter we have seen the dependence of animals upon plants for various nutritional factors. We saw how the dependence for the amino acid, methi-onine, was eased by synthetic chemistry. The same is true for vitamin E as we have already seen or will see later for other vitamins.

Auxin Content of Seeds and Seedlings:

—There have been a number of determinations of the auxin content of seeds and seedlings. These de-terminations were mostly made by the Went coleoptile assay methods. Parthenocarpic induction, leaf epinasty, and other responses have also been used as measures of auxin.

So far as the ovary is concerned free auxin begins to appear somewhat after anthesis or pollination and reaches a maximum a few weeks later after which it falls off. In tobacco (Muir 1942) there is little or no free auxin in the style or the body of the ovary until the pollen tubes begin growth in these organs. Auxin is formed in both organs as the pollen tubes penetrate them and there is a great production of auxin in the ovary after fertilization. Muir suggests that the growing pollen tubes produce an enzyme that hydrolyzes a pro-auxin in the ovary tissue and the auxin released in the ovary moves down the pedicel preventing abscission of the fertilized flower. The auxin may also be concerned in the development of conducting tissue through which food moves into the growing ovary.

Luckwill (1948) finds a similar situation for hormone formation in the developing apple seed. In Beauty of Bath hormones appear in large amounts with endosperm growth 30 days after petal fall, with maximum 75 days after petal fall and the lows are at June and pre-harvest drop. Hormones are believed to regulate fruit fall rather than development. Hormones are largely in the outer layer of seeds. Apples with few seeds show greater pre-harvest drop than those with many seeds.

Avery et al. (1942a, b and c) found little auxin in the maize grain before pollination. Following pollination the auxin rose rapidly for one to three weeks after which it fell off sharply to maturity. The auxin was mainly in the form of an inactive precursor. In the kernel 98 per cent of the auxin was alkali stable probably indoleacetic acid, IAA, while more than 70 per cent of the auxin in wheat grains was alkali labile. Alkali liberated IAA from precursor but of course destroyed alkali labile auxins. Sweet corn bore much more auxin than starchy corns but there is no relation between hybrid vigor and auxin content. Berger and Avery (1944a and b) isolated and purified the auxin precursor of dormant maize grains so it bore the equivalent of 3.7 per cent IAA. Precursor auxin was 95 per cent of the total auxin. They suggest that the precursor is a protein or is absorbed on a protein. Tryptophane or tryptophane containing proteins yielded small amounts of auxin compared with the purified precursor.

Hatcher (1945) summarized the work done by himself, associates and other investigators on the auxin content of cereal grains. Mature grains of maize were richest and rye, wheat, and barley successively poorer. In all mature grains the auxin exists largely as pro-auxin made active by alkali treatment. In rye grain the auxin is in the endosperm, largely in the aleurone adjacent to the embryo. In this grain free auxin appears the third week after anthesis and reaches a peak four weeks later falling to a very low value at maturity of the grain. If any alkali labile auxin exists in the rye grain Hatcher missed it for he used strong alkalies to release auxin from the precursor. By use of N/50 NaOH to free auxin from the precursor it was shown that ratio of the latter auxin to the former was 3:1 in the rye during auxin accumulation and 80:1 in the mature grain. If immature grains are picked and dried the free auxin is transformed to precursor auxin and dried immature grains bear a higher concentration of auxin than mature grains. The fall in total auxin and the rise in the ratio of total auxin to free auxin coincides with the change of the endosperm from the milk to the dough stage. Anthers show an accumulation and disappearance of auxin with development resembling that of the carpel. Hatcher does not agree with Muir or Luckwill as to the function of auxin but does not suggest any other function.

The Avery-Berger interpretation of bound auxin is quite different from the later findings of Schocken (1947), who suggests that the IAA alleged to be bound to proteins may be a transformation product of the essential amino acid, tryptophane, an indole compound that is released during hydrolysis of proteins. In a series of purified proteins that contained tryptophane all yielded IAA in the alkaline hydrolysates while hydrolysates of gelatine which are free of tryptophane did not. As early as 1944 Larsen (1949) had found indole acetaldehyde in the oat coleoptile and later found evidence that an enzyme in the coleoptile oxidizes it to active IAA. Bonner and Wildman (1946) found an enzyme in the oat coleoptile that transforms tryptophane to active IAA, also an enzyme that inactivates IAA. Tang and Bonner (1948) found a thermostable inhibitory factor for the IAA destroying enzyme. This factor is more abundant in tissue that has been illuminated than in etiolated tissue. This gives a new interpretation to origin of the alkali stable auxin. Even if tryptophane of seed proteins is the source of all the IAA of the seeds, the source of the alkaline unstable hormones has to be accounted for. There are likely many other growth regulators including inhibiting and promoting substances both of the regulators and of growth itself to be discovered in seeds, seedlings, and other parts of plants (Funke 1943; Engard and Nakata 1947).

Pinus jeffreyi seeds germinate promptly without low-temperature stratification while P. lambertiana seeds require two to three months of stratification at 36° F. for after-ripening. No correlation was found (Haddock 1942) between the auxin content of the seeds and promptness of germination. Also low-temperature treatment did not modify the auxin content. Auxin content was higher in immature than in mature seeds and auxin increased in the embryo and endosperm during early phases of germination. Seeds in air storage long enough to lose their vitality completely (maize, 36; oats, 29; and *Phaseolus*, 26 years) (Juel 1941) still contained considerable auxin. Evidently loss of auxin is not related to loss of vitality.

Estrone-like substances, animal hormones, have also been found in seeds (Tadokoro and Saito 1941; Sahasrabudhe 1945).

We have noted several processes in seeds (dormancy, after-ripening, vernalization, and aging) in which auxin seems to play no role as stated above. Muir, also Luckwill, conclude that auxin prevents abscission. Gordon (1946), reviewing the work of several other investigators, mentions that auxin may liberate enzyme from proteins by acting as an exchange adsorbate of the protein-adsorbing enzymes and it may act as a coenzyme, or enzyme activator. Berger and Avery (1943) have found alcohol dehydrogenase stimulated by auxin addition to plant tissue. They also confirm the findings of Commoner and Thimann that auxin stimulates respiration. We know little about the extent to which active auxin is released during germination and even less about its movement to the actively growing seedling (Funke 1943). As is well known, the auxins are extremely active in inhibiting the general development of plants and in modifying the growth form. Perhaps it is fortunate that the rather large amounts of auxins in seeds are largely bound in the inactive form in or to proteins or other precursors.

Vitamin Content of Seeds and Seedlings:

—Since seeds are a main source of food for man and animals it is of course natural for the nutritionist to inquire about the vitamin content of seeds. The plant physiologist is interested also in the vitamin content and the function of these vitamins in the growing seedling.

For quantitative methods for determining the amount of various vitamins in seeds and seedlings by biological or chemical assays, the reader is referred to the following general texts (Schopfer 1943, Chap. XXIV, p. 257-269; Bailey 1944, Chap. 16, p. 280-317; Rosenberg 1942).

Bailey (1944) summarizes the literature on the vitamin content of wheat and other cereal grains. Hard spring wheat contains 5.25, hard winter wheat 4.77, and soft winter wheat 3.54 p.p.m. of B_1 thiamin. There is a great difference in the concentration of B_1 in different parts of the grain. The embryo half of the wheat grain contains 5.8 times as much as the brush half; the germ contains 30; the bran 13.2; shorts 23; straight flour 1.5; and patent flour 0.7 p.p.m. of B_1. Maize, rye, barley, and sorghum grains are similar to wheat in B_1 content while oats are about 60 per cent higher. During development and maturing of the wheat grain the percentage of B_1 remains about constant on dry weight basis and there is a continuous movement of B_1 from the glumes and straw into the grain.

According to different investigators the wheat grain contains one-fifth to one-half as much B_2, riboflavin, as it does of B_1. B_2 content is less affected by environment and varies more with variety than B_1 content. B_2 shows an unequal distribution within the grain somewhat like B_1 but less markedly so. The grade flours contain a higher proportion and embryo a lower proportion than is true of B_1. The several cereals studied show little variation in B_2 content. Wheat grains are much richer in niacin, anti-pellagra factor, than white corn, and sweet corn much higher than starchy corn (Mather and Barton-Wright 1946; Burkholder *et al.* 1944) but none of these compares favorably with Brewer's yeast. Niacin content of wheat varies much with both variety and environmental conditions. It is especially abundant in bran. It is partly tied up as a precursor from which it is liberated by acids, bases, and enzymes.

The wheat grain is a good source of B_6, pyridoxin, with greater concentration in the embryo and integuments. Maize is also rich in B_6. Pantothenic acid, the anti-dermatitis factor, is found in the wheat grain with more nearly equal distribution throughout the grain than other vitamins mentioned above. The wheat embryo is rich in choline while the endosperm is relatively poor with considerable in the pericarp. Biotin is found in wheat with greater concentration in bran. Wheat oil, especially germ oil, is very rich in vitamin E (anti-sterility factor), alpha-tocopherol, and probably in beta- and gamma-tocopherol. The vitamin A and C content of the dormant wheat grain is, of course, low but they both increase with germination. Yellow corn is much richer in A than white corn and sweet corns are much richer (Mather and Barton-Wright 1946) in niacin than starchy corns. Some seeds and fruits are especially rich in certain vitamins. Varieties of pecans (Anon. 1943a), pinto beans (Anon. 1943b), and sweet sorghums (Bertagni 1943) are rich in B_1. Sunflower seed meal is a good source of B vitamins (Day and Mitchell 1945). Acorns of willow oak (King and Titus 1943) are a good source of A. Unripe fruits of several species of walnut and to a lesser degree unripe fruits of several other nuts are rich in C (Melville 1947). Seeds are in the main a poor source of vitamins A, C, and D.

Niacin content can be increased greatly in corn (Hunt et al. 1948; Richey and Dawson 1948) and in grain sorghum (Tanner et al. 1947) by breeding. Tanner et al. found in 42 samples of grain sorghums studied that the riboflavin, niacin, pantothenic acid, biotin, and pyridoxin varied considerably but only niacin content was mainly determined genetically.

The change in vitamin content of seeds, dry weight basis, has been determined for many seeds during development and maturing and during early stages of germination (Cheldelin and Lane 1943; Burkholder and McVeigh 1942, 1945). In Golden Bantam corn and pods of bush lima beans, riboflavin, niacin, pantothenic acid, biotin, inositol, and folic acid increase with early stage of development and fall with later stages and maturity. Pyridoxin was highest in the mature seeds. In the early stages of germination nicotinic and ascorbic acids, riboflavin, niacin, biotin, and pyridoxin increase and thiamin shows little change while folic acid rises in some seeds and falls in others. Thiamin is higher in seedling leaves of cereals than in the grains and is not destroyed by drying. Burkholder and McVeigh (1942) conclude that the oriental practice of eating sprouted seeds is well founded because sprouting increases the content of a number of vitamins. Much research is being done at present on the vitamin content of various seed and seedling organs during the course of seedling development (Hoffer et al. 1946; Wai et al. 1947; Terroine and Desveaux-Chabrol 1947; Kretovich et al. 1948; Robinson et al. 1948; Cailleau et al. 1949).

Several vitamins have already been synthesized. With the rapid advances in synthetic organic chemistry we may have new abundant and cheap sources of various vitamins for animals and non-chlorophyllous plants. Until we know and have synthesized all vitamins an entirely synthetic source will be impossible. In any case plant parts including seeds are the ultimate source of organic nutrients for animals. Along with nutrients go the vitamins often in insufficient amounts. It is likely that synthetic vitamins will be used to supply these deficiencies rather than become the main or sole source of vitamins.

What functions do the several vitamins in the seed, as well as those synthesized by the growing seedling, perform in the development of the organs of the seedling itself? The function of these vitamins in the nutrition of man and animals, including insects and worms, and in fungi, bacteria, and yeasts has been extensively studied; indeed fungi and bacteria furnish one of the two ways of assaying vitamins. The function of the various vitamins in the green plant, the great natural source of most of the vitamins, is more difficult to determine and has received relatively little attention (Schopfer 1943).

The storage organs (endosperm and/or cotyledons) are often rich in vitamins as well as nitrogenous carbohydrate and fat nutrients for the embryo. As a consequence one of the methods of determining the function of vitamins in the development of the root and stem of the seedling is to remove the storage organs from the seeds and grow the axis organs of the embryo on proper nitrogen and carbohydrate sources with and without various vitamins and combinations of vitamins. The pea has been a favorite seed. The cotyledons are removed before the vitamins from the cotyledons have an opportunity to move into the axis organs. By the use of this method it has been shown that thiamin and biotin are both necessary for epicotyl growth while the root gives little response to biotin and marked response to thiamin. The epicotyl lacks the capacity to synthesize either of these vitamins in adequate amounts and the radicle lacks this power for thiamin. In the intact embryos these deficiencies are supplied by the cotyledons. Robertson (1947) shows that the cotyledons are the organs that synthesize ascorbic acid in the germinating pea. Virtanen and Saubert-v. Hausen (1949) confirm this and give vitamin C a very important role in the growth of the pea seedling. C is the vitamin for growth and in sufficient additions will practically entirely displace the need of the cotyledons. While B complex, biotin, and certain amino acids favored the growth of the isolated axis organ they were not nearly as effective as C. C, they assume, acts as a reducing system enabling the axis organ to utilize nitrates rather than NH_4 salts as a nitrogen source. They state that vitamin C and other reducing substances regulate the Redox potential within the plant.

The culture of isolated root tips is another source of information on the significance of vitamins in the growth of organs of green plants. The root lacks chlorophyll and is limited in its synthetic power. In the early cultures of root tips yeast extract along with minerals, glucose, and peptone as carbohydrate and nitrogen sources proved effective. Thiamin is especially important in root culture. Pea roots can synthesize thiamin if the two component radicles, pyrimidine and thiazole, are present. The tomato root can synthesize the pyrimidine radicle but not the thiazole. It can also combine the two radicles. Some roots such as the sunflower require thiamin, niacin, and pyridoxin in addition to mineral and organic nutrients for best growth; carrot roots require thiamin and pyridoxin; while other roots, alfalfa, require thiamin and niacin.

Progress is being made on the intermediates involved in vitamin synthesis. Gustafson (1949) reviews the literature on tryptophane as an intermediate for nicotinic acid synthesis by microorganisms and offers evidence that tryptophane is an intermediate for the synthesis of the same vitamin by green plants.

The cursory statements above indicate that at least some of the vitamins stored in seeds or manufactured by the green parts of seedlings function in the growth of certain organs of green plants. A few years ago it was claimed that additions of B_1 to intact green plants increased their growth enormously. This was later proved to be entirely wrong. This does not prove that vitamins have no function in the growth of even the green organs of plants. It may mean merely that such organs with their almost unlimited capacity to synthesize organic compounds supply fully their own vitamin needs.

References:—

Avery, G. S., Jr., J. Berger & B. Shalucha, 1942a: Auxin content of maize kernels during ontogeny, from plants of varying heterotic vigor (Amer. Jour. Bot. 29:765-772).

————, ————, ————, 1942b: Auxin storage as related to endosperm type in maize (Bot. Gaz. 103:806-808).

————, ————, ————, 1942c: Total auxin extraction from wheat (Amer. Jour. Bot. 29:612-616).

Bailey, C. H., 1944: The constituents of wheat and wheat products (332 pp., Reinhold Publ. Corp., New York).

Berger, J., & G. S. Avery, Jr., 1943: The mechanism of auxin action (Science 98:454-455).

――――, ――――, 1944a: Isolation of an auxin precursor and an auxin (indoleacetic acid) from maize (Amer. Jour. Bot. 31:199-203).

――――, ――――, 1944b: Chemical and physiological properties of maize auxin precursor (Amer. Jour. Bot. 31:203-208).

Bertagni, P., 1943: Study on vitamins in sweet sorghum. I. Determination of aneurine in seeds of Sorghum saccaratum (Riv. Biol. 28:282-286; abstr. in Chem. Abstr. 37:6003, 1943).

Beumer, H., 1933: Über die Sterinbildung bei der Keimung (Biochem. Zeitschr. 259:469-470).

Bhargava, P. N., 1946: Chemical examination of the unsaponifiable matter of the fat from the fleshy arils of Celastrus paniculata (Proc. Indian Acad. Sci. Sec. A 24:506-509; abstr. in Biol. Abstr. 21:18253, 1947).

Bonner, J., & S. G. Wildman, 1946: Contributions to the study of auxin physiology (Growth 10(Suppl. 6 Sympos.):51-68; abstr. in Biol. Abstr. 22:2155, 1948).

Burkholder, P. R., & I. McVeigh, 1942: The increase of B vitamins in germinating seeds (Proc. Nat. Acad. Sci. 28:440-446).

――――, ――――, 1945: Vitamin content of some mature and germinated legume seeds (Plant Physiol. 20:301-306).

Burkholder, P. R., I. McVeigh & D. Mayer, 1944: Niacin in maize (Yale Jour. Biol. & Med. 16:659-663; abstr. in Exp. Sta. Rec. 92:44, 1945).

Cailleau, R., J. Lévy, T. Terroine, J. Adrian & R. Jacquot, 1949: Les variations de la riboflavine, des acides nicotinique, pantothenique et ascorbique dans les débuts de la germination du Blé et du Pois (Compt. Rend. Acad. Sci. [Paris] 228:1044-1045).

Cheldelin, V. H., & R. L. Lane, 1943: B vitamins in germinating seeds (Proc. Soc. Exp. Biol. & Med. 54:53-55).

Day, H. G., & H. H. Mitchell, 1945: B vitamins found in sunflower seed meal (Amico Lab. News 2:5).

Eisenschiml, O., & G., 1945: Postwar prospects for drying oils (Chem. & Eng. News 23:33-36, 85).

Engard, C. J., & A. H. Nakata, 1947: A growth inhibitor and a growth promotor in sugar cane (Science 105:577-580).

Feinholz, E., & H. E. Stavely, 1940: On brassicasterol, the characteristic sterol of rapeseed oil (Jour. Amer. Chem. Soc. 62:1875-1877).

Funke, H., 1943: Über Hemm- und Wuchsstoffe des keimenden Maiskorns (Jahrb. Wiss. Bot. 91:54-82).

Gloyer, S. W., & H. A. Schuette, 1939: The sterols of rye germ oil (Jour. Amer. Chem. Soc. 61:1901-1903).

Gordon, S. A., 1946: Auxin-protein complexes of the wheat grain (Amer. Jour. Bot. 33:160-169).

Green, T. G., T. P. Hilditch & W. J. Stainsby, 1936: The seed wax of Simmondsia californica (Chem. Soc. Jour. 1936. Pt. II:1750-1755).

Gregory, T. C., 1939: Uses and applications of chemicals and related materials. Vol. I (665 pp., Reinhold Publ. Corp., New York).

――――, 1944: Uses and applications of chemicals and related materials. Vol. II (459 pp., Reinhold Publishing Corp., New York).

Gustafson, F. G., 1949: Tryptophane as an intermediate in the synthesis of nicotinic acid by green plants (Science 110:279-280).

Haddock, P. G., 1942: A study of the rest period in seeds and buds of Pinus lambertiana Dougl. and Pinus jeffreyi Murr. (Diss. (Ph.D.) Univ. of Calif., 229 pp.).

Hatcher, E. S. J., 1945: Studies in the vernalization of cereals. IX. Auxin production during development and ripening of the anther and carpel of spring and winter rye (Ann. Bot. n. s. 9:235-266).

Heftmann, E., 1947: Antioxidant properties of carrot oil (Jour. Amer. Oil Chem. Soc. 24: 404-409; abstr. in Chem. Abstr. 42:1069-1070, 1948).

Hilditch, T. P., 1947: The chemical constitution of natural fats (2nd ed., 554 pp., John Wiley & Sons, Inc., New York).

Hilditch, T. P., & Y. A. H. Zaky, 1942: The component fatty acids of some vegetable seed phosphatides (Biochem. Jour. 36:815-821).

Hoffer, A., A. W. Alcock & W. F. Geddes, 1946: The distribution of thiamine in wheat seedlings at different stages of germination in the dark (Cereal Chem. 23:76-83).

Hoffpauir, C. L., D. H. Petty & J. D. Guthrie, 1947: Germination and free fatty acid in individual cotton seeds (Science 106:344-345).

Hunt, C. H., L. Ditzler & R. M. Bethke, 1948: Niacin and pantothenic acid content of corn (Ohio Agric. Exp. Sta. Bull. 674:43).

Ichiba, A., 1937: Unsaponifiable matter of wheat-germ oil (Sci. Papers Inst. Phys. Chem. Res. [Tokyo] 34:121-131; abstr. in Pharm. Abstr. 6:72, 1940).

Ivanow, S., 1912: Über die Verwandlung des Öls in der Pflanze (Jahrb. Wiss. Bot. 50:375-386).

Jamieson, G. S., 1943: Vegetable fats and oils (2nd ed., 508 pp., Reinhold Publ. Corp., New York).

Juel, I., 1941: Der Auxingehalt in Samen verschiedenen Alters, sowie einige Untersuchungen betreffend die Haltbarkeit der Auxine (Planta 32:227-233).

Karon, M. L., & A. M. Altschul, 1944: Effect of moisture and of treatments with acid and alkali on rate of formation of free fatty acids in stored cottonseed (Plant Physiol. 19:310-325).

King, T. R., & H. W. Titus, 1943: Acorns of the willow oak, Quercus phellos, a source of vitamin A activity (Poultry Sci. 22:56-60; abstr. in Chem. Abstr. 37:2784, 1943).

Kirschenbauer, H. G., 1944: Fats and oils, an outline of their chemistry and technology (154 pp., Reinhold Publ. Corp., New York).

Konen, J. C., 1944: Drying oils—past, present, future (Oil & Soap 21:202-204; abstr. in Chem. Abstr. 38:5419, 1944).

Kretovich, V. L., A. A. Bundel & T. V. Drozdova, 1948: Sulfhydryl compounds and ascorbic acid in sprouting and ripening seeds (Biokhimiya 13:332-336; abstr. in Chem. Abstr. 42:8888-8889, 1948).

Larsen, P., 1949: Conversion of indole acetaldehyde to indoleacetic acid in excised coleoptiles and in coleoptile juice (Amer. Jour. Bot. 36:32-41).

Lischkevitsch, M., 1939: Cottonseed phosphatides (Maslob. Zhir. Delo 2:6-8; abstr. in Pharm. Abstr. 6:411, 1940).

Luckwill, L. C., 1948: The hormone content of the seed in relation to endosperm development and fruit drop in the apple (Jour. Pomol. & Hort. Sci. 24:32-44).

Malisoff, W. M., editor, 1943: Dictionary of bio-chemistry and related subjects (579 pp., Philosophical Library, New York).

Manceau, P., & Bigé, 1931: Phytosterols of seeds and fruit (Compt. Rend. Soc. Biol. 107:635-636; abstr. in Chem. Abstr. 26:2765, 1932).

Mather, K., & E. C. Barton-Wright, 1946: Nicotinic acid in sugary and starchy maize (Nature 157:109-110).

Melville, R., 1947: The nutritive value of nuts (Chem. & Indus. 1947(22):304-306).

Miller, E. C., 1938: Plant physiology (2nd ed., 1201 pp.; Chap. X, p. 726-769; McGraw-Hill Book Co., Inc., New York).

Muir, R. M., 1942: Growth hormones as related to the setting and development of fruit in Nicotiana tabacum (Amer. Jour. Bot. 29:716-720).

Olcott, H. S., 1944: Cottonseed phospholipids (Science 100:226-227).

Ott, A. C., & C. D. Ball, 1944: The isolation of stigmasterol and β-sitosterol from the common bean, Phaseolus vulgaris (Jour. Amer. Chem. Soc. 66:489-491).

Painter, E. P., 1943: The composition of linseed oil (N. Dak. Agric. Exp. Sta. Bimo. Bull. 5(6):32-36; abstr. in Exp. Sta. Rec. 90:1-2, 1944).

Painter, E. P., & L. L. Nesbitt, 1943a: The stability of linseed oil during storage of flaxseed (N. Dak. Agric. Exp. Sta. Bimo. Bull. 5(6):36-40; abstr. in Exp. Sta. Rec. 90:2, 1944).

————, ————, 1943b: Thiocyanogen absorption of linseed oils: Thiocyanogen absorption of linoleic and linolenic acids and composition of linseed oils (Indus. & Eng. Chem., Anal. Ed. 15:123-128).

Poliakoff, M. Z., & G. B. L. Smith, 1948: Guanidine soaps (Indus. & Eng. Chem. 40:335-337).

Ralston, A. W., 1948: Fatty acids and their derivatives (986 pp., John Wiley & Sons, Inc., New York).

Rewald, B., 1942: Phosphatides from oil seeds (Biochem. Jour. 36:822-824).

Richey, F. D., & R. F. Dawson, 1948: A survey of the possibilities and methods of breeding high-niacin corn (maize) (Plant Physiol. 23:238-254).

Robertson, T. S. B., 1947: The accumulation of vitamin C during germination in peas (Austral. Jour. Exp. Biol. & Med. Sci. 25:41-46).

Robinson, A. D., L. E. Lynd & B. J. Miles, 1948: The distribution of thiamine and riboflavin in wheat, oats, and barley at successive stages of plant growth (Canad. Jour. Res. Sec. B 26:711-717).

Rosenberg, H. R., 1942: Chemistry and physiology of the vitamins (674 pp., Interscience Publishers, Inc., New York).

Sahasrabudhe, M. B., 1945: Estrogen potency of the defatted castor seed (Current Sci. 14:69; abstr. in Chem. Abstr. 39:5311, 1945).

Schocken, V., 1947: Bound auxin (Amer. Jour. Bot. 34:602-603).

Schoenheimer, R., 1946: The dynamic state of body constituents (78 pp., Harvard Univ. Press, Cambridge, Mass.).

Schopfer, W. H., 1943: Plants and vitamins (293 pp., Chronica Botanica Co., Waltham, Mass.).

Sherman, H. C., 1941: Chemistry of food and nutrition (6th ed., 611 pp., The Macmillan Co., New York).

Tadokoro, T., & T. Saito, 1941: Chemical properties of an estrone-like substance and an enzyme-containing protein in the rice germ. I (Jour. Chem. Soc. Japan 62:417-418; abstr. in Chem. Abstr. 37:4431, 1943).

Tang, Y. W., & J. Bonner, 1948: The enzymatic inactivation of indole acetic acid. II. The physiology of the enzyme (Amer. Jour. Bot. 35:570-578).

Tanner, F. W., Jr., S. E. Pfeiffer & J. J. Curtis, 1947: B-complex vitamins in grain sorghums (Cereal Chem. 24:268-274).

Terroine, T., & J. Desveaux-Chabrol, 1947: Synthesis of nicotinic acid in the course of germination (Arch. Sci. Physiol. 1:117-133; abstr. in Chem. Abstr. 42:2323, 1948).

Thornton, M. H., H. R. Kraybill & F. K. Broome, 1941: Sterol glucosides from cottonseed oil (Jour. Amer. Chem. Soc. 63:2079-2080).

Van Nostrand's, 1947: Scientific Encyclopedia (2nd ed., 1600 pp., D. Van Nostrand Co., Inc., New York).

Virtanen, A. I., & S. Saubert-v. Hausen, 1949: Role of substances formed during germination in growth of plants (Nature 163:482-483).

Wai, K. N. T., J. C. Bishop, P. B. Mack & R. H. Cotton, 1947: The vitamin content of soybeans and soybean sprouts as a function of germination time (Plant Physiol. 22:117-126).

Woods, R., 1945: The amino acids in nutrition (Borden's Rev. of Nutrition Res. 6(1):1-11).

————, 1947a: New concepts in fat metabolism (Borden's Rev. of Nutrition Res. 8(4-6):1-12).

————, 1947b: Vitamin review. II (Borden's Rev. of Nutrition Res. 8(3):1-16).

————, 1948: The essential fatty acids (Borden's Rev. of Nutrition Res. 9(4):1-12).

Anon., 1943a: Pecans as a source of vitamin B_1 and B_2 (Ariz. Agric. Exp. Sta. Ann. Rept. 1941/42(53):67-69).

Anon., 1943b: Variations in the vitamin B_1 (thiamin) content of pinto beans (Ariz. Agric. Exp. Sta. Ann. Rept. 1941/42(53):69).

Chapter V

WATER RELATIONS OF SEEDS

THE water relations of seeds involve complicated physical and chemical reactions. That these phenomena are of great importance is evidenced by the fact that water is the most abundant constituent to be found in living organisms. Water absorption and movement through different parts of the plant have been studied extensively and much literature is available on the subject. Progress has been made in the understanding and explanation of the observed phenomena, such explanations being based on experimental evidence for the most part. Some confusion has resulted from failure to recognize all of the determining factors, however, and from a lack of uniformity in definition of terms used. A recent article (Meyer 1945) on "A critical evaluation of the terminology of diffusion phenomena" may help to some extent.

There is a great irregularity in the rate of moisture absorption by plant material (Shull and Shull 1932). In a variety of materials, including cotyledons of peas, corn grains, seeds of *Xanthium, Gossypium,* and *Hibiscus,* and tissues of *Auricularia,* it was determined that the rate of intake is rapid at first, gradually falling off as more water is taken up until it approaches zero as the tissues become nearly saturated. Finally absorption ceases, due either to complete saturation or to the balance of outward diffusion of soluble substances from the tissues with inward diffusion from the surrounding solution. Constant temperature, accurate timing, uniform drying and weighing technique, physical and chemical homogeneity and chemical stability in the presence of water of the plant tissue used are required for reliable data on absorption rates.

The characteristics and the reactions of seeds in regard to internal and external water supply are of the greatest physiological significance. No attempt will be made here to discuss the complicated laws governing diffusion but a brief survey of the factors affecting the water supply in relation to the physiologic response of the seeds will be made. The initial movement of water into the seed is known as imbibition. Different methods have been devised for measuring the resulting swelling of the seeds. Suffice it to say that the seeds do increase in size and that heat is evolved in the process. Seeds are known to have a great power of water absorption from the surrounding medium.

Permeability of Seed Coverings:—The most obvious factor affecting absorption of water by seeds is the nature of the coverings surrounding them. The capacity of these coverings for allowing substances to pass through is known as their permeability. Permeability to both gases and water are important in the behavior of the seed. For example, difference in water imbibition did not explain the difference in the germination of the two seeds in the cocklebur (Crocker 1906). The lower seed in the bur germinated readily while the upper seed failed to germinate unless supplied with extra oxygen pressure. This was shown to be due to the impermeability of the seed coats of the upper seed to oxygen. Crocker pointed out that this was not the case in the delayed germination of the seeds of *Axyris amaranthoides* or *Abutilon avicennae* and many other seeds which owe their germination failure to the exclusion of water by the coats.

It is generally assumed that seeds must be in direct contact with water in order to absorb enough moisture for germination. It has been demonstrated, however, that rye, wheat and barley can absorb enough water from a saturated atmosphere to germinate (Machalica 1926). Not all seeds require the same amount of water for germination, nor do they absorb the same amount under any given set of conditions.

TABLE IX: *Moisture Contents of Seeds stored at various Temperatures and relative Humidities (moisture expressed as percentage of dry weight of seeds):—*

SEED + % MOISTURE AT TIME OF STORAGE	% REL. HUM.	PER CENT MOISTURE AFTER STORAGE FOR 105 DAYS			
		5° C.	10° C.	20° C.	30° C.
Lettuce	35	5.8	5.9	5.2	4.5
6.5	55	8.0	8.5	6.8	5.4
	76	10.5	19.6	11.1	10.4
Onion	35	9.2	9.1	8.3	7.2
10.2	55	12.4	15.1	11.0	8.8
	76	15.2	30.5	17.1	13.8
Tomato	35	8.1	8.3	7.4	6.3
8.9	55	11.4	13.1	9.7	7.7
	76	13.8	15.7	15.9	12.6
Flax	35	6.8	6.8	6.1	5.3
7.6	55	9.3	11.0	8.1	6.4
	76	11.4	16.5	13.0	11.2
Pine	35	7.0	7.4	6.3	5.5
8.1	55	9.8	10.8	8.4	6.9
	76	11.6	14.6	12.8	11.8
Peanut	35	4.8	4.8	4.5	3.9
5.8	55	7.0	7.7	5.9	4.6
	76	8.6	13.9	9.1	9.7

Barton (1941) found that seeds showed differential absorption of water from the air under the same conditions of temperature and relative humidity according to the species. Moisture contents of seeds of lettuce, onion, tomato, flax, pine, and peanut after storage for 105 days at 5°, 10°, 20°, and 30° C. at relative humidities of 35, 55, and 76 per cent are shown in Table IX. In the order of increasing water-absorption capacity, the seeds were peanut, lettuce, flax, pine, tomato, and onion. This order persisted regardless of storage temperature or atmospheric humidity. With a relative humidity of 35 per cent, seeds took up approximately the same amount of water at 5° and 10° C., but in every case, less water was absorbed at the higher temperatures of 20° and 30° C. At 55 and 76 per cent relative humidities, however, the peak of moisture absorption was at 10° C. and the lowest absorption at 30° C. The importance of these phenomena will be discussed further in connection with the keeping quality of seeds under different conditions. Stiles (1948) found that Rogers Acala cotton had a total water absorption of 320.53 per cent after 96 hours, while Sure Cropper corn had only 153.54 per cent. She stated that seeds are adapted to mesic, hydric, or xeric germination according to the habitat in which they grow, and that such adaptations are evident in the water requirements of the axis of the embryo and the imbibitional capacity of the cotyledons and endosperm. Thus one would expect varietal differences. Kisser and Schmid (1932) also pointed out the variation of the amount and course of water absorption with the kind of plant. Protein-rich peas were capable of faster water absorption than those with less protein. Also, the minimum water necessary for germination may be greater in seeds with low germination vigor (Dunin and Miazdrikova 1930). This is a phase of the water relations of seeds which needs more investigation.

Even when the seed is fully imbibed with water and apparently has all of the other conditions necessary for germination, it sometimes fails due to the mechanical restriction of the enveloping structures. This has been demonstrated for seeds of the water plant, *Alisma plantago,* the coats of which limit the swelling of the embryo (Crocker and Davis 1914). This restriction may be removed naturally only after years of lying in water. Dry storage of certain seeds may also make their coats more permeable both to oxygen and to water. The upper seed of the cocklebur is an example of the former (Crocker 1906). In studies at Boyce Thompson Institute with certain seeds which after-ripen in dry storage it has been shown that the initial rate of water absorption, as well as the total amount absorbed, tends to increase as the after-ripening proceeds (Crocker 1948, p. 126).

Semipermeable Membranes:—A membrane which will permit the solvent to pass through but not the solute is called semipermeable. The characteristic reaction of the membrane depends upon the type of walls surrounding the individual cells that make up the tissue.

Using disks of beet tissue, Skene (1943) found that the cellulose walls offered a differential resistance to the passage of solutes, but concluded that, in spite of this, the cell wall would have very little to do with the cellular exchange under ordinary conditions, for the protoplasmic permeability is so much lower.

Other published works have given evidence of the semipermeable character of the membranes surrounding seeds of different types. Shull (1913) working principally with *Xanthium* but also including a number of seeds in various families discovered that all seeds do not exhibit the same degree of semipermeability. *Xanthium* seed coats, for example, permit very slow passage of some solutes such as sodium chloride, copper sulphate, glycerols, sugars, and HCl, those of the sunflower and peach restrict the passage less, and bean coats are still more permeable. The importance of semipermeability in the effects of salts and other substances which must reach the embryo of the seed through the coats is stressed by Shull (1913). If semipermeability is commonly to be found in seeds, the physical and chemical characteristics of the seed coats must be considered in the study of germination behavior. The selective activity is independent of any living substance in the seed coat, for the coat of *Xanthium* can be removed and used as an osmotic membrane. The testa is composed of three layers, the outer of which cannot function as a semipermeable membrane. Both the middle and the inner membrane, which can be split apart by the use of strong alkalies, possess osmotic properties, the inner layer to a higher degree than the middle one.

The differences in the degree of permeability of cell walls to water in some seed coats were shown by Denny (1917a). The amount of water passing through equal areas in the same period of time from distilled water to a saturated solution of sodium chloride with an osmotic pressure of approximately 375 atmospheres was 0, 4.0, 9.3, 18.2, 88.5, and 565.1 milligrams for the seed coats of grapefruit, *Cucurbita pepo*, *Cucurbita maxima*, cocklebur, almond, and peanut respectively. In order to ascertain the possible cause of this differential permeability, Denny (1917b) made a study of the chemical composition of the membranes. After determining the flow of water through a membrane, it was extracted with a solvent and the flow again determined. Also cross sections of the tissues were studied microchemically to determine the nature of the substances present and the effects of the treatments upon them. The results proved the significance of lipoids in restricting water permeability. Their removal increased the water flow through the membrane and re-impregnation with the removed lipoid material decreased permeability though not to the point exhibited before extraction. The presence of tannins and pectic substances was also correlated with a reduction in permeability. Suberized layers usually considered important in the restriction of water movement were not a dominant factor in the membranes studied by Denny.

By the removal of different layers of the fruit or seed coats surrounding the seed and subsequent immersion in water the particular layer concerned in absorption inhibition can be determined. As a rule, natural swelling of a seed in water begins at the micropylar opening opposite which an extra thinness of the membranes has been found in some seeds.

Carefully selected, viable seeds of *Spinacea oleracea inermis*, *Cucumis sativus*, *Capsicum annuum*, *Triticum vulgare*, *Secale cereale*, and *Hordeum distichum* as well as commercial samples of the grain seeds were soaked for 16 hours in 1.5 per cent solutions of KNO_3 and $MnSO_4 \cdot 4H_2O$ and the intake of the salts by the seeds and the diffusion of the salts from the seeds in subsequent soaking was determined by means of electrical conductivity measurements of the external solutions (Kotowski 1927). As a result of these tests it was concluded that the seed coverings checked the intake of KNO_3, especially in the cereals. The absorption of salt also depended upon the kind of seed and the cation and anion of the salt. When the seed coverings were intact the absorbed salts were held superficially and a large percentage was lost when the seeds were washed one minute. This is a very important fact when seeds are treated with various substances for stimulatory effects.

The permeability of seed to iodine solution has been the subject of study by Harrington and Crocker (1923) for Johnson grass, by Braun (1924) for wheat, and by Malhotra (1931) for *Zea mays*. All are agreed that iodine enters the seeds. In some cases too much iodine penetrates the seed coat and kills the embryo, while in others the embryo is killed as soon as it emerges from the coat and comes in contact with a more concentrated solution of the toxic material. It was claimed by Malhotra (1931) that a very weak solution of iodine (0.05 per cent) stimulated, to a very slight extent, corn seeds which had been immersed in it, and the resulting seedlings showed somewhat better growth than the control lots. He was interested in the permeability of corn seeds to iodine from the point of view of obtaining seedlings with higher iodine content to help prevent endemic goiter.

The selective absorption of ions by seeds of soy beans and corn has been studied by Rudolfs (1925a and b). He recorded the changes in hydrogen-ion concentration and the rate of the reaction change after definite time intervals in solution of aluminum nitrate and aluminum sulfate. Only three minutes were required for soybeans to change the aluminum nitrate solutions from pH 4.5 to 3.6 and twelve minutes from 3.6 back to 4.5 while after 60 minutes the H-ion concentration was changed to pH 5.8, where it remained for the next 18 hours. In the sulfate solution and for corn seeds, the same general course was followed. Rudolfs believed that the absorption of the ions was greatly influenced by the nature of the protein material in the seeds. Seeds of rice, wheat, and peas were found to regulate the acidity of the solution in which they were soaked bringing it to a pH of about 7.0 if the soaking liquid was water and to a lower pH in solutions of monovalent salts and still lower if the solute was a bivalent salt (Kurbatov and Glückmann 1930). These changes in pH were independent of the swelling of the seed or of the temperature.

TABLE X: *Moisture Intake of Xanthium Seeds in Osmotic Solutions* (Temperature 23.5° C.; Intake in Percentage of Air-dry Weight; Shull 1916):—

SOLUTIONS VOLUME MOLECULAR	1 HR.	4 HRS.	7 HRS.	10 HRS.	24 HRS.	48 HRS.	OSMOTIC PRESSURE IN ATMOSPHERES
H₂O	16.39	44.38	48.78	50.38	51.18	51.58	0.0
0.1 M NaCl	16.79	39.43	45.87	46.48	46.39	46.33	3.8
0.2 M NaCl	17.12	38.67	45.00	45.57	45.93	45.52	7.6
0.3 M NaCl	16.07	34.05	40.75	41.95	42.24	42.05	11.4
0.4 M NaCl	14.36	31.21	38.08	39.97	40.33	40.27	15.2
0.5 M NaCl	13.96	30.26	35.87	38.08	38.70	38.98	19.0
0.6 M NaCl	13.80	25.57	32.41	33.57	34.77	35.18	22.8
0.7 M NaCl	13.32	26.29	30.99	31.73	32.79	32.85	26.6
0.8 M NaCl	13.13	25.22	29.21	29.95	31.12	31.12	30.4
0.9 M NaCl	12.58	24.34	27.64	28.95	29.14	29.79	34.2
1.0 M NaCl	11.90	22.92	25.42	26.48	26.21	26.73	38.0
2.0 M NaCl	8.19	14.55	18.25	18.43	18.60	18.55	72.0
4.0 M NaCl	4.81	8.37	9.84	10.08	11.00	11.76	130.0
Sat. NaCl	3.42	4.94	5.24	5.84	6.21	6.35	375.0
Sat. LiCl	−0.67	−0.77	−0.58	−0.58	−0.58	−0.29	965.0

Denny and Youden (1927) made further studies on the effect of plant materials of different kinds, such as disks of potato tubers, carrot roots, apple fruits, whole seeds of corn, rye, and wheat, and corn seed powder, upon the pH of surrounding solutions. They were not able to confirm the report of Rudolfs that plant tissues when placed in salt solutions of different concentrations brought the external pH to characteristic values for each kind of tissue. They stated (p. 328): "Although our results do not show that the tissue itself or the proteins take no part whatever in these changes in pH, they indicate that the soluble, non-protein, non-colloidal substances which diffuse out of the tissue into the salt solution and which then react with it are important factors in the acidifications that are produced in the external solution." Also, Muhlack (1929) concluded that the seed testa of the pea has no selective permeability properties as shown by solutions of dye and dialysis tests with electrolytes.

The absorption characteristics of seeds in salt solutions depend not only on the character of the membranes to be traversed but upon the nature, especially the osmotic value, of the cell sap and of the external solution.

The attraction of air-dry seeds of *Xanthium pennsylvanicum* for water was measured by Shull (1916) and was found to be nearly 1000 atmospheres. He used different concentrations of solutions of sodium chloride (from 0.1 M to saturated) and determined the intake of water by the seeds in each solution. With these data and the osmotic pressures of the salt solutions the attraction of the seeds for water could be calculated. Table X taken from Shull's publication (1916, Table III, p. 12) shows moisture intake of the lower seeds of *Xanthium pennsylvanicum* under the conditions just described.

In every mature living plant cell, the contents exert a pressure against the cell wall so that the cell is filled and perhaps somewhat expanded. With the release of this pressure due to removal of water from the cell, the cell contents contract and move away from the cell wall. This condition is known as plasmolysis. It may be caused by the higher osmotic concentration of the solution external to the cell resulting in a movement of water outward from the smaller concentration of osmotically active substances within the cell. Since plasmolysis is characteristic of living cells only, the method has been used with some success in determining the germinating capacity of seeds of some legumes and fruit trees (Doroshenko 1937).

In order to absorb water only when immersed in salt solutions seeds must possess semipermeable membranes. According to Atkins (1909), the membranes of seeds of beans and sweet peas become semipermeable only after germination begins, the cell protoplasm acting as a membrane at that time. There was no difference in absorption by living and dead seeds up to the time of germination. For these seeds he maintained that the forces concerned were capillarity and imbibition in the initial stages of water absorption and osmosis after germination.

The permeability of different seed coats has been studied extensively through their absorption of water from salt solutions. Barley grains have been the subject of several experiments by Brown (1907, 1909; Brown & Tinker 1916). It was demonstrated that the membrane was semipermeable to copper sulfate, ferrous sulfate, potassium chromate, silver nitrate, and potassium ferrocyanide, since water was taken up from solutions containing them but none of the solutes entered the seed. As regards other substances, among which were mercuric chloride, acetic, formic, propionic, and butyric acids, and ammonia, however, the membrane was permeable. This brings up the selective permeability character of seed coats, allowing certain solutes to be absorbed and certain others excluded. Brown (1932) claimed that there was evidence that the cuticle-like membranes of the semipermeable system of wheat grains carry electrical charges which affect the absorption of electrolytes. He concluded that the regulation of the absorption of the solute by the wheat grain was through: (A) electrical adsorption in the cuticle-like membrane, (B) mechanical adsorption in the testa and the tissues of the endosperm and embryo, (C) the imbibitional pressure developed in the endosperm, and (D) the size of the intermolecular spaces of the semipermeable membranes.

Temperature Effects:—There is no doubt that the temperature has an effect on the rate of water absorption. Brown and Worley (1912) in their study of barley grains found that the velocity with which they absorbed water was almost exactly an exponential function of the temperature. Shull (1920), using seeds of *Xanthium* and several varieties of peas, was not able to confirm the results of Brown and Worley, but found, rather, that the velocity of intake at any given moment was approximately an inverse exponential function of the amount of water previously absorbed. This same conclusion was reached by Singh and Tandon (1935). Therefore both physical and chemical changes are involved. The rate of moisture absorption by tobacco seeds has been shown to increase at higher temperatures but the total absorbed was less at higher temperatures (Poptzoff 1932). Other external factors as well as the age of the seed had an effect on the water-holding capacity of these seeds. Singh and Tandon (1935) also showed the unfavorable effect of immersion of seeds in water at temperatures as high as 40° or 45° C. They maintained that with prolonged immersion under these conditions seeds actually showed negative absorption to a certain extent, as indicated by a loss in weight. Ohga (1926) observed double maxima in the rate of absorption of water by Indian lotus seeds regardless of temperature. The cause of the second maximum was not known, but it was thought probable that it was determined by the nature and structure of the seed materials.

Experiments on temperature effects are thus seen to emphasize the complexity of the absorption process.

TABLE XI: *Absorption of Moisture by untreated Corn Kernels, placed on Blotters with Embryo and Endosperm down at Temperatures of 30°, 20°, 10°, and 5° C.* (Davis and Porter 1936):—

Exp. No.	Temp. ° C.	No. Kernels	Original Weight in Grams	Per Cent Water Absorbed		Per Cent Germination	
				24 hrs.	48 hrs.	24 hrs.	48 hrs.
			Embryo down:—				
1	30	20	5.5017	25.70	39.25	10.0	90.0
2	30	20	6.1520	28.46	31.44	15.0	75.0
3	30	20	6.2612	34.53	47.37	—	30.0
4	30	20	4.8022	30.34	45.98	10.0	95.0
5	20	20	5.1929	24.99	34.80	—	55.0
6	20	20	6.6535	17.79	22.79	—	—
7	10	20	5.1981	18.08	27.40	—	—
8	10	20	5.1528	18.12	26.09	—	—
9*	5	20	6.4764	—	15.4	—	—
*		20	6.2107	—	11.3	—	—
Summary		160	44.9144	24.57	34.27	4.37	43.12
			Endosperm down:—				
1	30	20	5.8192	18.56	28.82	—	5.0
2	30	20	6.0432	21.81	21.81	—	—
3	30	20	6.4713	26.47	36.48	—	—
4	30	20	5.2408	24.77	32.42	—	5.0
5	20	20	5.2681	22.59	29.22	—	—
6	20	20	6.5550	14.15	15.78	—	—
7	10	20	5.4865	15.89	23.37	—	—
8	10	20	5.1697	14.95	21.47	—	—
9*	5	20	5.8598	—	7.4	—	—
*		20	6.0938	—	7.4	—	—
Summary		160	46.1538	19.93	26.12	—	1.25

* Not included in summary.

Structure and Chemical Composition of the Seed:—The embryo and the endosperm of the seed appear to be independent in their moisture absorption.

The embryo of grains took up about twice as much water as the endosperm (Buchinger 1932). This was reflected in better germination with the embryo side down than with the endosperm side next to the moist medium. Similar results, some of which are shown in Table XI, were obtained with corn kernels (Davis and Porter

1936, part of Table 2, p. 64). In 48 hours there was a significant difference in moisture absorbed with embryo or endosperm side down. This same difference was observed when the embryos of corn were killed by heating to 180° C. before the absorption tests. Water absorption capacity would seem, then, to depend upon physical and chemical characteristics of the tissues of the different parts of the grains of corn. Further light has been thrown on this subject by the work of Dungan (1924). Corn was harvested at three different dates, the harvested grain representing three different stages of maturity: milk stage, the dent stage, and the mature stage. Grains in the three stages were subjected to the same curing conditions and all contained practically the same amount of water when the absorption tests were begun. More water was taken up and the rate was more rapid for seeds collected in the milk stage than for those collected in the dent stage, and absorption in the latter exceeded that of those in the mature stage. This effect was attributed to the larger proportion of soft starch in the immature seeds. The amount of oil in the corn grain had no effect on absorption capacity but there was a great difference in the percentage of water taken up by high and low protein strains (15.29 per cent and 6.10 per cent protein). A large part of the protein of the high-protein strain was found to be in the endosperm giving it a horny texture which doubtless contributed to the low absorption. Alberts (1927) corroborated these findings reporting that floury endosperm of corn takes up more moisture than horny endosperm. Singh and Tandon (1935) extended the work on chemical composition of seeds as an influence in moisture absorption. They chose six species having seeds of a starchy nature, and four and three species representative of a proteinaceous group and an oily and proteinaceous group respectively. Water intake was determined under 156 combinations of external variables. In spite of irregularities the seeds which were chemically and structurally similar showed more or less similar absorption rates. Starchy seeds showed high absorption under good air and water conditions and less when immersed except *Oryza* of which the reverse was true. Oily seeds absorbed less under water and responded to better aeration conditions with a marked increase. No saturation limit was reached by proteinaceous seeds, a continuous increase being obtained under adequate aeration and moisture supply.

The structure and chemical composition of each of the different parts of the seed exert an influence, either collectively or singly, on moisture absorption. It was pointed out by Shull (1920) that different factors might become limiting as the absorption progresses. If the seed coat transmits water more slowly than the seed substance can absorb it transmission is the limiting factor. If the transmission power of the coat exceeds the absorption power of the seed contents, the latter becomes limiting. If the seed coat, embryo, and endosperm are non-homogeneous, the absorption rate may be dominated by one structure then by the others in succession, giving irregular and peculiar absorption curves.

Variety of Seed:—The differential capacity of different species and varieties of seeds to absorb water from solutions has already been mentioned. Rudolfs (1921) found marked differences in the absorbing power of seeds of different species and Burke (1930) noted the fluctuation within varieties of *Triticum vulgare* and *T. durum*.

The behavior of seeds in solutions of different osmotic pressure has been used to identify varieties. A considerable literature has been developed on the subject. A critical review of the reports up to 1932 has been made by Schratz (1932) to whose article the reader is referred for details. One of the methods was that developed by Buchinger. The seeds were supported between glass rods or beads in contact with a series of sugar solutions of increasing concentration and allowed to germinate. At the conclusion of the germination period the osmotic pressure of the solution which permitted 50 per cent as much germination as water, expressed in atmospheres, was taken as the "suction-force maximum" of the species or variety examined. It was thought that the osmotic activity of the sugar solution balanced the osmotic and imbibitional forces within the seed and retarded the entrance of water into the seed. Hence the higher the concentration of sugar solution in which the seed would germinate, the greater was the water absorption capacity of the seed.

Successful use has been made of this method to distinguish between commercial and home-grown strains of *Phleum* sp., *Lolium italicum*, and *Lolium perenne* (Chippindale 1931). Commercial seeds exhibited consistently higher suction forces than corresponding home-grown strains. The possibility of using such germination tests as a criterion in the identification of any given sample of seed is suggested.

Wheat seeds selected by germinating under certain osmotic pressure conditions have proved drought and cold resistant, thus making possible a classification of strains as to desirability for growth in certain areas (Bolsunov 1927; Anon. 1937). The drought resistance of rice has been determined by the absorptive power of the seeds (Onodera 1934). In unknown variety tests a known standard must be included for comparison. It might be expected that the climatic conditions under which the specific seed lot matures would affect the plasma colloids and hence the osmotic properties. This is pointed out by Walker (1934) in his work with varieties of oats, in which no correlation between suction-force value of the seeds and subsequent growth behavior was found.

Artificial Membranes:—The question arises as to whether it is possible to make an artificial semipermeable membrane. Weatherby (1943) prepared asymmetric membranes by the addition of phospholipids (lecithin and cephalin) to collodion. The membrane containing lecithin showed electrical potentials at pH values less than approximately 7.0 to 7.5, the lower the pH the higher the potential. Membrane containing cephalin, on the other hand, usually exhibited electrical potentials throughout a pH range of from 2.75 to 11.0, the higher the pH the higher the potential. The signs of the potentials were reversed as the pH was changed from values below 4.5 to those above. Membranes containing either or both lipids were permeable to weak acids such as propionic and salicylic, and to weak bases such as nicotine, but were impermeable to their salts. Variations in permeability of the membranes containing both lipids to nicotine at different pH values paralleled the variations in toxicity of nicotine for *Paramacium caudatum* under similar pH conditions. It was suggested that the membrane potentials were the result of ionization of the acidic and basic groups in the lipids, and that these ions remain in the collodion membrane and thus impart their charges to the membrane. Such charged membranes repel ions or similar charges, so that salts do not permeate readily, as do the unionized molecules of acids and bases.

Another method of preparing "permselective" collodion membranes was described by Gregor and Sollner (1946). A solution of collodion in ether-alcohol was poured over a test tube rotating slowly in a horizontal position and then the film was allowed to dry for several minutes. This process was repeated until three layers of film had been applied. The tubes were then immersed in distilled water after which the membranes were oxidized in 1 M NaOH for 8 to 14 minutes, followed by soaking in water to remove the hydroxide. Still on the tubes the membranes were then dried in air. These membranes were said to combine great permeability with extreme ionic selectivity over wide concentration ranges.

After-Effects of Soaking Seeds:—Theoretically, soaking seeds accelerates the metabolic processes preparatory to germination. This is accompanied by the absorption of oxygen, the release of carbon dioxide and a diminishing of the food reserve. The effect of soaking is dependent upon the relative amount, kind and temperature of water or solution used, the length of the soaking period, aeration, size of the seed and density of the seed mass. The vernalization process described in another chapter is primarily a controlled soaking process. As pointed out there, vernalization has some very favorable effects on the further growth of the plant.

As for other soaking treatments, different investigators have reported favorable and unfavorable effects. The lack of uniformity of results has probably been due in a large measure to the variations in the conditions of the experiment.

Acceleration of germination has been produced by soaking in many instances. Some grass seeds, especially *Dactylis glomerata,* are favorably affected by soaking (Chippindale 1934). Instances of other types of favorable effects have been reported. Soaking seeds of nine different varieties of wheat as well as some oats, barley, and maize has prevented seed injury from disinfectants by diluting the chemicals as they enter the tissues and has increased the germicidal efficiency of the disinfectants by making the seed coat pathogens more susceptible (Braun 1919). The high boron requirement of cotton has been supplied by soaking the cotton seeds in boric acid before planting (Novikov and Sadovskaja 1939).

The temperature of soaking is of prime importance in any injury produced. Surprisingly, it has been found that soaking at 10° and 30° C. is more injurious to beans than soaking at 20° C. (Kidd and West 1919; Eyster 1936). Eyster (1939) attributed this difference to a greater loss of protein at 10° and 30° C. In a later paper (1940) he added enzymes and growth promoting substances to the constituents leached out of bean seeds during soaking and concluded that this also contributed to the injury. His results were based on chemical analyses of the water in which the seeds had been soaked. Kidd and West (1919) had previously noted that the rate of exosmosis of soluble food reserves was much greater at 30° than at 20° C. but only slightly greater at 10° than at 20° C., not enough to be significant in the latter case.

Harmful action of soaking seeds of several different kinds was reported by Kidd and West (1918). Both seed germination and subsequent growth of the plant were involved. Prolonged soaking in tap water was also found deleterious for many kinds of seed by Tilford *et al.* (1924). They did not exclude the possible leaching of soluble food from the seeds, but rather emphasized the much greater importance of the bacterial factor. That the capacity for germination was not destroyed by long continued soaking, even up to three months, in sterile media (Barton 1929) lends credence to this explanation. Thus it was demonstrated that the destructive changes were not brought about by the enzymes in the seeds and that any changes taking place in the seed did not affect the viability. The injurious effects of presoaking seeds of soy beans has been attributed by Resühr (1941) to the high water permeability of the testa. Injury due to the low oxygen present in water slows their germination and subjects the young seedlings to more hazards, such as bacteria and fungi. Soy beans are very sensitive to the amount of moisture in the soil.

Instead of the injurious effect of low oxygen present in the soaking water, Albaum *et al.* (1942) reported that oat seedlings were adversely affected after exposure of the seed to oxygen. Experiments conducted in this laboratory (Barton 1950) have confirmed these results, and have opened up possibilities of new lines of investigation to determine the mechanism of oxygen action. We have found that not only oats are injured by exposure to oxygen, but the same effects have been found in wheat, beans, corn, sunflower, and cocklebur. Furthermore, the deleterious effect of soaking beans may be overcome by supplying them with carbon dioxide during the soaking period. A pronounced reduction in the water absorption rate of bean seeds soaked in the presence of carbon dioxide has indicated a direct relationship between this behavior and injury from soaking. Also there is a tendency for absorption far beyond the point needed for germination when oxygen is supplied during the soaking process. Air induces greater absorption than nitrogen. It appears from the data at hand, however, that there are certain gas effects which are independent of the effects of moisture absorption. Further studies on these effects are in progress. Treatment has consisted in placing intact seeds or excised embryos in water through which different gases have been bubbled at different temperatures.

In contrast to the injurious effects of soaking just discussed, seeds of some plants native to the region of Cold Spring Harbor, N. Y., were found to survive long periods of submergence in water without apparent harmful effects (Shull 1914). Twenty-two different species were placed on a layer of soil and covered with water. Eleven of these germinated after a submergence of more than four years and at least three species were still represented by viable seeds at the end of seven years of continuous submergence. These were seeds of land and not water plants, and serve to indicate that soaking is not always as harmful as generally assumed.

The harmful action of distilled water on biological material was recognized at an early date. A search for the poisonous substances concerned revealed contamination of the water from metal stills. Following this, water distilled from glass was considered a safe medium. But a number of investigators found even that harmful through the action of impurities, perhaps dissolved ammonia. Later workers showed that organisms lost soluble material when in contact with distilled water.

Lupine roots were injured by distilled water (True 1914). The injury could be prevented by the addition of calcium salt in sufficient quantity to make it osmotically equal to tap water. Sugar or sodium chloride solutions of the same osmotic concentration as calcium did not remove the harmful effect of distilled water. Scarth (1924) found that distilled water free of metal ions but exposed to air was highly toxic to *Spirogyra*. Again, cations nullified the toxic action, their effectiveness varying according to their valency and of course limited by their own toxicity. The positive deleterious factor thus eliminated was the hydrogen-ion concentration, increased by dissolved carbon dioxide.

Bailey (1933), on the other hand, obtained very little modification of the injurious effect of distilled water on seeds soaked in it by the addition of calcium salt. A decreased germination rate was the first noticeable effect of distilled water soaking of the seeds. Some of the seedlings from seeds subjected to prolonged soaking were unable to reach maturity. Of those that survived, growth was reduced and a longer time was required for the plants to reach maturity. Certain morphological variations from normal were found, along with a higher percentage of carbohydrates and a lower percentage of proteins. These plants were thought to have lost some of their ability to form nitrogen compounds from the carbohydrates, and the consequent reduction in nitrogen compounds caused the reduced growth. Since the water used for soaking was sterile and aerated, bacterial action and lack of oxygen or accumulation of carbon dioxide were eliminated as deleterious agents.

Still another hypothesis to explain the retardation of growth of *Bacterium coli* by freshly distilled water was given by Hegarty and Rahn (1934). According to them distilled water immediately after condensation consists mostly of single water molecules as opposed to the predominance of the double-molecular form under ordinary conditions and the triple-molecular form to be found in melted ice. The growth rate of B. coli was retarded in mono-molecular water and was normal in the di- and tri-molecular forms. About four hours after distillation growth was normal indicating the assumption of a di-molecular character of the distilled water. Other reports have not emphasized the "age" of the distilled water used, but it is doubtful if this explanation would hold for many of the effects discussed above.

References:—

Albaum, H. G., J. Donnelly & S. Korkes, 1942: The growth and metabolism of oat seedlings after seed exposure to oxygen (Amer. Jour. Bot. 29:388-395).

Alberts, H. W., 1927: Relation of endosperm character in corn to absorption of hygroscopic moisture (Amer. Soc. Agron. Jour. 19:590-595).

Atkins, W. R. G., 1909: The absorption of water by seeds (Royal Dublin Soc. Sci. Proc. n. s. 12:35-46; *abstr. in* Exp. Sta. Rec. 21:725-726. 1909).

Bailey, W. M., 1933: Structural and metabolic after-effects of soaking seeds of *Phaseolus* (Bot. Gaz. 94:688-713).

Barton, A. W., 1929: The effect of long-continued soaking on seed germination (Trans. Kansas Acad. Sci. 32:37).

Barton, L. V., 1941: Relation of certain air temperatures and humidities to viability of seeds (Contrib. Boyce Thompson Inst. 12:85-102).

————, 1950: Relation of different gases to the soaking injury of seeds. (Contrib. Boyce Thompson Inst. 16:55-71).

Bolsunov, I., 1927: Selection of wheat seed by testing in salt solutions (Zap. Kiiv, Silsk. Gosp. Inst. [Mem. Agr. Inst. Kiev] 2:33-41; *abstr.* in Exp. Sta. Rec. 63:124. 1930).

Braun, H, 1919: Presoaking as a means of preventing seed injury due to disinfectants and of increasing germicidal efficiency (Science 49:544-545).

————, 1924: A gradient of permeability to iodin in wheat seed coats (a preliminary note) (Jour. Agric. Res. 28:225-226).

Brown, A. J., 1907: On the existence of a semi-permeable membrane enclosing the seeds of the *Gramineae* (Ann. Bot. 21:79-87).

————, 1909: The selective permeability of the coverings of seeds of *Hordeum vulgare* (Proc. Roy. Soc. London, B, 81:82-93).

Brown, A. J., & F. Tinker, 1916: Selective permeability: the absorption of phenol and other solutions by the seeds of *Hordeum vulgare* (Proc. Roy. Soc. London, B, 89:373-379).

Brown, A. J., & F. P. Worley, 1912: The influence of temperature on the absorption of water by seeds of *Hordeum vulgare* in relation to the temperature coefficient of chemical change (Proc. Roy. Soc. London, B, 85:546-553).

Brown, R., 1932: The absorption of the solute from aqueous solutions by the grain of wheat (Ann. Bot. 46:571-582).

Buchinger, A., 1932: Welchen Anteil haben Embryo und Endosperm an der Saugkraft der Getreidefrüchte? Dargestellt an *Triticum* spelta muticum! (Internat. Seed Test. Assoc. Proc. 4:46-64).

Burke, T. W. L., 1930: Studies of water absorption and germination with varieties of *Triticum vulgare* and *T. durum* (Sci. Agric. 10:369-388).

Chippindale, H. G., 1931: "Suction-force" measurements on the seeds of some strains of grasses (Welsh Jour. Agric. 7:168-182).

————, 1934: The effect of soaking in water on the "seeds" of some *Gramineae* (Ann. Appl. Biol. 21:225-232).

Crocker, W., 1906: Rôle of seed coats in delayed germination (Bot. Gaz. 42:265-291).

————, 1948: Growth of plants. Twenty years' research at Boyce Thompson Institute (459 pp., Reinhold Publ. Corp., New York).

Crocker, W., & W. E. Davis, 1914: Delayed germination in seed of *Alisma plantago* (Bot. Gaz. 58:285-321).

Davis, G. N., & R. H. Porter, 1936: Comparative absorption of water by endosperm and embryo of corn kernels (Assoc. Off. Seed Anal. No. Amer. Proc. 28:62-67).

Denny, F. E., 1917a: Permeability of certain plant membranes to water (Bot. Gaz. 63: 373-397).

————, 1917b: Permeability of membranes as related to their composition (Bot. Gaz. 63:468-485).

Denny, F. E., & W. J. Youden, 1927: Acidification of unbuffered salt solutions by plant tissue in relation to the question of tissue isoelectric points (Amer. Jour. Bot. 14:395-414; *also in* Contrib. Boyce Thompson Inst. 1:309-328, 1927).

Doroshenko, A. V., 1937: Plasmolytic method of determining the germinating capacity of seeds (Engl. summary) (Bull. Appl. Bot., Genet., & Plant Breed. Ser. IV 2:119).

Dungan, G. H., 1924: Some factors affecting the water absorption and germination of seed corn (Amer. Soc. Agron. Jour. 16:473-481).

Dunin, I. S., & M. N. Miazdrikova, 1930: Method of determining the minimum water quantity for seed germination (Jard. Bot. Princ., Ann. essais semences [Leningrad] 7(2):71-103; *abstr. in* Biol. Abstr. 6:12860, 1932).

Eyster, H. C., 1936: Sensitivity of seeds to soaking (Amer. Jour. Bot. 23:691).

————, 1939: Cause of decreased germination of bean seeds soaked in water (Amer. Jour. Bot. 26:18s).

————, 1940: The cause of decreased germination of bean seeds soaked in water (Amer. Jour. Bot. 27:652-659).

Gregor, H. P., & K. Sollner, 1946: Improved methods of preparation of "permselective" collodion membranes combining extreme ionic selectivity with high permeability (Jour. Phys. Chem. 50:53-70).

Harrington, G. T., & W. Crocker, 1923: Structure, physical characteristics, and composition of the pericarp and integument of Johnson grass seed in relation to its physiology (Jour. Agric. Res. 23:193-222).

Hegarty, C. P., & O. Rahn, 1934: Growth retardation by freshly distilled water (Jour. Bacteriol. 28:20-30; *abstr. in* Biol. Abstr. 9:4676, 1935).

Kidd, F., & C. West, 1918: Physiological pre-determination: The influence of the physiological condition of the seed upon the course of subsequent growth and upon the yield. I. The effects of soaking seeds in water (Ann. Appl. Biol. 5:1-10).

————, ————, 1919: The influence of temperature on the soaking of seeds (New Phytol. 18:35-39).

Kisser, J., & H. Schmid, 1932: Untersuchungen über die Permeabilität der Samenhüllen von *Pisum* und *Triticum* für Wasser sowie die Saugkräfte der Samen (Anz. Akad. d. Wiss. Wien, Math., Naturw. Kl. 69:197-200; *abstr. in* Bot. Centralbl. 166:145, 1934).

Kotowski, F., 1927: Semipermeability of seed coverings and stimulation of seeds (Plant Physiol. 2:177-186).

Kurbatov, V., & S. Glückmann, 1930: The influence of inorganic ions on the properties of seeds (Protoplasma 9:34-96).

Machalica, J. J., 1926: Germination of cereals in moist atmosphere (Roczniki Nauk Rolniczych i Lesnych [Polish Agr. & Forest. Ann.] 15:407-423; *abstr. in* Biol. Abstr. 6:21624, 1932).

Malhotra, R. C., 1931: Periodic permeability of iodine solution and water in the protoplasm of *Zea mays* seeds (Protoplasma 13:374-388).

Meyer, B. S., 1945: A critical evaluation of the terminology of diffusion phenomena (Plant Physiol. 20:142-164).

Muhlack, E., 1929: Zur Keimungsgeschichte der Erbse (Bot. Arch. 26:437-485).

Novikov, V. A., & R. O. Sadovskaja, 1939: Soaking of cotton seeds in boric acid as a means going to satisfy the boron requirement and increase salt resistance (Compt. Rend. Acad. Sci. U.R.S.S. 23:276-279).

Ohga, I., 1926: A double maximum in the rate of absorption of water by Indian lotus seeds (Amer. Jour. Bot. 13:766-772).

Onodera, J., 1934: On the experiments of germination and absorption power of water in the seeds of rice as a method of estimation of drought resistance among the varieties of rice plants (Crop Sci. Soc. Japan Proc. 6:20-43; *abstr. in* Exp. Sta. Rec. 71:470, 1934).

Poptzoff, A. V., 1932: Hygroscopic properties of tobacco seed (Krasnodar Inst. of Tobacco Indus. USSR, Bull. 88, 36 pp.).

Resühr, B., 1941: Ueber die Bedeutung konstitutioneller Mängel für das Auftreten von Keimlingschäden bei *Soja hispida* Moench. II. Beitrag (Zeitschr. f. Pflanzenkrankheiten [Pflanzenpathologie] u. Pflanzenschutz 51:161-192).

Rudolfs, W., 1921: Effect of salt solutions having definite osmotic concentration values upon absorption by seeds (Soil Science 11:277-293).

————, 1925a: Effect of seeds upon hydrogen-ion concentration equilibrium in solution (Jour. Agric. Res. 30:1021-1026).

————, 1925b: Selective absorption of ions by seeds (Soil Science 20:249-252).

Scarth, G. W., 1924: The toxic action of distilled water and its antagonism by cations (McGill Univ. Publ. Series II [Botany] 18(28):8pp.).

Schratz, E., 1932: Die Keimprüfung in Zuckerlösung ("Saugkraftbestimmung") und ihre Bedeutung für die Sortenkunde (ein kritischer Überblick) (Der Züchter 4:161-174).

Shull, C. A., 1913: Semipermeability of seed coats (Bot. Gaz. 56:169-199).

————, 1916: Measurement of the surface forces in soils (Bot. Gaz. 62:1-31).

————, 1920: Temperature and rate of moisture intake in seeds (Bot. Gaz. 69:361-390).

Shull, C. A., & S. P. Shull, 1932: Irregularities in the rate of absorption by dry plant tissues (Bot. Gaz. 93:376-399).

Shull, G. H., 1914: The longevity of submerged seeds (Plant World 17:329-337).

Singh, B. N., & R. K. Tandon, 1935: Temperature-absorption characteristics during germination in seeds of differing structure and biochemic constitution under varying concentrations of oxygen and water supply (Proc. Indian Acad. Sci. 1B:496-518).

Skene, M., 1943: The permeability of the cellulose cell wall (Ann. Bot. n. s. 7:261-273).

Stiles, I. E., 1948: Relation of water to the germination of corn and cotton seeds (Plant Physiol. 23:201-222).

Tilford, P., C. F. Able & R. P. Hibbard, 1924: An injurious factor affecting the seeds of *Phaseolus vulgaris* soaked in water (Papers Mich. Acad. Sci., Art and Letters 4:345-356).

True, R. H., 1914: The harmful action of distilled water (Amer. Jour. Bot. 1:255-273).

Walker, R. G., 1934: "Suction-force" measurements on the seeds of some varieties of oats (Welsh Jour. Agric. 10:289-295).

Weatherby, J. H., 1943: Concerning the mechanism of membrane semipermeability (Jour. Cell. and Comp. Physiol. 21:1-17; *abstr. in* Biol. Abstr. 17:15495, 1943).

Anon., 1937: Determination of winter hardiness by germinating seeds in sugar and salt solutions (Herbage Rev. 5:161).

Chapter VI

RESPIRATION

RESPIRATION has been defined as the process which goes on in every living cell by means of which energy is released. In the normal respiration process, oxygen is absorbed, organic compounds disappear, carbon dioxide and water are given off, and energy is produced. Hence the process is usually considered to be one of oxidation. Babcock (1912) claims that metabolic water sufficient for all the vital processes of the plant is provided by the slow oxidation taking place as a result of direct respiration. In seeds which are not germinating this constant production of water is thought to be essential for maintaining viability. The definite knowledge of the materials used and the end products obtained might lead to the assumption that the process is simple. On the contrary, the intermediate steps are little known and probably involve a series of complex processes.

In addition to aerobic respiration in which oxygen is absorbed and used, there is a breakdown of food reserves in plants when oxygen is excluded. In such anaerobic respiration, carbon dioxide is produced without a corresponding uptake of oxygen and alcohol is formed.

The many phases of the respiration process in plants have been presented by Miller (1938) in his "Plant Physiology," and by Stiles (1935) in a review article on the subject. We shall discuss here only those dealing with seeds and, for the most part, with respiration in seeds before actual germination has occurred.

It is obvious that, even in seeds which are in a dry and apparently quiescent state, there must be some metabolic activity for the continuance of life. Many investigators have measured the carbon dioxide produced under various conditions and have considered that a satisfactory index of the respiratory activity of the tissue being studied. Others have claimed that a true picture depends not only upon the amount of carbon dioxide given off but also upon the amount of oxygen absorbed. This relationship changes under certain altered conditions and might indicate the nature of the processes taking place within the plant tissue under examination. The ratio of the volume of carbon dioxide given off to the volume of oxygen absorbed during respiration is called the respiratory quotient, written CO_2/O_2. Further discussion of this quotient appears in another section.

Factors Affecting Respiration of Seeds:—A consideration of the various conditions which influence respiratory rate in seeds reveals the difficulties in separating the several effects one from the other. However, certain definite trends can be indicated.

Seed coats.—The first item to be considered is the permeability to gases of the seed coat membranes. Brown (1940) found that the seed coat of *Cucurbita pepo* consists of two membranes of which the outer is much less permeable to gases than the inner, as shown by the following table taken from his paper:

Permeability to various Gases of inner and outer Membranes of the Seed Coat of Cucurbita pepo (Diffusion as c.c./cm.^{2}/hr.):—

	Outer membranes			Inner membranes		
	(1) CO_2	(2) O_2	(3) N_2	(1) CO_2	(2) O_2	(3) N_2
	3.2	0.0	0.0	14.3	4.0	3.6
	2.5	0.7	0.0	10.5	4.6	3.3
	3.2	0.0	0.5	13.5	3.9	2.9
	3.0	0.8	0.7	21.3	4.3	3.8
	3.4	0.6	0.0	14.9	4.4	2.5
	2.8	0.0	0.7	18.4	4.5	3.3
Means	3.0	0.35	0.31	15.5	4.3	3.2

The inner coat is the important one in gaseous exchange, however, since there is a micropylar opening in the outer coat. Absorption of water by the inner membrane increases its permeability to gases by furnishing a medium in which the gases can dissolve. According to Brown, the water also removes in solution some impermeable constituent of the membrane. The resistance of the inner membrane to gas diffusion is due to living tissues in the membrane. When these are killed the rate of diffusion increases considerably. In a later paper, Brown (1942) reported that the removal of the inner coat of *Cucurbita pepo* increased the rate of gas exchange. Still further studies (Brown 1943) involved the excision of embryos of barley and the accompanying respiratory changes. Low rates of oxygen uptake and carbon dioxide emission by the embryo of the intact seed were attributed to the low permeability of the seed coat membranes. Both rates increased when the embryo was removed from the seed and transferred to water.

Shull had shown in 1914 that much more oxygen was used by naked embryos of both upper and lower seeds of *Xanthium glabratum* than with corresponding seeds with coats intact. With the coats off the upper embryos absorb 5 times as much oxygen as with coats on and the lower embryos 2.5 times as much. Very thin seed coats impose great restrictions on gas absorption by the embryo.

The carbon dioxide production of whole and dehulled sunflower and flax seed also indicates more rapid respiration with the coats removed (Larmour *et al.* 1944). Frietinger (1927), on the other hand, obtained reduced carbon dioxide output in pea seeds with the coats removed as compared to those with coats intact. However, the former took up more oxygen the second day than the latter.

Moisture content.—The amount of moisture contained in seeds held in storage determines, to a large extent, the respiratory rate.

A gradual increase in respiration followed increased moisture content of sorghum grains stored under uniform laboratory conditions (Coleman *et al.* 1928). Cracked or broken sorghum kernels with high moisture contents or heat-damaged kernels respire more vigorously than normal whole kernels. Bailey (1940) adjusted the amount of moisture in certain cereal grains and flax seed by adding water to weighed lots of air-dry seeds in large, tightly-stoppered bottles. He kept the samples at 2° C. to prevent the growth of organisms while the moisture equilibrium was being obtained. Carbon dioxide determinations were made after four days in a respiration chamber at 37.8° C. As the moisture content was increased in oats from 11 to 17 per cent the daily respiration rate went up from 0.2 mg. to 13.5 mg. per 24 hours per 100 g. of dry matter. Similar determinations made for barley, rye, and flax yielded similar results except that the respiration of flax seeds was at a higher level than that of the cereals. In resting seeds of *Hordeum distichum* respiration was found to increase gradually with water content up to 15 to 16 per cent moisture which represented a critical turning point according to Kolkwitz (1901). At 20 per cent moisture there was much stronger respiration.

Leach (1942) measured the carbon dioxide evolved by single grains of wheat during absorption of water and germination. He obtained data for five different kinds of wheat which show a sequence of three respiratory stages. The initial stage which begins shortly after the grain is brought in contact with water and extends over a ten-hour interval is marked by a slow rise in respiratory rate. This is followed in the next 10 to 20 hours by an acceleration and a slowing off in rate. After 30 hours comes the final stage with rising respiration rate accompanying the germination process. The author concludes that a fully developed oxidizing system and an immediately available supply of respiration substrate exist in the dry wheat grain.

Oxygen consumption of seeds of *Cajanus* (Thakurta and Dutt 1935/36) at pre-resting, resting, and post-resting stages depends upon the internal moisture condition of the seed. No water was supplied to these seeds but moisture determinations were made at each stage. In the beginning of the study of the pre-resting stage the moisture content of the seed was 80.5 per cent and the oxygen consumption was 456.7 cubic mm. per gram of dry weight per minute, a very high rate. As the seed approached the resting stage the moisture content was lessened and was accompanied by a marked reduction in respiration. At 66.1 per cent moisture, only 44.8 cubic mm. of oxygen were taken up per minute for each gram of dry weight. This rapid fall in respiration continued until at a moisture content of 12.01 per cent only 0.0053 cubic mm. of oxygen was used per minute for each gram of dry weight. The resting stage was attained at approximately 10 per cent moisture. During the resting stage which continued for 57 to 90 days, no oxygen consumption could be detected. Following this period, when the moisture content was between 7 and 8 per cent, 0.00056 cubic mm. of oxygen was used per minute for each gram of dry weight. Thus while the fall in respiration rate paralleled the loss of water by the seed up to the time the rest period began, it was not entirely dependent upon the moisture content since at the post-resting stage the moisture content was lower than at the onset of the resting stage and yet the respiration was higher. These facts have important implications in a study of metabolic activities of seeds in storage in relation to their longevity. Seeds of the river maple, *Acer saccharinum* L. (Jones 1920), have a high respiratory rate at the time of fall. In desiccating seeds the rate is reduced the first few days but this is followed by a gradual rise until a maximum is reached at a moisture content of approximately 44 per cent. This maximum is retained for several days, then there is a gradual decline until only a trace of carbon dioxide is given off. The decline is attributed to water deficiency, since the respiration again increases when the dead seeds are placed under germination conditions. Jones points out, however, that this CO_2 may have been given off by microorganisms attacking the dead seeds. This seems very likely and the decline in volume of gaseous exchange with decreased moisture content may have been due to the death of the embryos.

Spontaneous heating in damp grain has been thought to be largely the result of respiration of the embryos in the kernels. In this connection the respiration of wheat in storage has been studied. Moisture content of the grain is very important. We have seen that any gain in moisture content increases the rate of gas diffusion and hence accelerates respiration. In plump wheat grains this increase is gradual until the moisture exceeds 14.5 per cent when a marked rise occurs (Bailey and Gurjar 1918). Also because of the diffusion rate soft, starchy wheat respires more rapidly than hard, vitreous wheats with the same moisture content. In wheat as in sorghum injury of the grain is followed by higher respiratory activity.

In respiration and heating studies made on hard red spring wheat, Larmour *et al.* (1935) found an estimation of the true respiration of the damp grain complicated by the respiration of the fungi which developed. Exposure of damp wheat to vapors of carbon tetrachloride for 25 days had no harmful effect on the quality, maintained a low rate of respiration, and permitted no heating in wheat with 25 per cent moisture. Evaluation of respiratory intensity in these damp grains was by carbon dioxide output. Bakke and Noecker (1933), in their inquiry into the relation of moisture to respiration and heating in stored oats, used oxygen consumption as the index of respiration. They attributed irregularities in oxygen consumption even in oats of low moisture content to the differences in fungal flora of the different seed lots. Reference will be made again in the ensuing pages to the importance of pure cultures for respiration studies.

There seems little doubt that fungal growth as well as moisture content and external temperature must be considered as a factor in the heating of damp grain. In fact, Oxley and Jones (1944) have come to the conclusion that the carbon dioxide produced by stored wheat, apparently by respiration of the grain itself, is really produced almost entirely by microorganisms growing in the pericarp. The observed progressive increase in respiration rate with increased time in storage was not accompanied by any detectable increase in the size or differentiation of the wheat embryo. Thus no increase in amount of respiring tissue was evident. Furthermore, wheat grains from which the embryos had been removed by larval attack have respiratory rates nearly as high as that of intact grains from the same sample. It seemed, then, that the main source of carbon dioxide was outside of the embryo and much greater than that of the embryo. Removal of the pericarp by abrasion without injury to the seed contents reduced the carbon dioxide production to about 5 per cent of its original value. Examination of the actively respiring pericarp failed to show many living cells. A number of fungal hyphae were found on the inner surface of the pericarp, however, and to these was attributed the carbon dioxide formation. Moisture content of the stored grain was important in respiration in that it favored or inhibited fungal growth in the pericarp. These authors are now attempting to grow wheat to maturity from sterilized seeds under aseptic conditions in order to secure a crop of grain free from fungal contamination for comparison with normal wheat.

The hygroscopic equilibrium attained by various seeds depends not only upon the chemical and physical characteristics of the seed contents but upon the type of structure enclosing the seed. A comparative study of the respiratory rates of common and hull-less oats (Ramstad and Geddes 1942) disclosed that for equivalent sample treatments at corresponding moisture levels the latter showed an appreciably lower rate than the former. This difference is due to the lower hygroscopicity of the hulls and therefore higher moisture content of respiring materials. For the most part, investigators have regarded the total moisture content of seeds in their consideration of moisture effects on respiration. Shirk (1942) has established descending and parallel curves for respiration and freezable water for immature rye and wheat when plotted against time or against total water. This indicates a shifting of the free-bound water equilibrium with development and maturity of the seeds and a dependence of respiration rate, as measured by the amount of oxygen taken up, upon the amount of free water.

Temperature.—Plant tissues respire more rapidly with increased temperature up to the point of injury by over-heating. As is the case with other phases of respiration, more inquiries have been made into the responses of vegetative or floral parts of the plant than into respiration of the seeds themselves. Increasing temperatures have been found to accelerate the respiratory rate of stored wheat grains until 55° C. is reached (Bailey and Gurjar 1918). This effect is attributed to increased diastatic action upon the starch. The point is reached, however, at which enzyme activity and respiration diminish. Karchevski (1901) measured the carbon dioxide evolved by embryos of wheat placed in water for 24 hours before the tests were made and then held dry during the tests and observed a reduction in amount at 70° C. and a complete cessation of carbon dioxide production at 98.5° C.

Concentration of oxygen and carbon dioxide.—The influence of the concentration of oxygen on respiration of seed tissues depends upon the amount which is already held available within the seed as well as the condition of the seed and hence the special oxygen requirements at the time the observation is made. If the seeds have coverings through which the oxygen diffuses with difficulty, a higher supply of oxygen is needed to produce a certain rate of respiration or growth than when the coats are removed. This has already been mentioned for *Cucurbita pepo* and for barley. The oxygen requirements of the seed before germination as well as the output of carbon dioxide may be and often are very different from those existing after the germination process has been initiated. At the same time, the actual initiation of germination depends upon the physiological condition of the embryo inside the seed and hence indirectly upon its gaseous exchange. While a considerable amount of work has been done to ascertain effects of different amounts and pressures of oxygen and carbon dioxide upon germination, very few tests have been aimed at such effects upon the embryo while it is still within the seed. Such work as has been reported has dealt mainly with the accumulation of carbon dioxide in the respiratory chamber and its effect upon the respiration response of the seeds. Kidd (1915) found that 10 per cent carbon dioxide retarded the respiration of white mustard seed.

A depressing effect on respiration of accumulated carbon dioxide in the respiratory chamber was noted in 1918 by Bailey and Gurjar for stored wheat. Bailey later (1940) confirmed this effect for oats, barley, rye, and flax. The wheat grain was also used by Willaman and Beaumont (1928) in their investigation of the effect of accumulated carbon dioxide on plant respiration. The rate of carbon dioxide production decreased continuously with the time this gas was allowed to accumulate in a respiration chamber at 40° C. The rate of respiration immediately assumed a much higher value upon aspiration of the atmosphere which had accumulated around the grain. The authors gave two possible explanations for this phenomenon. First, that we are observing the establishment of an equilibrium between the carbon dioxide which has dissolved in the tissues and that in the surrounding atmosphere, the excess in the latter being removed slowly after the beginning of aspiration. The second possibility pointed out is that the accumulation of carbon dioxide increases the hydrogen-ion concentration in the tissues, that the proteins of the protoplasm are thus brought nearer their isoelectric point, increasing the permeability of the protoplasm, and that this is responsible for a real increase in the amount of carbon dioxide produced. Willaman and Beaumont (1928) favor the second of these explanations for they substituted air which had been bubbled through hydrochloric acid for the accumulated carbon dioxide and got the same results. Under the conditions of their experiment they did not believe the exhaustion of oxygen from the chamber was a factor. Thornton (1933), on the other hand, showed that carbon dioxide in the presence of oxygen did not increase the hydrogen-ion concentration of plant tissues such as fruits, roots, stems, tubers, bulbs, and entire plants. Instead there was a decrease in the acidity of the sap extracted from treated tissue. He believed that this change in pH depended upon the living process. This is in contrast to the direct action of carbon dioxide on the extracted juice of tissues which is to make it more acid. He did not use seeds but the presence of the living embryo in seeds might be expected to be similar in reaction to other living tissues.

A comparison of continuous and discontinuous methods for removal of carbon dioxide from the respiration chamber, in which wheat grains with 20 per cent moisture were placed, revealed higher respiration in the continuously aerated sample (Larmour et al. 1935).

It appears then that experiments concluded to date have verified each other in the demonstration of an inhibiting effect on respiration of accumulated carbon dioxide. Furthermore, the air seems to furnish sufficient oxygen to prevent its becoming a limiting factor, though the seed coat tissues themselves may limit the entrance of oxygen (Shull 1914).

Light.—Certain seeds are known to require light for, or at least be benefited by light in, the germination process. It is easy to understand how light would affect the respiration of seedlings once germination had taken place. It is more difficult to interpret a light effect on respiration of seeds after swelling in water. Such an effect was found in light-favored seeds of *Nicotiana tabacum* (Kipp 1929). In the dark respiration increased with swelling to a maximum, fell at the end point of swelling, and then decreased slowly. With lighting, the decrease did not occur. The respiration increased slowly at first and then more rapidly with the initiation of germination. Whatever the effect of light on the preparation of the seed for germination, the respiration process is involved.

Embryo versus endosperm respiration.—It is generally assumed that the embryo is the living part of the seed and therefore carries on the metabolic processes which are part of living tissue. That the embryo is primarily responsible for the respiratory behavior of the seed has been demonstrated.

Wheat grains have been test objects for much of this work. The energy of carbon dioxide respiration has been reported to be twelve times as great in the embryos as in the wheat grain itself (Karchevski 1901). Shriveled wheat respires two or three times as fast as plump wheat at moisture contents above 14 per cent. This has been attributed to the higher ratio of embryo to endosperm and hence a larger percentage of enzyme to substrate in a given weight of seeds (Bailey and Gurjar 1918). Leach

(1943) observed that the kernel size of wheat has a definite effect on respiration on the basis of the quantity of carbon dioxide produced per unit weight of grain, kernels of large size evolving less carbon dioxide than those of small size. Also for barley it has been found that for equal weights of different sized kernels, the smaller kernels have the highest respiration rate (Bailey 1940). The embryo of wheat and rice under any given oxygen tension evolves 65 to 85 per cent of the total amount of carbon dioxide given off according to Taylor (1942). The remainder of the carbon dioxide is produced by the endosperm.

More definite proof that the endosperm may contribute to the total respiration of the seed has been presented by Stoward (1908). He prepared endosperm tissue of both *Hordeum* and *Zea* so as to prevent the possible diffusion of respiratory enzymes from either the embryo or the aleurone layer. This tissue exhibited gaseous exchange of a respiratory nature. It was not established whether this respiratory activity was due to vital activity of living protoplasm or to respiratory enzymes which had been formed as the seed matured. Considerable evidence of the possession of vitality by the aleurone layer is available but there is less concrete proof that the endosperm is composed of living tissue.

With the present knowledge of the respiration behavior of uncontaminated seeds, it is safe to conclude that by far the major portion of the gaseous exchange mechanism is centered in the embryo.

Age of seed.—There can be no doubt that the rate of respiration is affected by the loss of viability of the seed. This would mean, then, that the storage conditions rather than the age of the seed determine the amount of gaseous exchange. The length of the storage period for wheat up to 30 months is without significant effect on the respiratory activity, when the gaseous exchange per kernel is considered (Leach 1943). This is related to the number of embryos included in the samples as described above.

Ohga (1926*a* and *b*) compared the life activity of century-old and recently harvested Indian lotus fruits. He was unable to secure a measurable amount of carbon dioxide from air-dry fruits in a three-day test. Liberation of carbon dioxide from old soaked fruits from which the plumule had just begun to emerge was more intense than that of new ones.

Dormancy.—The chapters on dormancy describe the different types and the conditions which impose them. Secondary dormancy in the embryos of *Ambrosia trifida* is dependent on seed membranes which have been found to restrict gaseous exchange (Davis 1930). The reduction of oxygen available to the embryo is necessary for the development of dormancy. But dormancy does not develop in the absence of oxygen. The delayed germination of the upper seeds of *Xanthium* is also due to certain seed coat and embryo characters which are related to the need and availability of oxygen (Ota 1925). The seed coats have low permeability and the embryo has a high oxygen requirement for germination. These upper seeds when placed on a moist medium without extra oxygen pressure will remain ungerminated for long periods of time. Under such conditions the respiratory rate rises rapidly during the first day or two reaching a maximum after which it falls rapidly during the second and third days to a low level and continues to decrease slowly for three weeks, at which time the experiment was terminated. The carbon dioxide eliminated after the first sixty hours was ten times that liberated at the 20*th* day.

A similar reduction in respiration of seeds held moist without germination has been found by Barton (1945) for *Amaranthus retroflexus, Impatiens balsamina,* and *Rumex obtusifolius.* These seeds were held dormant on a moist medium by placing them, soon after harvest, at temperatures which inhibit germination at that time. The beginning of the curtailment of respiration of *Amaranthus retroflexus* seeds at 20° C. became apparent after two days and was definite after eight days in moist storage. Measurements continued on these *Amaranthus* seeds held moist at 20° C. at intervals up to 901 days showed gradual reduction in the volume of gaseous exchange to about 10 per cent of the original. This rate was reached by the end of a year. Respiratory intensity of Johnson grass seeds held in a germinator at 20° C. for a year has also been found to be much reduced (Crocker and Harrington 1918). Reduction in respiratory intensity is doubtless one of the factors affecting the life span of seeds buried in the soil. This will be discussed more fully in another chapter.

Amaranthus retroflexus, Chenopodium album, and *Rumex crispus* were among the dormant seeds the respiration of which was investigated by Sherman (1921). These seeds were held dry from the time of harvest until 24 hours before respiration measurements were to be taken. The carbon dioxide given off and the oxygen absorbed by seeds of *Amaranthus retroflexus* were determined after dry storage for 3 to 176 days. The values for respiration intensity were higher than those reported above for seeds of the same species held moist and ungerminated. This may be accounted for by the progressive after-ripening in dry storage and the persistence of an initial dormancy or the formation of a secondary dormancy in moist storage at a temperature unfavorable for germination.

Some respiration investigations have been made on seeds with dormancy imposed by the contents within the seed coats. When the coats are permeable enough to water and to gases to supply the demands of the embryo for after-ripening and germination, we must look for germination failure to the embryo itself or to the endosperm which may be in a form not available for use by the embryo. Such dormancy is usually overcome by moist, low-temperature pretreatment (*see* chapters on dormancy).

Seeds of *Crataegus,* peach, apricot, cherry, sand cherry, Blue Gage plum, and Burbank plum, all of which exhibit dormancy of this type, were included in the respiration studies made by Sherman (1921). In these rosaceous forms the respiratory intensity varied greatly for different seeds and for different lots of the same kind of seed under the same experimental conditions. This, the author explained, may be characteristic of seeds with dormant embryos.

In contrast to the seeds of river maple, those of sugar maple, *Acer saccharum,* are dormant. Very little respiration could be measured on these dormant air-dry seeds (Jones 1920). When they were soaked 48 hours, however, and transferred to a respirometer, the respiratory intensity attained approximately the same level as that of seeds which had been fully after-ripened by moist, low-temperature pretreatment. Jones was unable from his data to correlate respiration and after-ripening.

The respiration intensity of dormant apple seeds is low (Harrington 1923) but becomes much higher with after-ripening when the seeds are capable of germination. A seed coat effect is coupled with the internal dormancy of these seeds for the removal of the coats increases the respiration and accelerates germination.

Northern red oak acorns which are dormant, and white oak acorns which are nondormant, differ only slightly in their gas exchange (Brown 1939). The carbon dioxide given off by both species remained constant during over-winter storage at 2.5° C., but the oxygen consumed by red oak acorns increased rapidly during the first three weeks of storage while the increase in oxygen consumption by white oak acorns was not evident until after the first three weeks. The extra oxygen consumption of the dormant acorns may have served to convert fatty acids to carbohydrates, an accumulation of which was necessary for after-ripening according to Brown. Red oak acorns are known to contain approximately three times as much fat as those of white oak.

Fungi and bacteria effects.—In the process of measurement of respiration of seeds as well as other tissues, it is essential that they be kept free of fungi and bacteria. As soon as these organisms are introduced respiration is altered. The first effect is usually an acceleration caused either by the respiration of the invading organisms added to that of the host tissue or by increased respiration of the invaded tissue itself (Pringsheim *et al.* 1931). Milner and Geddes (1945), measuring simultaneously the oxygen consumption and carbon dioxide production of soybean seed containing about 18.5 per cent moisture, found that the respiration curves were similar in form to the microbiological population growth curves. That mold growth on the seeds accounted for much of the gaseous exchange was further demonstrated when the seeds were killed by heating to 50° C., a temperature not lethal for mold spores. Subsequent respiration at 30° C. was found to be higher than that of viable seed combined with mold at the optimum temperature of 40° C. Sterilization is difficult for the chemicals used may themselves affect respiration. Nabokich (1903) found no depressing effect on carbon dioxide output in seeds during the first few days after sterilization by chemicals such as mercuric chloride. In some instances the respiration of the sterilized seeds exceeded that of the controls. Uspulun soaking of corn grains for one hour has no effect on their respiration (Lantz 1927).

Most reliable gaseous exchange measurements are to be had on material which is held under aseptic conditions requiring no special treatment which might alter respiration.

Chemical composition of the seed.—Since respiration is considered primarily as an oxidation process, some substrate must be combined with the oxygen taken in to complete the process. The nature of the respiration especially as measured by the oxygen used and the carbon dioxide given off will depend upon the form in which food is stored in the seeds. If the food reserve is carbohydrate and if the oxidation is complete, the volume of oxygen taken in will be equal to the volume of carbon dioxide given off. If fats are oxidized a greater amount of oxygen is required. Furthermore, it is recognized that since the stored food materials undergo a series of changes during after-ripening, germination, and seedling development, there are qualitative and quantitative differences in the materials available for respiration.

With the idea of investigating the carbon dioxide emission and oxygen absorption resulting from the breakdown of the reserve food supply of the barley grain, James and James (1940) conducted an extensive study. They germinated seeds in the dark at 21° C. in a normal mixture of atmospheric gas and made continuous records of the carbon dioxide given off. Their data yielded a respiratory curve which was analyzed into five phases. Starting with the seed which shows low carbon dioxide output, a gradual rise in respiratory intensity characterizes the first phase in which water is absorbed, the embryo develops rapidly, and the embryonic reserves are used. The phase lasts for two days. The respiratory rise continues through the second phase in which the endospermic carbohydrates are mobilized and reaches a maximum the *7th* day. Greatest respiration intensity is reached between the second and the third phase the latter extending to the *12th* day.

The decline in the third phase is due to the exhaustion of the endospermic carbohydrates. A slight decrease in respiration continues in the fourth phase in which a mixture of reserves including protein are utilized. The decrease is arrested and a slight rise is evident during the 22nd day in the beginning of the fifth phase in which the seedling are dead due to the presence of saprophytic organisms. Since these seedlings were kept in the dark they were entirely dependent upon the food stored in the seed. Embryos germinated independently of their endosperm show similar first respiration phase but the later phases are much modified. Although this work was done with the germinating seed and the resulting seedling rather than with the seed itself, it serves as a good illustration of the relationship between respiration and the substrate and emphasizes the fact that the gaseous exchange at a given time is dependent upon the food material available at that time. Stiles and Leach (1932) earlier had followed the course of respiration of *Lathyrus odoratus* seeds during germination and young seedling development and had reported five phases similar to the ones just discussed.

Bonnier and Mangin (1884) divide seeds into two classes dependent on their respiration: (A) oleaginous seeds which absorb, during germination, a volume of oxygen greater than that of carbon dioxide exhaled, and (B) amylaceous seeds which exhibit an equality between the volume of oxygen absorbed and carbon dioxide given off.

Respiratory Quotient:—The ratio of the volume of carbon dioxide given off to the volume of oxygen absorbed during respiration is called the respiratory quotient and is written CO_2/O_2. It will be remembered that many of the measurements of respiration reported in this chapter consisted of records of carbon dioxide output only. In a few instances oxygen consumption only was used as an index of respiratory rate. It is obvious that a measurement of the volume of both gases would contribute more to our knowledge of the processes involved. Authorities differ, however, in their opinions of the value of the respiratory quotient in interpretation of results.

In many cases where the research worker has determined the oxygen uptake as well as the carbon dioxide output of respiring material, there has been some discussion of the significance of the relationship of the volume of one gas to the other. It should be kept in mind that the RQ may not give an index of all the oxygen actually used or all the carbon dioxide which is released by the living tissues for some of either or both of these gases may be held in the tissues. Also a quantity of oxygen is used in processes which do not involve a production of carbon dioxide. An incidence of anaerobic respiration induced by low permeability to oxygen results in a higher RQ while low RQ values accompany the accumulation of new respiratory carbohydrates. Cases like this alter the quotient from that usually characteristic of the material and, when the RQ alone is considered, give a distorted picture of the actual happenings inside the tissues.

From the foregoing section on the effect of the chemical composition of the seed on respiration, it is obvious that the available substrate is of prime importance in determining the value of the respiratory quotient. If the material being respired is carbohydrate where the volume of oxygen taken in exactly equals the volume of carbon dioxide given off, the RQ is 1. More oxygen is required for the complete breaking down of fats so that the RQ in this case is 0.7. However, because a seed, especially the endôsperm is composed principally of carbohydrates, it does not follow that the RQ will be unity. For example the value found for the RQ of *Amaranthus retroflexus* seeds shortly after they had been moistened was approximately 0.7 (Barton 1945) in spite of the fact that an analysis of the constituents of these seeds made by Woo (1919) showed 47.03 per cent carbohydrates and only 7.86 per cent lipins. These fats are probably concentrated in the embryo so that when respiration is first accelerated in the embryo this is the substrate used. This is in agreement with Stiles and Leach (1933) who said that the small reserve of fat in the germinating seed of *Fagopyrum esculentum* was consumed at a very early stage in seedling development in spite of the fact that the principal food reserve in the seed was starch. Eight different kinds of starchy seeds and eight of fatty seeds were used as test material by Pringsheim *et al.* (1933) to determine the relation between reserve food material in the seed and the RQ during the swelling of the seeds for 12 or 24 hours. In the starchy seeds RQs varying from 0.72 to 1.00 were obtained and in the fatty seeds from 0.60 to 0.86. When the soaking time was extended to 36 hours, the RQ decreased in *Lens esculenta,* a starchy seed, and in *Helianthus annuus,* an oily seed. *Triticum sativum* seeds, also starchy, showed the reverse condition. Thus it is demonstrated again that the RQ does not necessarily depend upon the principal food reserve but upon the substrate being used at a given time, and upon whether oxidation is complete.

Peas show an exceptionally high RQ value (about 6.0) after four hours' soaking, with a decrease to 1.8 after eight hours' soaking (Smith 1935). Even after soaking for 24 hours the RQ was well above unity. In a similar experiment with maize an RQ of 1.0 was obtained and in another with mustard an RQ greater than unity. All of these values are high and are in contrast to the findings of other research workers. Smith measured the carbon dioxide and oxygen in separate but parallel experiments. This may have altered the relationship of one gas to the other.

Sherman (1921) found the RQ of *Amaranthus retroflexus* seeds approximately 0.8 regardless of changes in actual amounts of oxygen taken in and carbon dioxide given off and of time of storage from 3 to 176 days. The seeds were stored dry and were placed in distilled water 24 hours before gaseous exchange was determined. A very different relationship between the oxygen consumed and carbon dioxide evolved is obtained when seeds of this same species are held on a moist medium at 20° C. which keeps some of the seeds dormant for at least 901 days (Barton 1945). The RQ tends to decrease with increased time in moist storage from approximately 0.69 at the beginning to 0.43 after 564 days with a still greater reduction evident after 901 days. Both carbon dioxide produced and oxygen absorbed were decreased with storage but the proportions did not remain constant. Brown (1939) also found a lowered RQ in dormant red oak acorns with increased time in storage up to three weeks at 2.5° C. Unlike the case of *Amaranthus retroflexus* this altered RQ was due to increased oxygen consumption while carbon dioxide production remained constant.

Just how many factors affect the relationship of one gas to the other in the exchange characteristic of living tissues is not known. It is evident that there are many variables and that their exact natures and effects are unknown. For example, Tang (1932) reports that the temperature characteristics for oxygen consumption and carbon dioxide production of germinating seeds of *Lupinus albus* are different and that, therefore, the respiratory quotient is a function of temperature. This may be due to a change in the nature of the food material with change in temperature or as the author suggests to the control of carbon dioxide production and oxygen consumption by two different mechanisms. The RQ of dormant apple seeds increases with increase in temperature and decreases with decrease in temperature (Harrington 1923). Whatever may or may not be the significance of the respiratory quotient itself, certainly the quantity of both gases concerned in the respiratory process is of importance in the interpretation of the physiological condition of the seed and its component parts. New findings may necessitate a revision of some of the accepted ideas of the mechanics and the chemistry of the respiratory process.

Respiratory Enzymes:—Obviously there must be some chemical substances present in living tissue which are capable of bringing about oxidation of available materials to supply energy for life processes. Data on respiratory enzymes have been collected and presented in book form by Elvehjem and Wilson (1939). Most of the work has been done with vegetative parts of plants but some attention has been given to enzymes present in seeds.

Catalase activity has been variously reported as paralleling or diverging from respiratory activity. Whether a close correlation exists between these two processes apparently depends upon the material under investigation and the conditions of the experiment. Crocker and Harrington (1918) found a close correlation between catalase activity and respiratory intensity of Johnson grass seeds held moist in a germinator but no such correlation seemed to exist for *Amaranthus retroflexus* seeds. A divergence of catalase activity and respiration in six different kinds of seeds was reported by Rhine (1924) who concluded that catalase could be used as an indicator of metabolism only in cases where there is no rapid change in respiration and that therefore catalase can not be considered as part of the respiration mechanism. When conditions are stable for respiration, however, catalase activity could be used as a convenient and fairly accurate index of this process. Results obtained by Lantz (1927) also failed to show a close correlation between catalase activity and respiration, thus excluding catalase as the enzyme chiefly concerned in physiological oxidation. Report of research by Davis (1939) available in abstract only describes ratios of oxygen used by intact seeds to that of seeds with membranes removed as similar to the ratios of catalase of the same in terms of oxygen released.

Other enzymes thought to be concerned in respiration are the oxidases. Their activities parallel physiological behavior of seeds much less generally than does that of catalase according to Crocker and Harrington (1918). The presence of cytochrome oxidase in wheat embryos was demonstrated by Brown and Goddard (1941). They found this oxidase inhibited by HCN, $NaNO_3$, and CO. The respiration of the wheat embryos was similarly inhibited by these poisons. Indications were, then, that a major portion of the respiration is accomplished by cytochrome oxidase though no direct evidence of this was obtained. According to Mikhlin and Kolesnikov (1947) the cytochrome oxidase system is predominant only in plant embryos and during the initial stages of development of grasses. Otherwise, they believe that the polyphenoloxidase system is the most common and the most important of the oxidative mechanisms. They demonstrated the presence of the cytochrome oxidase system in barley embryos by the use of special substrates, by inhibitors, and spectroscopically. On further development of the barley plant, this system is replaced by another as evidenced by the slight sensitivity to the action of cyanides and the complete insensitivity to carbon monoxide. Further studies indicated that amino acids, β-hydroxybutyric acid, glyceraldehyde, and hypoxanthine were all oxidized, even in the presence of the cyanides, when infiltrated into barley leaves. This proved the presence of flavoprotein enzymes, with the resultant formation of hydrogen peroxide, which is used for the oxidation of polyphenols. These, in turn, act as intermediate catalysts for the oxidation of amino acids and other metabolites. Peroxidase was found in all stages of barley development, but its activity and the flavin content increased as the plant ripened.

The presence of dehydrogenases has been demonstrated in the embryos of barley and garden peas (Fink *et al.* 1936; Bach 1938*a* and *b*).

That a measurement of respiratory rates obtained from a quantity of seeds is the sum of the respiratory rates of a number of seeds in different stages of development is indicated by the difference in germination rate often exhibited by seeds which are apparently alike and subjected to the same external conditions. As more studies on respiration and related phenomena are completed we will be able to add to the facts which contribute to a fuller understanding of the life processes of the seed.

References:—

Babcock, S. M., 1912: Metabolic water: its production and role in vital phenomena (Wis. Agric. Exp. Sta. Res. Bull. 22:87-181).

Bach, D., 1938*a*: Respiratory complex of dormant seeds. Dehydrogenases and co-enzyme of *Pisum sativum* (Compt. Rend. Soc. Biol. 127:175-177; *abstr. in* Chem. Abstr. 32:3453, 1938).

————, 1938*b*: The respiratory complex of dormant seeds. Separation of coenzyme by ultrafiltration of extracts of dried garden peas (Compt. Rend. Soc. Biol. 127:1063-1065; *abstr. in* Chem. Abstr. 32:5442-5443, 1938).

Bailey, C. H., 1940: Respiration of cereal grains and flaxseed (Plant Physiol. 15:257-274).

————, & A. M. Gurjar, 1918: Respiration of stored wheat (Jour. Agric. Res. 12:685-713).

Bakke, A. L., & N. L. Noecker, 1933: The relation of moisture to respiration and heating in stored oats (Iowa Agric. Exp. Sta. Res. Bull. 165:320-336).

Barton, L. V., 1945: Respiration and germination studies of seeds in moist storage (Ann. New York Acad. Sci. 46:185-208).

Bonnier, G., & L. Mangin, 1884: Sur les variations de la respiration des graines germant avec le développement (Bull. Soc. Bot. France 31:306-309).

Brown, A. H., & D. R. Goddard, 1941: Cytochrome oxidase in wheat embryos (Amer. Jour. Bot. 28:319-324).

Brown, J. W., 1939: Respiration of acorns as related to temperature and after-ripening (Plant Physiol. 14:621-645).

Brown, R., 1940: An experimental study of the permeability to gases of the seed-coat membranes of *Cucurbita pepo* (Ann. Bot. n. s. 4:379-395).

————, 1942: The gaseous exchange of seeds and isolated cotyledons of *Cucurbita pepo* (Ann. Bot. n. s. 6:293-321).

————, 1943: Studies in germination and seedling growth. I. The water content, gaseous exchange, and dry weight of attached and isolated embryos of barley (Ann. Bot. n. s. 7:93-113).

Coleman, D. A., B. E. Rothgeb & H. C. Fellows, 1928: Respiration of sorghum grains (U.S.D.A. Tech. Bull. 100, 16 pp.).

Crocker, W., & G. T. Harrington, 1918: Catalase and oxidase content of seeds in relation to their dormancy, age, vitality, and respiration (Jour. Agric. Res. 15:137-174).

Davis, W. E., 1930: Primary dormancy, after-ripening, and the development of secondary dormancy in embryos of *Ambrosia trifida* (Amer. Jour. Bot. 17:58-76).

————, 1939: The relation between respiration and catalase based on studies of intact dormant seed and seed with certain membranes removed (Amer. Jour. Bot. 26:16s).

Elvehjem, C. A., & P. W. Wilson, directors, 1939: Respiratory enzymes (236 pp., Burgess Publ. Co., Minneapolis, Minn.).

Fink, H., H. Haehn & E. Zenger, 1936: Formation of respiration enzymes during germination of barley (Wochschr. Brau. 53:65-69, 73-77, 83-87, 93-95, 101-103; *abstr. in* Chem. Abstr. 30:7587-7588, 1936).

Frietinger, G., 1927: Untersuchungen über die Kohlensäureabgabe und Sauerstoffaufnahme bei keimenden Samen (Flora 122:167-201).

Harrington, G. T., 1923: Respiration of apple seeds (Jour. Agric. Res. 23:117-130).

James, W. O., & A. L. James, 1940: The respiration of barley germinating in the dark (New Phytol. 39:145-176).

Jones, H. A., 1920: Physiological study of maple seeds (Bot. Gaz. 69:127-152).

Karchevski, 1901: Influence of the fluctuation of temperature on the respiration of seeds and embryos of wheat (Mem. Warsaw Unit 9:114 pp.; *abstr. in* Exp. Sta. Rec. 14:839, 1903).

Kidd, F., 1915: The controlling influence of carbon dioxide. Part III. The retarding effect of carbon dioxide on respiration (Proc. Roy. Soc. London, B, 89:136-156).

Kipp, M., 1929: Die Abgabe von Kohlensäure und die Aufnahme von Sauerstoff bei der Keimung lichtgeförderter Samen von *Nicotiana tabacum* (Jahrb. Wiss. Bot. 71:533-595).

Kolkwitz, R., 1901: Ueber die Athmung ruhenden Samen (Ber. Deut. Bot. Gesell. 19:285-287).

Lantz, C. W., 1927: Respiration in corn with special reference to catalase (Amer. Jour. Bot. 14:85-105).

Larmour, R. K., J. S. Clayton & C. L. Wrenshall, 1935: A study of the respiration and heating of damp wheat (Canad. Jour. Res. 12:627-645).

Larmour, R. K., H. R. Sallans & B. M. Craig, 1944: Respiration of whole and de-hulled sunflower seed and of flaxseed (Canad. Jour. Res. Sec. F, 22:9-18).

Leach, W., 1942: Studies on the metabolism of cereal grains. I. The output of carbon dioxide by wheat grains during absorption of water and germination (Canad. Jour. Res. Sec. C, 20:160-168).

————, 1943: Studies on the metabolism of cereal grains. II. The effect of age and kernel size on the course of respiration of wheat during early germination stages (Canad. Jour. Res. Sec. C, 21:289-296).

Mikhlin, D. M., & P. A. Kolesnikov, 1947: Respiratory systems of plants (Biokhimiya 12:452-464; *abstr. in* Chem. Abstr. 43:728, 1949).

Miller, E. C., 1938: Plant physiology (2nd ed., 1201 pp., McGraw-Hill Book Co., Inc., New York).

Milner, M., & W. F. Geddes, 1945: Grain storage studies. II. The effect of aeration, temperature, and time on the respiration of soybeans containing excessive moisture (Cereal Chem. 22:484-501).

Nabokich, A. J., 1903: Ueber den Einfluss der Sterilisation der Samen auf die Atmung (Ber. Deut. Bot. Gesell. 21:279-291).

Ohga, I., 1926a: A comparison of the life activity of century-old and recently harvested Indian lotus fruits (Amer. Jour. Bot. 13:760-765).

————, 1926b: The germination of century-old and recently harvested Indian lotus fruits, with special reference to the effect of oxygen supply (Amer. Jour. Bot. 13:754-759).

Ota, J., 1925: Continuous respiration studies of dormant seeds of *Xanthium* (Bot. Gaz. 80:288-299).

Oxley, T. A., & J. D. Jones, 1944: Apparent respiration of wheat grains and its relation to a fungal mycelium beneath the epidermis (Nature 154:826-827).

Pringsheim, E. G., Fr. Jedlitschka & Br. Görlich, 1931: Untersuchungen über Samenquellung. II. Mitteilung. Die Atmung quellender Samen (Planta 15:419-458).

————, ————, ————, 1933: Untersuchungen über Samenquellung. III. Mitteilung. Der Atmungsquotient quellender Samen (Planta 19:653-712).

Ramstad, P. E., & W. F. Geddes, 1942: The relative respiratory rates and hygroscopic equilibria of common and hull-less oats (Jour. Agric. Res. 64:237-241).

Rhine, L. E., 1924: Divergence of catalase and respiration in germination (Bot. Gaz. 78:46-67).

Sherman, H., 1921: Respiration of dormant seeds (Bot. Gaz. 72:1-30).

Shirk, H. G., 1942: Freezable water content and the oxygen respiration in wheat and rye grain at different stages of ripening (Amer. Jour. Bot. 29:105-109).

Shull, C. A., 1914: The role of oxygen in germination (Bot. Gaz. 57:64-69).

Smith, A. J. M., 1936: The respiratory quotient of the initial metabolism of soaked seeds (Great Britain Dept. Sci. & Indus. Res. Food Invest. Board Rept., 1935: 132-135).

Stiles, W., 1935: Respiration (Bot. Rev. 1:249-268).

Stiles, W., & W. Leach, 1932: Researches on plant respiration. I. The course of respiration of *Lathyrus odoratus* during germination of the seed and the early development of the seedling (Proc. Roy. Soc. London, B, 111:338-355).

————, ————, 1933: Researches on plant respiration. II. Variations in the respiratory quotient during germination of seeds with different food reserves (Proc. Roy. Soc. London, B, 113:405-428).

Stoward, F., 1908: On endospermic respiration in certain seeds (Ann. Bot. 22:415-448).

Tang, P. S., 1932: On the respiratory quotient of *Lupinus albus* as a function of temperature (Jour. Gen. Phys. 15:561-569).

Taylor, D. L., 1942: Influence of oxygen tension on respiration, fermentation and growth in wheat and rice (Amer. Jour. Bot. 29:721-738).

Thakurta, A. G., & B. K. Dutt, 1935/36: Investigation on the oxygen consumption of the seed of *Cajanus* (Bose Res. Inst. Trans. 11:39-53).

Thornton, N. C., 1933: Carbon dioxide storage. IV. The influence of carbon dioxide on the acidity of plant tissue (Contrib. Boyce Thompson Inst. 5:403-418).

Willaman, J. J., & J. H. Beaumont, 1928: The effect of accumulated carbon dioxide on plant respiration (Plant Physiol. 3:45-59).

Woo, M. L., 1919: Chemical constituents of *Amaranthus retroflexus* (Bot. Gaz. 68: 313-344).

Chapter VII

FACTORS AFFECTING GERMINATION, I

Temperature Effects on Non-Dormant Seeds:—The failure of many seeds to germinate may have no relation to a need for pretreatment but may be due merely to the requirement of specific conditions. Temperature is among the most important of these conditions. Edwards (1932) in discussing the temperature relations of seed germination has listed 55 citations dealing with the subject. This list represents only a small portion of the work which has been done. Between different lots of seeds of the same variety there will be some differences in sensitivity to environmental conditions for germination. Also the individual seeds making up one sample may show a lack of physiologic uniformity which distributes germination over an extended period of time. The ideal germination conditions result in a prompt, complete stand of seedlings which is the goal of germination requirement trials.

The use of daily alternations of temperature has brought about the germination of a great number of flower, grass, and vegetable seeds which give poor seedling production under other conditions (Harrington 1923). The alternating temperatures most frequently used are 15° to 30° C. or 20° to 30° C. There have been many variations in the time of exposure to each of the temperatures. Usually, however, the seeds have been left in a germinator at the lower temperature for about 16 hours and at the higher temperature for about 8 hours each day. The change from one temperature to another may be effected in two ways. In a daily 20° to 30° C. alternation, for example, cultures may be moved from an oven with a controlled temperature of 20° to one of 30° C. each morning and returned to the 20° C. oven each evening; or, instead of moving the cultures the temperature of a single oven may be changed in the morning and in the evening. In the temperate zone spring planting approximates these conditions. The nights are usually cool and the days much warmer. There is no doubt of the significance of alternating temperatures in germination.

Because of the economic importance of vegetable seeds, detailed studies have been made on some of the more difficult forms. The speed of pepper seed germination was found to increase rapidly as the temperature was raised from 50°-60° F. to 90°-100° F. (Cochran 1936). In a greenhouse at 40°-50° F. no seedlings emerged in 45 days but upon shifting to a greenhouse at 90°-100° F. good germination resulted in 5 days. Twenty degrees C. has been determined as the best temperature for germinating potato seeds, which are very important in breeding experiments though commercial propagation is by tubers (Stier and Cordner 1937). A fairly low temperature is necessary for successful germination of celery seed. A constant temperature of 15° C. or a daily alternation of 10° to 25° C. has been effective (Hopkins 1928). Variations in germination of New Zealand spinach seeds can be decreased by using a daily alternation of 20° to 30° C. (Heit and Munn 1941).

Many flower seeds have specific temperature requirements for germination. For example, seeds of annual *Delphinium* do not germinate if planted at high temperatures (Barton 1935). Very poor germination is obtained if the temperature is above 20° C. These seeds may be induced to germinate at high temperatures which are ordinarily inhibitive by pretreatment in a moist medium at 10° or 15° C. for one, two, or three weeks. Seeds of the perennial form of *Delphinium* are not so sensitive to high temperatures as the annual seeds. Although wild columbine (*Aquilegia canadensis* L.) will germinate under a variety of conditions, too high temperature must be avoided here also. Constant temperatures as high as 25° C. permit only a small percentage of the germination obtained when there is a daily alternating temperature of 15° to 25° C. Honeysuckle (*Lonicera tatarica* L.) seeds respond in the same manner. Many rock garden forms require low temperatures for germination, some actually germinating near the freezing point. *Camassia leichtlinii* Wats. germinates poorly at temperatures above 5° C. and *Lewisia rediviva* Pursh. requires a temperature lower than 10° C. for germination (Schroeder and Barton 1939).

In cotton growing it is essential to have a complete stand of seedlings early in the season. Cold weather immediately after planting causes germination failure for many varieties. Thus it is desirable to select types which will germinate at lower temperatures or at least will not be injured by temporary exposure to low temperature (Ludwig 1932).

It is of importance to know the conditions under which weed seeds will germinate in order to develop proper measures for control of weed production. Some perennial weed seeds have been the subject of a study by Brown and Porter (1942). Minimum, maximum, and optimum temperatures for the germination of five species were determined as follows:

	MINIMUM ° C.	MAXIMUM ° C.	OPTIMUM ° C.
Convolvulus arvensis	0.5	40	30, 20-30, 20-35
Euphorbia esula	0.5	40	20-30, 20-35
Lepidium draba	0.5	40	20, 20-30, 20-35
Centaurea repens	0.5	35	20-30, 20-35
Solanum carolinense	20.0	40	20-30, 20-35

It will be noted that the germination of all of these seeds was favored by a daily alternation of temperature. The wide range of temperature between minimum and maximum at which germination can occur accounts in part for the success of these weeds. Seeds of crabgrasses (Toole and Toole 1941) and *Portulaca* (Heit 1945), other obnoxious weeds, also germinate at daily alternating temperatures, though the former are difficult to germinate when they are freshly harvested and some collections of the latter respond to prechilling for one month at 3° to 5° C. Russian pigweed seed (*Axyris*

TABLE XII: *Amaranthus retroflexus. 1942 Crop. Germination after various Periods on moist Glass Wool at 20° C. (2500 seeds in each lot):—*

Lot No.	NUMBER OF GERMINATIONS AT END OF EACH TWO-MONTH PERIOD																			
	2	4	6	8	10	12	14	16	18	20	22	24	26	28	30	32	34	36	38	40
1	8	4	0	0	242	171	14	1	0	95	168	17	506	198	184	21	40	75	15	0
2	7	3	0	4	430	73	19	0	1	59	500	58	184	75	101	66	95	172	28	4
3	12	0	0	3	404	36	9	0	0	58	181	63	594	14	202	13	56	110	18	3
4	14	1	2	0	95	18	13	0	1	115	208	12	1028	39	132	19	63	111	13	1
5	13	1	1	4	1360	39	7	0	0	4	210	59	251	8	13	33	22	7	7	0
6	11	2	3	2	1668	65	16	2	3	13	61	41	98	6	6	51	38	41	5	0
7	11	3	3	6	1764	35	6	1	0	18	48	46	102	7	26	6	22	21	7	1
8	12	1	0	5	1562	163	11	0	0	19	53	22	196	7	2	9	9	16	5	0
9	14	1	0	1	56	33	5	3	3	71	648	982	3	4	23	4	4	31	3	2
10	12	0	3	1	339	71	18	0	1	120	510	907	1	0	9	4	3	16	1	0
11	13	2	2	2	74	69	34	5	1	75	491	1233	6	0	5	2	0	21	4	0
12	13	2	0	2	29	199	28	2	2	49	936	750	5	1	2	0	1	28	2	0
13	9	5	0	3	1178	120	21	1	6	15	389	367	1	19	0	3	4	26	1	1
14	10	0	0	1	215	19	10	1	1	25	1740	133	6	0	3	3	25	8	0	0
15	6	1	0	4	620	97	33	6	0	25	1331	91	4	0	0	0	0	4	0	0
16	11	0	0	2	612	12	8	1	0	16	1430	122	5	0	0	2	17	5	1	0
17	8	3	1	3	284	36	21	2	1	27	1869	21	5	0	0	0	1	5	0	0
18	4	2	0	2	1043	141	10	0	2	11	1074	23	2	1	1	1	2	5	0	0
19	11	2	0	4	255	25	35	1	2	65	1903	30	1	0	0	0	0	0	0	0

Lot No.	NUMBER OF GERMINATIONS AT END OF EACH TWO-MONTH PERIOD																			TOTALS
	42	44	46	48	50	52	54	56	58	60	62	64	66	68	70	72	74	76	78	
1	25	47	87	19	17	0	0	2	18	6	0	0	0	11	41	5	0	0	0	2037
2	17	80	60	5	5	0	0	1	3	0	1	0	0	1	40	5	0	0	0	2097
3	10	36	35	7	1	0	0	0	2	0	0	0	0	8	16	0	0	1	0	1892
4	22	14	94	16	11	0	0	2	10	6	1	0	0	60	70	8	1	0	0	2200
5	32	12	32	4	3	0	0	0	3	6	0	0	0	4	14	2	0	0	0	2215
6	9	8	19	2	2	1	0	1	2	2	1	0	0	2	7	0	0	0	0	2188
7	10	13	30	11	2	2	0	1	3	1	0	0	0	7	7	0	0	0	0	2220
8	3	7	11	4	5	1	2	1	4	9	0	0	0	8	13	2	0	0	0	2162
9	6	15	31	8	3	0	0	0	12	10	1	0	2	10	34	10	0	0	0	2033
10	4	7	19	5	16	1	1	1	22	7	1	0	2	9	94	4	0	0	0	2209
11	2	5	22	5	8	1	0	0	8	10	0	0	0	15	67	8	0	0	0	2190
12	3	12	26	12	6	0	0	4	8	5	0	0	1	6	67	5	2	0	0	2208
13	0	10	26	3	5	0	0	2	0	0	0	0	0	3	4	1	0	0	0	2223
14	4	8	9	8	1	0	0	4	6	1	1	0	1	3	25	0	0	0	0	2271
15	0	2	3	2	3	0	0	2	0	0	0	0	1	5	1	0	0	0	0	2241
16	2	3	21	10	5	0	0	3	9	7	0	0	0	4	15	1	1	0	0	2325
17	1	1	4	2	0	0	0	1	2	1	0	0	0	0	7	0	0	0	0	2306
18	0	1	4	2	0	0	0	1	1	0	0	0	0	5	5	0	0	0	0	2343
19	0	1	6	0	0	0	0	0	1	0	0	0	0	0	0	0	0	0	0	2342

amarantoides L.) have been reported to germinate in ice and on frozen soil (Aamodt 1935). This means that the weed could become established very early in the growing season.

Certain weed seeds present in the soil exhibit a seasonal periodicity in germination. Warington (1936) believed this character to be connected with external factors of which temperature plays an important part. For example, germination of weed seeds that normally showed one peak period in the year when the soil samples were kept in a cold house during the winter, showed two maxima when heat was supplied. She states further (Warington 1936, p. 203): "External factors alone, however, cannot provide the full explanation for this phenomenon of periodicity, since a weed such as *Alchemilla* will germinate chiefly in the autumn in spite of the fact that very similar temperature fluctuations also occur in the spring. Neither can it be solely a matter of the seeds needing a definite period of after-ripening, or one would expect a continuous spell of germination with a gradual falling off after the rush in autumn, whereas actually the decrease is fairly sharp and is followed by a second maximum in the following autumn without any fresh seed having been introduced."

Periodicity in germination has also been observed for seeds of *Amaranthus retroflexus* L. held moist in a 20° C. room for 78 months after harvest (Barton 1945 and Table XII). Germination behavior at this temperature which is unfavorable for germination of the freshly harvested seed is difficult to understand. A few seeds germinated immediately and others germinated at intervals with no apparent cause. Careful records of germination have been kept for four different lots of seeds including collections for three different years. They have all exhibited a remarkably uniform periodicity in germination. Within a period of two months after the seeds of 1942 crop, Collection A, had been moistened and placed at 20° C., 4 to 32 seedlings had appeared in each of the cultures of 2500 seeds. Very few additional seedlings were obtained up to eight months of moist storage. Between eight and ten months many seeds germinated. The number varied greatly in the different cultures but germination occurred in all. Some increases were evident up to the 14*th* month of storage, but by the 16*th* month only occasional seedlings were found. Most of the remaining seeds continued ungerminated until between the 18*th* and 20*th* month of storage when a second germination pulse was noted. Here, again, seedling production occurred over a period of approximately two months. The seed lots which had many germinations after 10 months of storage yielded fewer seedlings in the second germination period, as was to be expected. Similarly, those with fewer germinations during the first period produced more seedlings during the second period. Under natural storage conditions in the soil, *Amaranthus retroflexus* seeds germinate before 10 months. The periodicity in their germination under controlled conditions was apparently independent of external conditions. That the germination of seeds of any one lot was so distributed indicates the absence of uniformity of physiologic behavior. The difficulties in separating the several factors involved in determining germination are apparent.

Comparatively low constant temperatures, *i.e.*, as low as 10° C. and not exceeding 25° C., or combinations of low with moderately high temperatures were found necessary for the germination of certain winter annuals characteristic of desert flora (Barton 1936). *Daucus pusillus* Michx., *Lepidium lasiocarpum* Nutt., *Lesquerella gordoni* (Gray) Wats., *Plantago fastigiata* Morris, and *Streptanthus arizonicus* Wats. were the forms studied. The temperature requirements for germination coupled with a certain amount of dormancy exhibited by the seeds when freshly harvested prevent their germination during the first summer rainy season when the prevailing high temperatures would kill the seedlings. Germination then takes place at the first winter rainy period after harvest.

Some of the fundamental physiological changes which accompany the germination process are known. Increased respiration and enzyme activity as well as chemical changes in the embryo and endosperm and growth of the embryo are among these. However, each type of seed possesses an internal mechanism for releasing germinative forces which is sensitive to one or several external conditions.

Maturity:—For several reasons it is important to know the effect of the stage of maturation of the seed on its germination. In many plants a period of several days elapses between the first and final dates of ripening of the seeds. At what stage, then, is it most profitable to harvest all of these seeds? One of the causes of failure to germinate is the presence of impermeable seed coats. When, in the course of maturation, does the seed coat become impermeable? Could the percentage of impermeable seeds be reduced by early harvest? It is also of interest to know whether the dormancy of the embryo itself is affected by the stage of maturity. In breeding experiments much time can be gained by immediate planting of seeds collected at the earliest possible date. Also in weed control a knowledge of the germination behavior of the seeds at different stages of maturity is important. Fall frost or other adverse weather conditions may necessitate early harvest. Are these seeds of good quality?

Although the stage of maturity of seeds has a definite relation to their keeping quality in storage, we shall consider in this section only germination effects with a brief reference to effects on seedling growth and vigor. The germination of corn harvested at milk, dent, and mature stages at 15°, 20°, 25°, and 30° C. was the subject of a study made by Dungan (1924). Seeds in the milk stage began germinating earlier than the others. Higher germination percentages were obtained during the first three days from dent than from mature seeds. However, when the final germination was taken, the superiority of mature seeds was evident both in number germinated and quality of seedlings produced. Sweet corn seeds harvested 13 to 55 days from silk showed low germination in the very immature samples (Walker 1933). After 31 days from silk excellent germination was obtained. The conclusion was drawn that good germination and strong plants could be secured from quite immature but fairly well developed seeds that had been well cured and properly stored.

It is well known that the quality of sweet corn as a table product depends to a large extent upon the stage of maturity. The lack of a definite relationship between sugar content of the grain at maturity and at the time when the table quality is at a maximum has been pointed out by Culpepper and Moon (1941). They found that sweet corn could be harvested at the time of maximum table quality (20 days from flowering) and chemical analyses and other tests for desirable characteristics made upon a portion of the ear and the remainder dried for subsequent planting without any impairment of germination. This simplified the selection and continuance of desirable traits which would not be apparent in the mature grain.

In connection with the slow and irregular germination of corn planted shortly after harvest, the relation of moisture content and time of harvest has been investigated (Sprague 1936). Seeds were collected 10, 21, 25, 30, 36, 41, 45, 50, and 55 days after pollination. A portion of a table taken from the report of this work is as follows:

| DAYS FROM | | MOISTURE, % | GERMINATION, % |
POLLINATION TO HARVEST	HARVEST TO SAMPLING		
10	0	83.79	0
	4	76.63	5
	8	50.63	25
	12	17.35	50
25	0	60.47	20
	4	45.14	55
	11	24.24	90
36	0	40.59	70
	2	33.54	100
	8	17.97	100
50	0	27.25	95
	5	13.76	100

Immature seeds became capable of germination with reduction of moisture to approximately 25 per cent. Moist sand was used for germination tests after the seeds had reached the moisture contents indicated. Sprague suggested that the mechanism inhibiting the normal germination of freshly harvested immature corn operates in the scutellum of the embryo since for germination corn kernels require only 35 per cent moisture in the whole grain but 60 per cent in the embryo.

Another publication appearing the same year as that of Sprague (Koshimizu 1936) also reported that a decrease of water content of unripe corn brings about germination, but attributed the effect to resulting increase in supply of nutrient solution and oxygen. Since Koshimizu found that excised embryos of unripe seeds germinated more quickly than intact seeds and that endosperm juice of unripe seeds inhibited germination, he reasoned that drying out of the seed might change the nature of the inhibiting substance so that it no longer would prevent germination. This places the cause for poor germination of immature seeds on the quality of the endosperm rather than the nature of the scutellum as postulated by Sprague. No work done since 1936 has shed any further light on this question.

Because there is a great loss in grass seeds in harvesting due to shattering, it would be advantageous to harvest before the seeds were fully mature. Before this can be done with safety it is necessary to know the earliest stages at which the seed can be harvested without subsequent reduction in germination capacity, longevity, and vigor of seedlings produced. Such a study for some western range and pasture grasses has been made (McAlister 1943). In general, immature seeds were inferior to mature seeds in seedling emergence in field plantings and in keeping quality though some exceptions were noted. However, at the end of the seedling year the plants which were produced from immature seeds were equal in survival and size to those produced from mature seeds.

Experiments conducted to determine whether a half grown crop of alfalfa seed in late fall was worth harvesting, revealed that if the seeds were one-half or more grown, even if the majority of the pods were still green, a seed crop of fair quality could be secured (Grunder and Megee 1929). It was necessary, however, to screen out the seeds less than one-half grown and fan out those light in weight.

The stage of maturity of the fruit has a direct effect upon the germination of pimiento seeds (Cochran 1943). Seeds planted immediately upon removal from green fruits did not give more than 6.1 per cent germination. Even when the fruits had ripened sufficiently to be streaked with red, only 68.5 per cent of their seeds germinated. Bright red fruits as well as those which had remained on the plant until they were dark red and shriveled yielded seeds with 96 per cent germination capacity. Thus it is not desirable to save seeds at the end of the season from imperfectly ripened fruit.

In the elimination of weeds, many of them are cut down after their seeds have started to develop and allowed to lie on the ground. Some of these seeds may be viable and hence germinate. A rather extensive piece of work on the viability of weed seeds at various stages of maturity has been reported by Gill (1938). Some common weeds were cut near the base of the plant and allowed to dry in the sun. Seed samples of each species were taken at stages of development from that at which the flower was still in the bud through the various stages of maturity after fertilization. Control lots of seeds allowed to mature fully on the growing plants were used for comparison. Certain plants within the family *Compositae* produced viable seeds when cut in the flowering stage while others did not. In the first group were *Sonchus oleraceus, Senecio jacobaea, S. vulgaris,* and *Aster tripolium* and in the second group were *Taraxacum vulgare, Hypochaeris radicata, Cirsium arvense,* and *C. lanceolatum.* Certain species in other families were found to produce viable seeds when cut down at various stages of maturation of the fruit following fertilization. According to La Rue (1935) who cut off dandelion heads at various stages, then allowed them to dry and tested their germination, there is no danger of spreading the weed from cut heads until the white of the pappus begins to extend beyond the green involucre tips. The achenes from less mature heads all decayed within 10 days and none of them showed normal embryos upon dissection.

The relation of the maturity of the seed to the development of an impermeable coat has been the subject of study for various forms. In *Brassica alba* the testa prevents germination when the seeds are green (Kidd and West 1920). As the seeds ripen and turn yellow the seed coat is less effective in preventing germination until with complete maturity no appreciable influence is shown. Excised embryos germinate freely in all stages of development from green to fully ripe. The authors believed that the living testa limited the gaseous exchange of the embryo.

Desiccation studies of sweet clover (*Melilotus alba*) seeds collected at two different maturity levels showed that the seed coats changed from the permeable to the impermeable state as a final step in the maturation of the seed (Helgeson 1932). Dehydration was thought to bring about an irreversible change in some colloidal material in the coats. Slightly immature seeds were practically all permeable and gave high germination percentages.

On the other hand, delaying the harvest of *Trifolium subterraneum* seeds for six weeks after the normal stage of maturity caused a considerable reduction in the percentage of hard seeds (Hills 1942). It is possible that these differences in reaction are due to the different types of seeds used but other investigations including studies of seeds harvested prematurely as well as after the normal harvesting stage might be worth while. Hills (1944) pointed out that hard-seededness is not a varietal character of *T. subterraneum* or, if it is, it is masked by the much more important environmental conditions.

Many varieties of lettuce seed do not germinate readily immediately after harvest. Immaturity at the time of harvest has been demonstrated to be an important contributing factor to this dormancy (Thompson 1936). Immature seeds are introduced into lettuce seed harvests by the practice of cutting and drying the plants and threshing all the seeds, some fully mature and the others immature. The retarding effect of immaturity on germination decreases with increase in time after harvest. This may be the drying effect mentioned above.

Other seeds which normally require low temperature pretreatment for germination or possess impermeable coats failed to exhibit any dormancy when immature, *i.e.*, just past the milk stage (Titus 1940). These effects have not been confirmed by other workers, probably principally because of the difficulty of selecting the seeds at the proper stage of maturation. Indeed throughout the reports on the subject of maturity, the descriptive terms used have been inadequate, since subject to the judgment of the particular investigator.

This difficulty has been recognized especially in the collection of cones of *Pinus ponderosa*. In this case a more accurate method for determining seed maturity has been developed (Maki 1940). It was found that the specific gravity of the cones decreased from 0.92 on July 27 to 0.74 on September 5. In the same period the germination capacity of the seed rose from 0 to 74.1 per cent. Thus the specific gravity of the cone can be used as an index of the maturity of the cone and hence of the seeds within it. The method can be used in the field by dropping cones in a test liquid of desired specific gravity and if three or more of five sound cones float, they are mature. In central Idaho, the specific gravity accompanying good self extraction of seeds as the cones dry as well as good germination was found to be 0.85. Therefore kerosene was used as the test solution. In cases where the degree of maturity is important the development of objective measurements is essential to a standardization of procedure.

Having ascertained the earliest stage of maturity which will yield seeds capable of good germination it is of interest to know whether there is an effect on the resulting seedlings. Immature rye seeds (one-sixteenth the weight of the normal grain) were viable and produced plants that for the greater part of the duration of the experiment exceeded those grown from normal grains in (1) relative growth rate, (2) rate of tiller production, and (3) rate of leaf formation (Nutman 1941). As a result all plants, regardless of original grain weight, were approximately the same size at the termination of the experiment. This was attributed to the higher rate of meristem development in the small grains.

On the contrary field stands of corn from immature seed were found to be inferior to those from mature seed even though only ears showing 100 per cent germination in laboratory tests were used (Koehler et al. 1934). This points to the lessened vigor of seedlings from immature seeds. This lessened vigor has been reported to result in increased development over reproductive as opposed to vegetative parts of the plant causing greater fruit yield (Arthur 1893; Goff 1892, 1900). The data on this point are meager, however, and are not conclusive.

Seed Size:—Seeds vary in size from that of the *Lodoicea maldivica,* a species of palm, which sometimes weighs as much as 40 pounds (Hodge 1949) to the small dust-like seeds of such forms as *Lobelia* or *Nicotiana.* Occasionally one sees a report about the relation between seed size and germination or between seed size and the rate of growth and final size of the plants produced. Six comparatively recent papers have dealt with this subject in different species of seeds.

Hatcher and Purvis (1945) obtained dwarf grains of rye, wheat, and barley by premature harvesting, and found that they would germinate readily and produce normal plants, even though the grain size might be only one-tenth that of the fully developed grain. The growth rate of the plants from the dwarf grains was higher than that of plants from normal grains but both types of plants tended to attain the same final size. The authors did not discuss the cause of the differential growth rates, but they pointed out that it is known for Petkus rye that the embryo weight is proportional to the grain weight, so the effect was not due to a relatively larger embryo in the dwarf grain.

Small alfalfa seeds, *i.e.,* half the size of the larger seeds, showed a germination capacity of only 10 per cent of the large seeds and the seedlings produced were less vigorous than those from the large seeds. These small seeds were mature, however, and never had the capacity for making normal-sized seeds while those of the premature grain seeds described in the preceding paragraph were probably capable of continuing development to full size (Erickson 1946).

Seeds of turnips vary in size within wide limits. It has been demonstrated that the smaller seeds tended to produce roots which were flatter in shape than those produced from the larger sizes and that the former did not give as good a stand in the field as the latter (Leggatt and Ingalls 1949). Consequently, it was recommended that the smallest size seeds be eliminated from the seed stock in spite of the fact that they were as prompt to germinate and of as high germination capacity as the larger seeds.

Righter (1945) pointed out that seeds of a pine tree may vary in weight so that the heaviest sound seed is more than twice as heavy as the lightest sound seed. Also, the seed size is reflected in the seedlings under uniform conditions, but experiments have shown that there are no lasting advantages to the seedling regardless of the size of seed from which it was produced. Seeds of identical weights from the same tree gave rise to seedlings differing widely in size. Also there were large, medium, and small hollow seeds. He concluded that seed weight is correlated in a positive manner with seedling size, but not with inherent vigor of the plant, so that grading the seed would not make a more vigorous stock.

On the other hand, Larson and Peng-fi (1949) suggested that the size of tomato seeds might be used successfully in segregating generations of this plant, since large seeds were found in preliminary tests to be associated with hybrid vigor as measured by yields of fruit. They found that the mean yield of the F_2 progenies produced from the largest of three seed-size classes was comparable to the mean yield of progenies from all seed sizes of the F_1. The smallest seed producing the F_1 generation produced less fruit, especially early in the season. In conclusion they stated (p. 568): "If a measurable association can be shown to exist between size of seed extracted from F_1 fruits and productivity in the F_2 generation progenies, a new method of producing hybrid seed in volume may result. Breeders of pure line tomato strains may also benefit by being able to select for vigor by seed size, thus eliminating the growing of considerable undesirable material."

The seeds of the mangosteen, *Garcinia mangostana* L., vary from 0.1 to 2.2 grams and average 1.0 gram in a typical lot according to Hume and Cobin (1946). Seed size affected the percentage germination of seed weighing less than 1.0 gram, so that the germination of seeds weighing less than 0.2 g. was very poor. Although seeds weighing 1.0 g. or above all gave about 100 per cent germination, seedling survival from seeds weighing less than 1.3 g. was reduced. The size of the plants after one year of growth was also positively correlated with the size of the seed. These results are in contrast to the reports for other types of seeds, which may show an effect of seed size on the seedling in the early stages of growth, but such effects tend to disappear with the maturation of the plant. The peculiar behavior of the mangosteen is attributed by Hume and Cobin to three characteristics of the plant. First, the embryo within the seed is not differentiated and therefore the ability of the seed to develop depends chiefly on the amount of stored food in the seed. Secondly, there are no root hairs on the roots of either seedling or mature trees, so that the better developed root systems of the larger plants from the larger seeds provide a better chance of survival of the seedlings. Thirdly, a large reserve of food in the seed makes good early growth of the seedling possible after which there may be a period of several years before further growth is initiated. They conclude (p. 301): "Because of these peculiarities the effect of seed size is particularly important in mangosteen. The seed supplies the energy for generation and differentiation of the embryo, the development of two root systems and the development of the plant until the synthetic mechanism can become established. The effect of seed size is not masked by independent growth of the mangosteen seedling during the first year."

Symbiosis and Germination:—The investigation of the association of various plants and the attending influence upon the germination of the seeds of one of the associated forms has been pursued intermittently for about a century. One of the earliest comprehensive treatises on this subject appeared in print in 1909 (Bernard). Evidence was presented to show that the germination of orchid seeds as well as the subsequent growth of the seedlings was dependent upon their infection by certain strains of the fungus which is generally found living in the orchid root. In the germinating embryo, the fungus disintegrated in the infected zone and was believed by Bernard to have been digested by the orchid embryo. His case for the need of the fungus by the embryo was weakened by the common germination failure in inoculated seed cultures. He obtained only a few hundred seedlings out of about 50,000 seeds.

Also, in certain of his experiments with Cattleya and Laelia, seeds were germinated without the fungus by using a concentrated solution of a dry powder obtained by pulverizing orchid tubers. This non-symbiotic germination was corroborated 13 years later by Knudson (1922) who obtained germination of seeds of these two forms without the aid of fungus provided soluble organic substances, particularly sugar, were present. He pointed out that the necessity of a fungus for orchid seed germination had not been proved. Germination is made extremely difficult because of the small size of the embryo and its susceptibility to unfavorable factors such as desiccation or death caused by a cover of fungal or algal growth or their decomposition products.

Further detailed studies by Knudson (1925, 1927) led him to explain the failure of orchid seeds to germinate as due to their food relations. The seeds are lacking in food reserves which must be supplied. The fungus is of value in germination only in that it makes food available to the embryo by digestion or by excretion of favorable substances. By supplying a suitable nutrient solution germination may be obtained without the presence of a fungus, i.e., non-symbiotically. Other workers have also secured orchid seed germination without fungal infection. A recent report (Watkins 1945) refers to the work of Meyer who germinated sterile seeds of representatives of six genera of orchids in a sterile agar medium containing tomato juice. Cappelleti (1947) demonstrated that the fungal mycelium stimulated the metabolism of the protocorms of Cymbidium as measured by water and nitrogen metabolism which was twice as great as in asymbiotic cultures. Bahme (1949) stimulated orchid embryo growth by the addition of 1 mg./l. of nicotinic acid. Since he obtained similar stimulation by the mycorrhizal fungus, he suggested that one of the possible functions of the fungus was to supply this substance. Adding aneurine, pyrimidine, or pyrimidine + thiazole to an inorganic nutrient medium increased the growth of Cattleya embryos (Mariat 1948). Addition of thiazole alone was ineffective. Germination of seeds of Calluna vulgaris has also been claimed to depend upon the presence of a fungus, but workers are not agreed upon this point. According to Chabrolin (1934b), Thesium humile seeds germinate only when the walls of the akene are infiltrated with a saprophytic fungus. This plant is parasitic on cereals but does not require the presence of any part of the host plant for the germination of its seeds.

Other seeds of parasitic or semi-parasitic plants have been said to depend upon secretions from the roots of the host plants for germination. Among these are Orobanche (Chabrolin 1934a), Alectra vogelii (Botha 1948), and Pyrola species (Lihnell 1942). The claim by Heinricher that there was no germination of the seeds of Lathraea clandestina without some fragment of the living host plant was refuted by Chemin (1931). In a series of papers, Brown and others (Brown and Edwards 1945, 1946; Brown, Johnson, Robinson and Todd 1949; Brown, Robinson and Johnson 1949) have reported the results of their findings on the germination of Striga lutea seeds. Tests with different dilutions of a standard solution of the host stimulant (from roots of *Sorghum vulgare* plants) led Brown and Edwards (1946, p. 142) to the tentative hypothesis "that the seed itself forms a stimulating substance, which is the same or similar to that which originates in the host root, and that the decreasing concentration of host substance necessary to induce maximum germination during the first 21 days is due to the accumulation of the stimulating substance self-formed in the seed. Similarly that the increasing concentration necessary after 21 days is due to the metabolic decrease of the accumulated quantity." Some of the chemical and physical properties of the stimulating substance have been determined, but it has not yet been isolated in its pure form (Brown *et al.* 1949). It can be replaced by thiourea or allylthiourea (Brown and Edwards 1945).

The physiologic responses of all seeds in this category are especially complicated and difficult of interpretation. This explains, at least in part, the many conflicting reports of their germination behavior.

The special behavior of these seeds together with that of many spores and pollen grains which are said to germinate only when associated with active independent tissues have led to a postulation by Brown (1946) that the same phenomenon is involved in the several groups. He thinks the effect may be due to the production by the active tissue of chemical activators which promote germination of the associated organism. These chemicals are not necessarily of the vitamin or hormone type but may actually act as a nutrient supply. However, the small concentrations necessary suggest hormones or similar compounds. Brown's contribution is a critical review of 34 different articles on the subject of seeds, spores, and pollen grains that require stimulation for germination and should be consulted by the student in this field.

Moon Effects:—Planting practices for different economic crops have included sowing at some given phase of the moon for best results. Controlled experiments in the greenhouse using tomato and maize seeds, both reputedly sensitive to lunar effects, have failed to reveal any consistent effect of the moon on germination (Mather 1942). Similarly outside plantings of radish, cabbage, bean, carrot, and onion were not affected by moon phases (Mather and Newell 1941). Fluctuations in germination were obtained but were due to other causes. No correlation was found by Rohmeder (1938) between moon phases and germination or early seedling development of spruce. Temperature, moisture, and soil conditions do influence germination significantly and these factors rather than the phase of the moon should be considered when plantings are to be made.

A recent short paper, however, has described a beneficial effect on germination of the bright moonlight of South Africa (Semmens 1947). The seed varieties used were not stated, but those seeds in which the testa was thin and transparent showed increased germination after exposure to the night sky at periods of half-moon, as compared to no moon. The maximum moon effect is evident at half-moon since moonlight is partially polarized. The effect of moonlight upon starch, both as raw and boiled starch grains and in the leaves of *Tropaeolum* and spinach as well as in the sap of trees, was found to be a hydrolytic one, *i.e.*, moonlight acted as a "digestive tonic." The starch disappeared from uncovered portions of the leaves upon exposure to moonlight, and there was nearly twice as much reduction to sugar in the sap of trees after a period of half-moon than after a period of minimum light. These results were similar to those secured with artificially polarized light.

References:—

Aamodt, O. S., 1935: Germination of Russian pigweed seeds in ice and on frozen soil (Sci. Agric. 15:507-508).

Arthur, J. C., 1893: Deviation in development due to the use of unripe seeds (Bot. Gaz. 18:341-342).

Bahme, R. B., 1949: Nicotinic acid as a growth factor for certain orchid embryos (Science 109:522-523).

Barton, L. V., 1935: Germination of delphinium seeds (Contrib. Boyce Thompson Inst. 7:405-409).

————, 1936: Germination of some desert seeds (Contrib. Boyce Thompson Inst. 8:7-11).

————, 1945: Respiration and germination studies of seeds in moist storage (Ann. New York Acad. Sci. 46:185-208).

Bernard, M. N., 1909: L'évolution dans la symbiose, les Orchidées et leur champignons commensaux (Ann. Sci. Nat. Bot. 9:1-196).

Botha, P. J., 1948: The parasitism of *Alectra Vogelii* Benth. with special reference to the germination of its seeds (South African Jour. Sci. 44:119).

Brown, E. O., & R. H. Porter, 1942: The viability and germination of seeds of *Convolvulus arvensis* L. and other perennial weeds (Iowa Agric. Exp. Sta. Res. Bull. 294:473-504).

Brown, R., 1946: Biological stimulation in germination (Nature 157:64-69).

Brown, R., & M. Edwards, 1945: Effects of thiourea and allylthiourea on the germination of the seed of *Striga lutea* (Nature 155:455-456).

————, ————, 1946: The germination of the seed of *Striga lutea*. II. The effect of time of treatment and of concentration of the host stimulant (Ann. Bot. n. s. 10:133-142).

Brown, R., A. W. Johnson, E. Robinson & A. R. Todd, 1949: The stimulant involved in the germination of *Striga hermonthica* (Proc. Roy. Soc. London, B, 136:1-12).

Brown, R., E. Robinson & A. W. Johnson, 1949: Effect of *Striga* germination stimulant on extension growth on the roots of peas (Nature 163:842-843).

Capelleti, C., 1947: Ricerche fisiologiche sulla simbiosi nelle orchidee (Physiological researches on symbiosis in orchids) (Lavori Bot. Torino 8:56-76; *abstr. in* Biol. Abstr. 22:12331, 1948).

Chabrolin, C., 1934a: La germination des graines d'*Orobanche* (Compt. Rend. Acad. Sci., Paris, 198:2275-2277).

————, 1934b: La germination des graines de *Thesium humile* exige l'intervention de champignons saprophytes (Compt. Rend. Acad. Sci., Paris, 199:225-226).

Chemin, E., 1931: Les graines de *Lathraea clandestina* peuvent germer sans l'assistance d'aucune autre plante. Réponse à E. Heinricher (Bull. Soc. Bot. France 78:708-721).

Cochran, H. L., 1936: Some factors which influence the germination of pepper seeds (Proc. Amer. Soc. Hort. Sci. 33(1935):477-480).

————, 1943: Effect of stage of fruit maturity at time of harvest and method of drying on the germination of pimiento seed (Proc. Amer. Soc. Hort. Sci. 43:229-234).

Culpepper, C. W., & H. H. Moon, 1941: Effect of stage of maturity at time of harvest on germination of sweet corn (Jour. Agric. Res. 63:335-343).

Dungan, G. H., 1924: Some factors affecting the water absorption and germination of seed corn (Amer. Soc. Agron. Jour. 16:473-481).

Edwards, T. I., 1932: Temperature relations of seed germination (Quart. Rev. Biol. 7:428-443).

Erickson, L. C., 1946: The effect of alfalfa seed size and depth of seeding upon the subsequent procurement of stand (Amer. Soc. Agron. Jour. 38:964-973).

Gill, N. T., 1938: The viability of weed seeds at various stages of maturity (Ann. Appl. Biol. 25:447-456).

Goff, E. S., 1892: A breeding experiment with tomatoes (Wis. Agric. Exp. Sta. Rept. 8(1891):152-159).

————, 1900: The effects of continued use of immature seed (Wis. Agric. Exp. Sta. Ann. Rept. 17:295-299).

Grunder, M. S., & C. R. Megee, 1929: Maturity influences quality of alfalfa seed (Mich. Agric. Exp. Sta. Quart. Bull. 12:61-62).

Harrington, G. T., 1923: Use of alternating temperatures in the germination of seeds (Jour. Agric. Res. 23:295-332).

Hatcher, E. S. J., & O. N. Purvis, 1945: On the behaviour in the field of small grain obtained by premature harvesting (Jour. Agric. Sci. 35:177-183).

Heit, C. E., 1945: Physiology of germination (New York [Geneva] Agric. Exp. Sta. Ann. Rept. 1943/44:45).

Heit, C. E., & M. T. Munn, 1941: New Zealand spinach germination studies (Proc. Assoc. Off. Seed Anal. 33:90-95).

Helgeson, E. A., 1932: Impermeability in mature and immature sweet clover seeds as affected by conditions of storage (Wis. Acad. Sci., Arts & Letters, Trans. 27:193-206).

Hills, K. L., 1942: Dormancy and hardseededness in T. subterraneum. 1. The effect of time of harvest and of certain seed storage conditions (Jour. Austral. Counc. Sci. & Indus. Res. 15:275-284).

————, 1944: Dormancy and hardseededness in T. subterraneum. 4. Variation between varieties (Jour. Austral. Counc. Sci. & Indus. Res. 17:242-250).

Hodge, W. H., 1949: The Goliath of seeds (Nat. Hist. 58:34-35).

Hopkins, E. F., 1928: Further studies of celery seed germination (Proc. Assoc. Off. Seed Anal. N. Amer. 20:69-70).

Hume, E. P., & M. Cobin, 1946: Relation of seed size to germination and early growth of mangosteen (Proc. Amer. Soc. Hort. Sci. 48:298-302).

Kidd, F., & C. West, 1920: The rôle of the seed-coat in relation to the germination of immature seed (Ann. Bot. 34:439-446).

Knudson, L., 1922: Nonsymbiotic germination of orchid seeds (Bot. Gaz. 73:1-25).

————, 1925: Physiological study of the symbiotic germination of orchid seeds (Bot. Gaz. 79:345-379).

————, 1927: Symbiosis and asymbiosis relative to orchids (New Phytol. 26:328-336).

Koehler, B., G. H. Dungan & W. L. Burlison, 1934: Maturity of seed corn in relation to yielding ability and disease infection (Amer. Soc. Agron. Jour. 26:262-274).

Koshimizu, T., 1936: On the relation between the ripening stages of the maize-seed and its germination (Bot. Mag. [Tokyo] 50:504-513).

Larson, R. E., & L. Peng-fi, 1949: Embryo size and productivity in segregating generations of tomatoes (Science 109:567-568).

La Rue, C. D., 1935: The time to cut dandelions (Science 82:350).

Leggatt, C. W., & R. A. Ingalls, 1949: Size of seed in relation to size and shape of root in swede turnips (Sci. Agric. 29:357-369).

Lihnell, D., 1942: Keimungsversuche mit Pyrolasamen (Symbolae botanicae Upsalienses 6(3):1-37).

Ludwig, C. A., 1932: The germination of cotton seed at low temperatures (Jour. Agric. Res. 44:367-380).

McAlister, D. F., 1943: The effect of maturity on the viability and longevity of the seeds of western range and pasture grasses (Amer. Soc. Agron. Jour. 35:442-453).

Maki, T. E., 1940: Significance and applicability of seed maturity indices for ponderosa pine (Jour. Forest. 38:55-60).

Mariat, F., 1948: Action des composants de l'aneurine sur le développement des embryons d'Orchidées (Compt. Rend. Soc. Biol. 142:840-841).

Mather, K., & J. Newell, 1941: Seed germination and the moon (Roy. Hort. Soc. Jour. 66:358-366).

Mather, M., 1942: The effect of temperature and the moon on seedling growth (Roy. Hort. Soc. Jour. 67:264-270).

Nutman, P. S., 1941: Studies in vernalisation of cereals. VII. A study of the conditions of formation and the subsequent growth of dwarf embryos of rye (Ann. Bot. n. s. 5:353-374).

Righter, F. I., 1945: Pinus: The relationship of seed size and seedling size to inherent vigor (Jour. Forest. 43:131-137).

Rohmeder, E., 1938: Der Einfluss der Mondphasen auf die Keimung und erste Jugendentwicklung der Fichte (Forstwiss. Centralbl. 60:593-603).

Schroeder, E. M., & L. V. Barton, 1939: Germination and growth of some rock garden plants (Contrib. Boyce Thompson Inst. 10:235-255).

Semmens, E. S., 1947: Chemical effects of moonlight (Nature 159:613).

Sprague, G. F., 1936: The relation of moisture content and time of harvest to germination of immature corn (Amer. Soc. Agron. Jour. 28:472-478).

Stier, H. L., & H. B. Cordner, 1937: Germination of seeds of the potato as affected by temperature (Proc. Amer. Soc. Hort. Sci. 34(1936):430-432).

Thompson, R. C., 1936: Some factors associated with dormancy of lettuce seed (Proc. Amer. Soc. Hort. Sci. 33(1935):610-616).

Titus, G. R., 1940: So-called 2-year seeds germinated first year (Amer. Nurs. 72(11): 22).

Toole, E. H., & V. K. Toole, 1941: Progress of germination of seed of Digitaria as influenced by germination temperature and other factors (Jour. Agric. Res. 63: 65-90).

Walker, J., 1933: The suitability of immature sweet corn for seed (Sci. Agric. 13:642-645).

Warington, K., 1936: The effect of constant and fluctuating temperature on the germination of the weed seeds in arable soil (Jour. Ecol. 24:185-204).

Watkins, J. V., 1945: Raising orchid seedlings in tomato juice (Flor. Exch. 105(10): 15).

Chapter VIII

FACTORS AFFECTING GERMINATION, II

Chemicals:—Some of the effects of chemicals on the germination of seeds will be considered in the chapter on "Seed Transmission of Disease," as incidental responses to treatments for disease control. Other chemical treatments given to seeds have been concerned with the direct effect upon the seed and its germination. These latter results will be reported briefly here.

Gases.—Moist and dry seeds of radish and rye exposed to a continuous flow of ammonia, chlorine, hydrogen cyanide, hydrogen sulphide, and sulfur dioxide gases revealed greater toxic effects for moist than for dry seeds (Barton 1940c). Concentrations of 1000 and 250 parts per million for periods of 1, 4, 15, 60, 240, and 960 minutes were used. Delay in germination due to gas treatment was the principal effect noted. This delay was sometimes accompanied by reduction in germination percentage and in some instances all the seeds were killed. Hydrogen cyanide and hydrogen sulfide had no effect on germination percentage; ammonia and chlorine were more toxic while sulfur dioxide proved most toxic under the conditions of this experiment.

Inorganic salts.—The action of potassium nitrate in fulfilling the requirements for germination of some light-sensitive seeds is well known (*see* Light and Dormancy). Manganese sulfate in a wide range of concentrations has been found to accelerate the rate of germination of the mungo bean, maize, and cabbage (Loo and Tang 1945). Salts of lead in concentrations of 0.01 per cent to 0.2 per cent caused a delay or inhibition in germination of seeds of cress and mustard (Dilling 1926). Thorium, zinc, and beryllium salts in equivalent concentrations gave similar though less marked effects. Copper stunted the growth of the seedlings and thallium destroyed the vitality of the seed. The amount of fertilizer applied to the soil during the maturation of the seed not only affects the yield but may affect the physiological behavior of the seeds themselves. Lettuce seeds from plants that had been fertilized twice gave fewer dormant seeds at harvest time than those that had been fertilized once, while those which had received no fertilizer produced twice as many dormant seeds (Thompson 1938).

Organic substances.—Organic substances, such as alfalfa powder, casein, and peptone, may injure germination if applied in large quantities (Fred 1918). This injury may be produced by an accumulation of poisonous decomposition products or by the increased growth of harmful organisms. Tests have been conducted using organic substances usually found in seeds and seedlings in an effort to increase the germination capacity of poor seeds. Asparagine and leucine increased the germination capacity without exerting any harmful effect while pepsin and diastase both produced an excess of mold and varied from no effect to a harmful effect in some cases and beneficial in others (Stone and Smith 1901).

Growth substances.—In the decade between 1930 and 1940 numerous reports appeared in the literature concerning the treatment of seeds with so called growth-promoting or hormone-like substances. The claims made for these treatments have varied from harmful effects through no effects to beneficial effects. Extensive studies made at Boyce Thompson Institute and reported in 1940 (Barton 1940*a*; Youden 1940) failed to reveal the beneficial effects claimed. Twenty-five different forms of flower, vegetable, and cereal seeds served as test objects for vapor, liquid, and dust treatments. Statistical analyses of some of the data corroborated the absence of stimulatory or beneficial effects. Harmful effects with large dosages, on the other hand, were easily demonstrable. It is recognized that the interpretation of such data is accurate only under the set of conditions which prevailed during a given experiment. Factors such as soil type and moisture, light, seed variation, selection of seedlings, position in the field, etc. complicate the chemical effects and doubtless account in part for the conflicting results obtained.

More recently the deleterious effects of 2,4-dichlorophenoxyacetic acid have been used to advantage in preventing the germination or killing the very young seedlings of some weeds. This acid is being used extensively as a herbicide and it becomes of interest to determine its effect on seed germination. It has been applied as a dust and in liquid form to soil and to seeds and the subsequent effect on germination noted (Hamner *et al.* 1946; Mitchell and Marth 1946). Added to muck soil infested with weed seeds 1 p.p.m. of 2,4-D reduced the number of plants 20 per cent. Muck soil containing 10 and 100 p.p.m. of the acid were entirely free of weed growth. There is a residue of the acid in treated soils which inhibits germination for periods up to 18 months after treatment. The length of time the toxic effects remain in the soil depends upon the kind of soil, the dosage of the chemical, moisture content, etc. Application to manure is also feasible to prevent germination of any weed seeds which might be present. Tests in which the 2,4-D was applied directly to the seeds revealed that grass seeds as a whole are less sensitive to injury than other seeds. However, it has been demonstrated that applications of 2,4-D do reduce the stands of grasses (Pridham 1946). Seeds of some dicotyledons, such as beans and peas are very susceptible to injury. The lethal dosage for seeds in the soil has been found to be in the neighborhood of 10 p.p.m. This is much less than the 1000 p.p.m. commonly used in herbicidal sprays of mature plants. The successful sterilization of soil with 2,4-D and its inactivation with storage after treatment suggests the possibility of weed control by this method.

Effect of 2,4-D on 22 different species including both monocotyledons and dicotyledons showed a lack of specificity in inhibiting germination of the seeds in moist chambers and indicated a more general herbicidal effect upon very young than upon older plants (Allard *et al.* 1946). When the acid was applied to the soil, differences in species response became marked. Germination and establishment of broadleaf species were completely inhibited at rates of application which merely stunted cereals. Similar effects from soil treatments have been described by Mitchell and Marth (1946).

Mitchell and Brown (1947) found that dormant seeds of subterranean clover, whether dry or wet, were resistant to 2,4-D, while seeds which had started to germinate were injured.

A spray of 2,4-D on ryegrass, rye, and oat plants when the flower primordia were showing, when the seed stalk was elongating, or when the seed was developing resulted in no significant differences in the germination of the mature seeds (Marth *et al.* 1948).

Hsueh and Lou (1947) obtained stimulation of seed germination using a 0.01 per cent solution of 2,4-D, but 0.07 per cent completely inhibited barley germination and delayed the germination of rice. In seeking to explain the different responses of these two grains, they compared the germination rate of treated seeds with that of seeds kept under aerobic and anaerobic conditions, and found a striking resemblance. It appeared that oxygen was no longer available to the seeds treated with 2,4-D, so that the germination of the aerobic barley seed was inhibited while that of rice, which is capable of germinating anaerobically, was only delayed. This hypothesis was supported by results of gas analyses by means of microrespirometers.

Chemical effects on dormant seeds.—Dormancy of seeds which normally show some delay in germination could not be broken by treatment with growth substances (Barton 1940*b*). On the other hand, the germination of seeds of *Cornus* and *Pyrus* which had had their dormancy broken by a period in a moist medium at 5° C. was inhibited by treatment with growth substances. This inhibiting effect was partly removed by a second period at 5° C., but abnormalities often appeared in the seedlings so produced. Also growth substances failed to initiate the growth of dormant epicotyls in germinated seeds of *Lilium auratum*, *Paeonia suffruticosa*, and *Viburnum* sp. (*see* chapter on Dormancy). Very little success has attended efforts to break dormancy by chemical means, though Deuber (1932) was able to shorten the rest period of red and black oak acorns by immersion in a solution of thiourea or by vapors of ethylene chlorohydrin.

Johnson (1946) has substituted chemical treatments for low temperature pretreatment to augment the germination of some forest tree seeds. These treatments have included soaking the seeds in 1 to 4 per cent potassium nitrate for 24 hours, soaking in 1 per cent solutions of thiourea and ethylene chlorohydrin for 1 minute after which the seeds were drained and left in corked vials for 24 hours, and the application to the seeds of red copper oxide and zinc oxide as dusts. Although the low-temperature pretreatments were, as a rule, more effective than the chemical treatments, Johnson believed that chemicals showed promise for treating the seeds of a number of forest tree species.

More success has attended the use of thiourea for forcing the germination of freshly harvested lettuce seeds at temperatures that ordinarily inhibit germination. Lettuce seeds, when freshly harvested, usually require temperatures of 20° C. or below for germination. The use of thiourea to stimulate the germination of such seeds at higher temperatures was reported first by Thompson and Kosar in 1938. They tried several chemicals but found that 0.5 per cent thiourea gave the highest germination of Grand Rapids and Hubbard Market varieties. Later tests reported in 1944 (Thompson and Horn) revealed marked increases in germination of lettuce seed treated with thiourea and germinated at high temperatures. That the variety of lettuce seed as well as the age from harvest at the time of treatment has a direct bearing on the effectiveness of thiourea treatment has been shown by Garman and Barton (1946). Seeds of four varieties (White Boston, Grand Rapids, Iceberg, and Black-seeded Simpson) which were soaked in 0.5 and 1.0 per cent thiourea solutions and germinated immediately after treatment displayed a gradual increase in germination with the lengthening of the period of dry storage between harvest and treatment. The amount of stimulation of seed germination by thiourea treatment also depended upon the variety. Presoaking seeds in a 0.5 or 1.0 per cent thiourea solution for 16 hours at 20° C. resulted in greatest stimulation of germination at 30° C. Soaking at 20° C. was more effective than soaking at 30° C. when the seeds were germinated at 30° C.

Colchicine.—The interest in the use of colchicine, a poison drug obtained from autumn crocus, *Colchicum autumnale,* as a method of obtaining polyploid, especially tetraploid, plants has led inevitably to a study of its effect on germination. As is true of so many chemicals, low concentrations of colchicine have been shown to stimulate germination while higher dosages inhibit germination or kill the seed. It is the opinion of Bond (1942) that weak solutions should be used, for the optimum concentration (0.04 per cent) for stimulating germination of *Petunia* seeds was high enough to induce polyploidy and the growth of the seedlings was not retarded as when high concentrations of the drug are used for seed treatment.

Penicillin.—Ribeiro (1944, 1946) has demonstrated that sulfanilamide and penicillin act to inhibit the germination of lettuce seeds. Replacement of penicillin solutions by water after 48 hours permitted normal germination. Thus penicillin acts as a phytostatic. He did not describe the penicillin used. Smith (1946) pointed out that therapeutic or crude penicillin prevented seed germination through the presence of impurities of phenylacetic, indoleacetic, and furoic acids, all of which are known to be active inhibitors of seed germination. He found that crystalline penicillin did not retard germination.

DDT.—The insecticide, DDT, was without effect on either seed or fungi when applied as a powder or liquid on 111 different seed lots (Patrick *et al.* 1947).

Pelleting.—In the pelleting process the surface of the seeds is coated with some inert material to which chemicals of various kinds may be added. Some of the pulverized materials used have been fly ash, feldspar, celite, bentonite, or vermiculite made to stick by means of a water-soluble plastic known as methylcel (Carolus 1949) and a mineral known as Montmorillonite which could be processed and made to adhere to the seed without a binder (Althaus 1949). Some of the advantages claimed for pelleting are:

1) The incorporation of fertilizer material in the pellet furnishes the young seedlings with needed nourishment.
2) Fungicides and insecticides are more effective when in direct contact with the seeds.
3) It permits a more uniform planting and eliminates the necessity of thinning.
4) Small seeds are made larger and heavier making for greater ease in planting and permitting planting from airplanes for reseeding prairie lands or forests.

5) Plant growth regulators or stimulants may promote rooting or hasten emergence of the seedlings.

6) The addition of certain types of carbon to the pellet may absorb the toxic properties of 2,4-D or other substances and thus reduce the injury to the young seedlings.

7) A coating that reduces the rate of moisture penetration may delay emergence of the seedling for 24 to 48 hours, thus allowing more time for weed seed germination and control.

Before using any particular type of pelleting on a commercial scale, however, it would be wise to determine the effect of the coating on the species of seeds to be used. The inert material alone, without any substance added, delayed cucumber germination 34 hours and onion two days, while there was no delay with turnip seeds (Carolus 1949).

Heavy Water:—No extensive reports on the effects of deuterium oxide (D_2O) on seeds are available but three short descriptions may be considered indicative of what may be expected. Tobacco seeds placed in small test tubes with ordinary and heavy water germinated in the former but not in the latter (Lewis 1933). Two varieties of *Pisum sativum* germinated in water containing up to 40 per cent D_2O (Brun and Tronstad 1935), but with 50 per cent or more D_2O no germination occurred. No stimulation was noted at low concentrations of D_2O. Melot (1934) germinated seeds of wheat, *Triticum vulgare,* in 14.8, 38.0, and 94.0 per cent D_2O. In all cases the seeds germinated and no macroscopical differences were detected. Also there were no differences in respiration of treated and control lots during the first and second days of germination. Much more detailed work is needed to determine the effects of heavy water on the physiology of the seed.

Pressure:—The question of the effect of the air pressure at different altitudes on seed germination has been considered (Lute *et al.* 1938). For these tests an altitude laboratory at Fort Collins, Colorado was used. Germination tests were made at pressures ranging from sea level to elevations of 5,000 and 10,000 feet using seeds of alfalfa, red clover, sweet clover, lettuce, wheat, and cabbage. No significant differences were noted and it was concluded that altitude is not an important factor in making laboratory germination tests.

The influence of high pressures on seed germination has been determined for some hard-coated as well as for some dormant seeds. Davies (1928*a* and *b*) applied hydraulic pressures up to 2000 atmospheres to seeds of *Melilotus alba* and *Medicago sativa* for periods up to 40 minutes. The germination of *Medicago* seeds was increased over 50 per cent when treated seeds were dried and their germination tested after 30 days and 6 months, while the germination of treated *Melilotus* seeds was increased from 150 to 200 per cent. Increased germination was brought about by the softening of impermeable coats. Other hard-coated seeds have had their germination hastened by the application of hydrostatic pressures (Rivera *et al.* 1937) but the treatment was not effective for dormant embryos of *Hamamelis virginiana, Cornus florida, Crataegus malus,* or *Rosa* sp. Very high pressures may be injurious to the soft seeds in a lot. Increased water absorption is one of the effects secured by high hydrostatic pressures. Mutation studies of *Oenothera* species have been accelerated by subjecting the seeds, which normally germinate very slowly, to pressures of 6 to 8 atmospheres for two or three days (de Vries 1915).

We have described external pressures of different kinds and their effects on germination. The internal pressure necessary to break fruit or seed coats is also of importance in germination. A recent publication (Crocker et al. 1946) reviews the work which has been done by others and present‐ a report of direct measurements of internal pressures. Breaking pressures of black walnut (*Juglans nigra* L.), hickory nut (*Carya ovata* [Mill.] K. Koch), and butternut (*Juglans cinerea* L.) were determined by boring a hole in the nut and then applying pressure to force the shell open by pumping water into the nut. Though any one lot of seeds showed in‐ dividual variations, the average internal pressure necessary for breaking the shells of the three kinds of nuts was several times that previously re‐ ported for breaking the shells of hazelnuts and *Pinus pinea*. Walnut shells of fruits held at low temperatures long enough for germination to occur had a breaking strength of about 28 to 33 atmospheres. Intact walnuts in germinators at temperatures of 17°, 23°, and 28° C. had weaker shells but no germinations occurred. The pressure that breaks coats in germination is growth pressure of the embryo, sometimes involving the endosperm and possibly the swelling pressure of colloids.

Electrical and Similar Effects:—One of the best-known methods of treating seeds electrically is the so-called Wolfryn electrochemical process described in detail by Fraser and Pidgeon (1933). Essentially this process consists in subjecting seeds to an electric current passing through a con‐ ducting solution in which the seeds are immersed. The seeds are then taken out of the solution and dried. The kind of salt used, the strength of the solution, the length of treatment, the strength of the current and the rapidity and amount of drying are all varied according to the type of seed used or the germination conditions. Benefits claimed from the treat‐ ment are: (1) increased yield, (2) better quality of the crop, and (3) in‐ creased resistance to disease. Subsequent tests of the process by different investigators have yielded conflicting reports. The preponderance of the evidence seems to indicate that there are few if any beneficial effects from the treatment. One of the most extensive field trials which has been re‐ ported is that of Fraser and Pidgeon (1933) with wheat. Statistical analyses of their data failed to show beneficial effects on the yield.

Electrodialysis studies have been made using seeds of peas (Mullison 1939; Nelly 1944) with resulting detrimental effects upon germination, resistance to infection, and seedling development.

X-ray effects.—That seeds are sensitive to X-rays has been demonstrated repeatedly. Maxwell and Kempton (1939) classified the biological effects of X-rays into three stages as follows:

1) Absorption of the quanta with liberation of primary electrons and subsequent ion-pair formation.

2) Ion-pair reactions with the surrounding medium which are expected to be independent of temperature and involving chemical reactions which may require both low and high energies of activation.

3) All subsequent low-energy, including thermal, reactions affecting the life of the material.

In this same paper and a later one (Kempton and Maxwell 1941) these men investigated a delayed killing effect of X-rays when air-dry maize seeds were treated with high dosages. This effect was characterized by death of the resulting seedlings following apparently normal germination and development to the stage where the first leaf began to emerge from the coleoptile. All the common cereals and many dicotyledonous species gave similar response. Since the number of thermal reactions occurring at the time of irradiation could be expected to depend, at least in part, upon the temperature at the time of treatment a temperature range from $-187°$ C. (liquid air) to $66°$ C. was used. X-ray dosages ranged from 35 to 45 kr. The heights and survival ratios of the plants grown from treated air-dry (8 per cent moisture) maize seeds were used as criteria of X-ray sensitivity. It was found that maximum sensitivity occurred at temperatures between $0°$ C. and room temperature. Either an increase or decrease of seed temperatures from these values reduced X-ray sensitivity.

Further work (Maxwell et al. 1942) confirmed these findings, and determined that to decrease the X-ray sensitivity at high or low temperatures, those temperatures must prevail during the time of irradiation. Also cold treatments following irradiation increased the X-ray effects, and heat treatments prior to irradiation increased the X-ray sensitivity. Extension of the time between X-raying and planting of the seeds resulted in a general but varying amount of recovery with all treatments. According to the authors, reduction in X-ray sensitivity by low temperature during the irradiation period may be caused by the absence of certain thermal or low energy reactions that would normally take place at room temperature but no definite explanation of decrease in X-ray sensitivity at temperatures higher than room temperature was given.

A modification of X-ray effects on dormant seeds of Himalaya barley by pretreatment and post-treatment with heat has been reported by Smith and Caldecott (1948). Root tips of the seedlings were examined for chromosomal bridges at late anaphase and early telophase, the frequency of bridges being considered a measure of induced chromosomal aberrations. Heat alone produced few bridges. Heat applied before or after irradiation reduced the frequency of bridges resulting from irradiation by more than half. There was an indication that heating the seeds after irradiation increased their ability to survive as compared with the survival of seeds heated before irradiation. In further tests Caldecott and Smith (1948) inactivated barley and einkorn seeds by applying heat at barely lethal temperatures and then treating with different dosages of X-ray. They were able to reactivate the seeds which had apparently been killed by heat by irradiation with X-ray. This is an amazing effect and one which should be investigated more extensively.

Stimulation of growth of plants has been reported in some cases where small dosages of X-rays have been given to the seeds. Twelve thousand seven hundred and fifty-one Manchu soybean plants and 13,824 plants of Wilson Black soybeans grown from irradiated seeds showed a slight stimulation of growth as measured by the average wet weight of the parts of the plants above ground (Long and Kersten 1936). Similarly wheat plants from seeds irradiated with small dosages had increased tillering and height at maturity as compared with the controls (Johnson 1939).

Many experiments have demonstrated that soaked seeds are more sensitive to X-ray than dry seeds.

Some of the physiological effects of the X-rays on the seeds themselves have been reported by Benedict and Kersten (1934). Wheat seeds were soaked in distilled water for twelve hours and then irradiated with the embryo end toward the target. There was an increase in diastatic activity and in sugar content during five seconds of irradiation but a decrease in these substances with longer exposure. The amount of respired material showed no increase over the controls but decreased with prolonged irradiation. The percentage of water in the seedlings at the end of the germination period indicated that the irradiated seeds could not absorb water as readily as the controls.

Structural changes occurred in the leaves of soybean plants grown from irradiated dry seeds (Long and Kersten 1937). Abnormal or deformed leaves of different types were found. Light colored spots were due either to a failure of the upper layer of palisade cells to develop chloroplasts or to the wider spacing of apparently normal palisade cells. Some of the green leaves had albino patches and some leaves were entirely white. Other abnormal leaves had dark green areas due to the development of many chloroplasts with unusually large amounts of chlorophyll. Geneticists are well aware of the chromosomal aberrations which are apt to follow X-ray treatment of living tissue.

Cathode rays.—A different type of radiation, cathode rays, has been used on a variety of seeds and the morphological changes produced in the seedlings noted (Busse and Daniels 1929). The treatment of the seeds injured the embryos causing dwarfing as well as local injuries in the seedlings. Cathode rays can penetrate only about a half millimeter of tissue, but when they are stopped by matter some of the energy is transformed into radiations of different wave lengths. Some of these radiations were probably X-rays. The amount of cathode ray treatment necessary to injure or kill the seeds depended upon the size of the seed and the thickness of the seed coat as well as other factors. It was noted that such treatment rendered the seed coats very permeable to water.

In general it may be said that electrical treatments or X-rays are without beneficial effect on germination but are of value for certain morphological and genetic studies.

Radioactive Effects:—*Uranium compounds.*—Řetovský (1934, 1939, 1942) reported a favorable effect of seed treatment with uranyl nitrate. Increased speed and percentage germination of wheat, rye, barley, maize, and horse chestnut, stimulation of germination of old seeds of barley, and shortening of the rest period of dormant seeds of horse chestnut were the claims made for such treatment. Verducci (1945) found alterations in the growth of plants from seeds treated with uranyl nitrate, sulfate, or acetate. Increased yield was obtained from seeds of *Pisum sativum* which had been soaked 24 hours in solutions of uranyl nitrate or manganese sulfate (Becquerel and Rousseau 1947). When the two solutions were mixed their favorable activity was lost. However, either one of them in combination with phenylacetic acid increased the yield from 6 to 40 per cent, while combinations with β-indoleacetic acid were not effective. The favorable effect of the manganese compound indicates that a similar effect of the uranium compound may have had nothing to do with its radioactive properties. Uranium acetate and uranium oxide in dilutions of 1:10,000 for several days or 4:10,000 for 24 hours stimulated the germination of vegetable seeds and the growth of plants produced from them according to Bevilotti (1945). Similar effects were noted for thorium oxide (Bevilotti 1944).

Radium.—Oat seeds exposed to radium emanations at distances not greater than 0.75 inch were killed. Beyond that point the retarding effect on germination decreased with increasing distance, and a stimulating effect was noted at 5 inches (Lawrence 1913). Using peas, Agulhon and Robert (1915) exposed them to radioactivity as follows:

1) They were exposed to emanations which traversed the walls of sealed tubes of thin glass containing radium bromide.

2) They were germinated in a solution containing the radioactive material.

3) The emanation was permitted to diffuse from the radium directly into the space containing the seeds.

The first treatment was unfavorable, the second was without effect, and the third had an accelerating effect on early growth, associated with some etiolation. The authors discussed the possibility of ozone formation in the third instance. Stoklasa (1922) demonstrated the value of radium emanations in overcoming the toxicity of selenium salts to the germination of seeds of buckwheat, oats, vetch, rye, and wheat. In his report of a study of radium dosages on the germination of 12 different kinds of seeds, Montet (1932) emphasized the importance of the size of the seed and the type of seed coat. Hard coats showed a greater opacity to radiation.

Atomic rays.—Naturally there is a great deal of interest in the possible effects of atomic rays on seeds. Dried corn seed were distributed on 22 ships anchored in the Bikini lagoon for the atomic bomb test in July, 1946 (Randolph et al. 1948). All samples of seeds were planted later. The seeds were not killed but the plants grown from them were defective and abnormal, resembling plants grown from X-rayed seeds. Undoubtedly much work is being done at the present time to determine further what effects radioactive materials have on plants, but the nature of the work prevents the publication of some of the detailed results. Dempsey (1949) states that there is little basis in fact for the claims of the beneficial effects of radioactive materials on the growth of plants, since the U.S.D.A. has conducted experiments with 19 crops in 14 states and has not been able to demonstrate better growth or higher quality.

An extensive study of the effects of radioactive mud upon germination of seeds and growth of seedlings has been made by Havas (1935). Both seeds and mud were of Hungarian origin. Dry untreated seeds were enclosed in a sealed glass cylinder which was buried near the center of a sack containing about 25 kg. of mud and allowed to stay there for 24 hours to 7 days. The mud consisted principally of the sediment of thermal springs mixed with some humus. Except radish, the 17 kinds of seeds showed marked response to irradiation. For example, seeds of *Triticum, Avena, Pisum, Phaseolus,* and *Soja* were stimulated by exposure for one day but repressed by two, three, and seven days' exposure. This repressive effect was not lasting, since after a latent period growth was resumed.

References:—

Agulhon, H., & T. Robert, 1915: The action of radium and radio-activity on germination in the higher plants (Ann. Inst. Pasteur 29:261-273; *abstr. in* Exp. Sta. Rec. 34:730, 1916).

Allard, R. W., H. R. DeRose & C. P. Swanson, 1946: Some effects of plant growth-regulators on seed germination and seedling development (Bot. Gaz. 107:575-583).

Althaus, H. C., 1949: Seeds with overcoats! Pelletizing allows precise planting with seeds (South. Seedsman 12(2):13, 40-41).

Barton, L. V., 1940*a*: Some effects of treatment of non-dormant seeds with certain growth substances (Contrib. Boyce Thompson Inst. 11:181-205).

————, 1940*b*: Some effects of treatment of seeds with growth substances on dormancy (Contrib. Boyce Thompson Inst. 11:229-240).

————, 1940*c*: Toxicity of ammonia, chlorine, hydrogen cyanide, hydrogen sulphide, and sulphur dioxide gases. IV. Seeds (Contrib. Boyce Thompson Inst. 11:357-363).

Becquerel, P., & J. Rousseau, 1947: Action de quelques substances de croissance, additionées, soit de nitrate d'urane, soit de sulfate de manganèse, sur la germination et la productivité du *Pisum sativum* (Compt. Rend. Acad. Sci. [Paris] 224:773-775).

Benedict, H. M., & H. Kersten, 1934: Effect of soft X-rays on germination of wheat seeds (Plant Physiol. 9:173-178).

Bevilotti, V., 1944: Biological action of radioactive substances. II. Action of colloidal thorium oxide on germination of seeds (Boll. Soc. Ital. Biol. Sper. 19:283-285; *abstr. in* Chem. Abstr. 41:1733-1734, 1947).

————, 1945: Biological action of radio-active substances. VI. Action of uranium on the germination of vegetable seeds (Boll. Soc. Ital. Biol. Sper. 20:558-559; *abstr. in* Soils & Fert. Imp. Bur. Soil Science 10:160, 1947).

Bond, L., 1942: Colchicine stimulation of seed germination in *Petunia axillaris* (Jour. Hered. 33:200-201).

Brun, J., & L. Tronstad, 1935: Some germination experiments with peas in heavy water (K. Norske Vidensk. Selsk. Forhandl. [Trondheim] 7:171-173; *abstr. in* Biol. Abstr. 11:18267, 1937).

Busse, W. F., & F. Daniels, 1929: Some effects of cathode rays on seeds (Amer. Jour. Bot. 16:139-153).

Caldecott, R. S., & L. Smith, 1948: Resuscitation of heat-inactivated seeds with x-radiation (Jour. Hered. 39:195-198).

Carolus, R. L., 1949: Possibilities with the use of pelleted seed (Ohio Veg. & Potato Grow. Assoc. Ann. Proc. 34:56-62).

Crocker, W., N. C. Thornton & E. M. Schroeder, 1946: Internal pressure necessary to break shells of nuts and the role of the shells in delayed germination (Contrib. Boyce Thompson Inst. 14:173-201).

Davies, P. A., 1928*a*: High pressure and seed germination (Amer. Jour. Bot. 15:149-156).

————, 1928*b*: The effect of high pressure on the percentages of soft and hard seeds of *Medicago sativa* and *Melilotus alba* (Amer. Jour. Bot. 15:433-436).

Dempsey, P. W., 1949: A candid estimate of radioactivity and plants (Hort. 27:80).

Deuber, C. G., 1932: Chemical treatments to shorten the rest period of red and black oak acorns (Jour. Forest. 30:674-679).

de Vries, H., 1915: Ueber künstliche Beschleunigung der Wasseraufnahme in Samen durch Druck (Biol. Centralbl. 35:161-176).

Dilling, W. J., 1926: Influence of lead and the metallic ions of copper, zinc, thorium, beryllium and thallium on the germination of seeds (Ann. Appl. Biol. 13:160-167).

Fraser, J. G. C., & L. M. Pidgeon, 1933: Electrolysis of seed of cereals (Sci. Agric. 14:141-148).

Fred, E. B., 1918: The effect of certain organic substances on seed germination (Soil Sci. 6:333-349).

Garman, H. R., & L. V. Barton, 1946: Response of lettuce seeds to thiourea treatments as affected by variety and age (Contrib. Boyce Thompson Inst. 14:229-241).

Hamner, C. L., J. E. Moulton & H. B. Tukey, 1946: Effect of treating soil and seeds with 2,4-dichlorophenoxyacetic acid on germination and development of seedlings (Bot. Gaz. 107:352-361).

Havas, L., 1935: Some effects of radioactive mud upon germination of seeds and growth of seedlings (Jour. Agric. Sci. 25:198-216).

Hsueh, Y. L., & C. H. Lou, 1947: Effects of 2,4-D on seed germination and respiration (Science 105:283-285).

Johnson, E. L., 1939: Growth of wheat plants from dry and soaked irradiated grains (Plant Physiol. 14:493-504).

Johnson, L. P. V., 1946: Effect of chemical treatments on the germination of forest tree seeds (The Forestry Chron. 22:17-24).

Kempton, J. H., & L. R. Maxwell, 1941: Effect of temperature during irradiation on the X-ray sensitivity of maize seed (Jour. Agric. Res. 62:603-618).

Lawrence, H., 1913: The influence of radiations of radium upon the germination of seeds (oats) (Rept. Austral. Assoc. Adv. Sci. 14:325, 326; abstr. in Exp. Sta. Rec. 34:626, 1916).

Lewis, G. N., 1933: Heavy water prevents seeds from sprouting (Science News Letter 24:116).

Long, T. P., & H. Kersten, 1936: Stimulation of growth of soy bean seeds by soft X-rays (Plant Physiol. 11:615-621).

———, ————, 1937: Structural changes produced in leaf tissue of soy bean plants by irradiation of the dry seeds with soft X-rays (Plant Physiol. 12:191-197).

Loo, T.-L., & Y.-W. Tang, 1945: Growth stimulation by manganese sulphate, indole-3-acetic acid, and colchicine in the seed germination and early growth of several cultivated plants (Amer. Jour. Bot. 32:106-114).

Lute, A. M., M. L. Thornton & K. Dixon, 1938: Study of the effect of altitude on germination of seeds (Proc. Assoc. Off. Seed Anal. No. Amer. 23/26(1930/33): 83-86).

Marth, P. C., E. H. Toole & V. K. Toole, 1948: Effect of 2,4-dichlorophenoxyacetic acid on seed development and germination in certain cereal and grass crops (Amer. Soc. Agron. Jour. 40:916-918).

Maxwell, L. R., & J. H. Kempton, 1939: Delayed killing of maize seeds X-rayed at liquid-air temperature (Jour. Washington Acad. Sci. 29:368-374).

Maxwell, L. R., J. H. Kempton & V. M. Mosley, 1942: Effect of temperature and time on the X-ray sensitivity of maize seeds (Jour. Washington Acad. Sci. 32: 18-24).

Melot, G. J., 1934: Effects of deuterium oxide on respiration of germinating seeds (Proc. Soc. Exp. Biol. & Med. 32:79-83).

Mitchell, J. W., & J. W. Brown, 1947: Relative sensitivity of dormant and germinating seeds to 2,4-D (Science 106:266-267).

Mitchell, J. W., & P. C. Marth, 1946: Germination of seeds in soil containing 2,4-dichlorophenoxyacetic acid (Bot. Gaz. 107:408-416).

Montet, D., 1932: De l'influence des faibles radioactivités sur la germination (Compt. Rend. Soc. Biol. 109:678-680).

Mullison, W. R., 1939: Electrodialysis of pea seeds (Plant Physiol. 14:583-587).

Nelly, J. D., 1944: Electrodialysis of seeds (Plant Physiol. 19:19-32).

Patrick, S. R., W. F. Crosier & C. E. Heit, 1947: The tolerance of seeds to DDT (Proc. Assoc. Off. Seed Anal. 37:166-169).

Pridham, A. M. S., 1946: 2,4-Dichlorophenoxyacetic acid reduces germination of grass seed (Proc. Amer. Soc. Hort. Sci. 47:439-445).

Randolph, L. F., A. E. Longley & C. H. Li, 1948: Cytogenetic effects in corn exposed to atomic bomb ionizing radiation at Bikini (Science 108:13-15).

Řetovský, R., 1934: Azotate d'uranyle et l'énergie de la germination de la sémence de la vieille orge (Bull. Int. Acad. Sci. de Bohême, 4 pp.).

————, 1939: Stimulace klícení semen uranylnitrátram (The stimulation of the germination of seeds by uranyl nitrate) (Rozpr. Česke Akad. Věd. a Umění Tr. 2. 49(12):31 pp.; *abstr. in* Biol. Abstr. 21:15584, 1947).

————, 1942: Verkürzung der Ruheperiode der Samen von *Aesculus hippocastanum* L. durch Uranylnitrat (Ber. Deut. Botan. Ges. 60:355-366).

Ribeiro, F., 1944: Influence of sulfanilamide on the germination of seeds (Jour. Biol. Chem. 152:665-667).

————, 1946: Penicillin action on the germination of seeds (Science 104:18).

Rivera, R., H. W. Popp & R. B. Dow, 1937: The effect of high hydrostatic pressures upon seed germination (Amer. Jour. Bot. 24:508-513).

Smith, L., & R. S. Caldecott, 1948: Modification of X-ray effects on barley seeds by pretreatment and post-treatment with heat (Jour. Hered. 39:173-176).

Smith, W. J., 1946: Effect of penicillin on seed germination (Science 104:411-413).

Stoklasa, J., 1922: Influence du sélénium et du radium sur la germination des grains (Compt. Rend. Acad. Sci. [Paris] 174:1075-1077).

Stone, G. E., & R. E. Smith, 1901: Influence of chemical solutions upon the germination of seeds (Mass. Agric. Exp. Sta. Rept. 13:74-83).

Thompson, R. C., 1938: The germination of lettuce seed as affected by nutrition of the plant and the physiological age of the plant (Proc. Amer. Soc. Hort. Sci. 35(1937):599-600).

Thompson, R. C., & N. L. Horn, 1944: Germination of lettuce seed at high temperature (25 to 35 degrees C.) stimulated by thiourea (Proc. Amer. Soc. Hort. Sci. 45:431-439).

Verducci, P., 1945: Comparative effect of radioactivity of uranium compounds on germination and development of seeds (Boll. Soc. Ital. Biol. Sper. 20:333-334; *abstr. in* Chem. Abstr. 40:6123-6124, 1946).

Youden, W. J., 1940: Seed treatments with talc and root-inducing substances (Contrib. Boyce Thompson Inst. 11:207-218).

Chapter IX

DORMANCY IN SEEDS, I

DORMANCY in seeds has been one of the major problems studied at this Institute since its beginning. The results of our experiments with hundreds of species have been published in separate articles and in two books (Barton and Crocker 1948; Crocker 1948). The reader is referred to these sources for details. In the present discussion an outline of the general types of dormancy and methods of overcoming them will be presented. The chemical changes involved are discussed in other chapters.

Significance:—With the relatively small amount of information at hand, failure of seeds to germinate was interpreted as late as the beginning of this century to mean the absence of some special stimulus. It was understood that hard seeds did not germinate because they did not absorb water, but if a seed did absorb water and still failed to sprout it was thought to need some special stimulus to release the germination mechanism. Consequently workers tried to find such stimuli. It was shown rather early that light would bring about germination of some seeds and would accelerate the germination of others, but this, too, was thought to be a stimulus response. Now it seems much more likely that light brings about chemical or physical changes which result in germination. In fact, as more and more information becomes available, it becomes increasingly evident that definite chemical and physical changes rather than a mysterious response to a release stimulus accounts for the initiation of germination. Recent work (Barton and Solt 1948) has demonstrated the presence of inhibitors to the growth of wheat roots in both dormant and non-dormant seeds, but failed to show any definite relationship between dormancy and degree of after-ripening and amount of the inhibitor present. There may, however, be other types of substances, such as those which might be removed by long leaching, causing failure to germinate.

We shall see how some seeds must be held moist at a low temperature to after-ripen the dormant embryos or bring about a digestion of food for the embryos. Other seeds will after-ripen in dry storage without any special treatment. In certain other cases, what appears at first to be dormancy is nothing more than a special temperature requirement for germination. Not only can dormancy be overcome by following certain definite procedures, but it can also be induced under certain conditions. Holding seeds in a high-temperature germinator under reduced oxygen pressure or treating with growth-regulating chemicals bring about this effect.

Some of the chemical and physical changes occurring in seeds during after-ripening, dormancy induction, and germination are discussed more in detail in other chapters. All of these considerations make it evident that the old conception of the failure of seeds to germinate as being due to a hard seed coat or to a lack of a release stimulus is over-simplified and entirely inadequate.

Delayed germination is of value to the plant, especially in the temperate zone where winters are apt to be severe and the seeds must be protected from germination when they fall to the ground in autumn. Seedlings produced at that time would be killed by the cold weather. This has been a factor in the success of wild oats in spreading and becoming a serious weed in some sections. The wild oat seeds are dormant enough to carry over to spring without germination. Cultivated oats and false wild oats are not weeds because they germinate in the fall and are killed by the cold weather which prevails where they grow. Seeds of some other wild plants lie dormant in the soil for years, thus assuring the continuance of the species. Hard seed coats permit the extension of life of many seeds, so that they are distributed in time as well as in space.

Delayed germination is often of value to man as well as to the plant. It is essential that grains have at least a short dormant period after harvest, so that they do not sprout and ruin. Mangelsdorf (1923, 1926) describes types of maize in which the grains have no dormant period, but form seedlings in the ear. On the other hand, very dormant varieties of barley can be made to germinate in the head by placing moist filter paper on the embryo of the immature grain (Pope and Brown 1943). Dormancy in grains of cereals is caused by genetic factors, or by the environmental conditions at the time of growth and maturation of the fruit. Maturing during rainy weather has been reported as the cause of dormancy in barley seeds, resulting in difficulty in the production of malt. Such dormancy as is exhibited by cereals requires no special treatment to overcome, since normal germination proceeds upon placing in a germinator after dry storage for several weeks.

An inconvenience to man in dormant cereal seeds is in their failure to sprout when a test is made to determine the viability. It is sometimes desirable to make this test soon after harvest, in which case it becomes necessary to give the grains some special pretreatment such as using 12° C. germinators instead of 20° C. or higher, breaking the coats over the embryo, or using high oxygen pressure (Harrington 1923).

Geneticists, anxious to grow as many generations in as short a time as possible, are also faced with the need to recognize dormancy in freshly harvested seeds and to know the methods for overcoming it.

Dormancy in Moist Seeds:—We shall see later how some dormant seeds after-ripen during a period of moist storage at a low temperature. This means that the necessary changes preliminary to germination take place there, so that after a definite length of time, they will sprout. There are other cases in which the seeds remain dormant indefinitely in a moist medium. One of the most noteworthy of these is the dormancy of seeds in the soil.

An explanation of this type of dormancy may be found in the special temperature requirement of the seed for germination (see *Temperature Effects on Non-Dormant Seeds*). Also light and the chemicals present in the soil may be factors. Nitrates and other nitrogen compounds promote the germination of certain seeds. This is especially true of many of the light-stimulated seeds, which may be buried too deep to receive any light (Crocker 1936). Inhibiting chemicals in the fruits, seed coats, or the seeds themselves may also play a part in preventing germination in the soil (Evenari 1949; Evenari *et al*. 1942; Shuck 1935; Stout and Tolman 1941). For example, the fleshy fruits of the tomato, cucumber, pawpaw (*Carica papaya*), and others contain chemicals which inhibit their own seeds while still enclosed within the fruits. The fibrous material of the seed balls of beets and the coats of lettuce seeds also inhibit germination, while endosperm or embryo of other seeds have the same effect. The inhibitory chemicals do not seem to be specific in their action, since they will inhibit germination of other seeds than the ones which produce them. Some of the chemicals are volatile while others are not. For the most part they seem to be heat stable, although some workers have found that they are destroyed at the boiling point of water. Substances present in seeds and found to inhibit germination are ammonia, hydrocyanic acid (from amygdalin of rosaceous seeds), essential oils, alkaloids, glycosides, and a substance not identified but known as "Blastokolin" (Köckemann 1936). These inhibitors are more effective in ordinary germinators than in the soil, for the soil moisture allows them to diffuse away from the seeds; also soil, like animal charcoal, adsorbs the inhibitors and removes them from action on the seeds. These inhibitors would need to be very stable and held within the seeds by special membranes in order to account for the failure of many seeds to germinate in the soil. Although these conditions may be met by such substances as alkaloids and glycosides, it is doubtful if inhibiting chemicals play a major role.

Secondary Dormancy:—Unfavorable germination conditions often throw seeds into dormancy so they will not germinate when shifted to a favorable condition. Kinzel (Crocker 1936) showed that seeds of *Nigella sativa*, which are prevented from germinating by light, if placed in an illuminated germinator soon change so that they will not later germinate in darkness. Similar effects are to be found in other light-inhibited seeds. Also, many seeds which are light-favored, when placed in a dark germinator, will not germinate when they are later transferred to light. High pressures of carbon dioxide, about 24 per cent, inhibit germination of some seeds and if continued will throw them into dormancy (Kidd 1914). If the oxygen pressure is reduced, the carbon dioxide becomes effective in lower concentrations. Dormancy induced in seeds by unfavorable germination conditions has been called "secondary dormancy" (Crocker 1916). No doubt many of these conditions prevail in the soil and may account for the existence of viable, non-germinated seeds. Davis has made a very thorough study of the induction of dormancy in seeds of *Ambrosia trifida* and *Xanthium* (1930). He was able to throw these embryos into and out of dormancy by varying the temperature and the oxygen supply. Relatively high temperatures and restricted oxygen caused the seeds to develop a secondary dormancy which could be overcome by relatively low temperatures and increased oxygen pressure. Each of these changes took a considerable time to develop.

After-Ripening in Dry Storage:—For many seeds which have characteristic dormancy only when freshly harvested, a period of dry storage is sufficient to prepare them for germination. A surprising number and variety of seeds fall in this category. Although there are some exceptions,

TABLE XIII: *Effect of Period of Dry Storage upon the Germination of four Varieties of Lettuce (Lactuca sativa) Seeds at Various Temperatures:—*

VARIETY	GERM. TEMP., °C.	PER CENT GERMINATION AFTER WEEKS OF DRY STORAGE				
		0	1	4	8	16
White Boston	20	69	33	100	99	100
	25	2	1	1	1	5
	30	0	0	0	0	0
	15 to 30*	97	42	98	95	100
	20 to 30*	4	2	2	58	22
Grand Rapids	20	92	97	96	94	95
	25	11	25	28	47	87
	30	0	2	0	1	3
	15 to 30*	98	97	94	97	96
	20 to 30*	91	92	92	94	96
Iceberg	20	96	97	95	97	97
	25	90	95	90	95	94
	30	1	0	11	6	38
	15 to 30*	98	97	97	97	97
	20 to 30*	99	97	99	99	97
Black-seeded Simpson	20	87	94	98	98	96
	25	49	5	9	51	41
	30	0	1	1	1	0
	15 to 30*	90	79	99	96	95
	20 to 30*	90	75	91	89	94

* Daily alternation. Cultures left at the lower temperature for sixteen hours and at the higher temperature eight hours each day.

many light-sensitive seeds lose this characteristic after several months in dry storage. Seeds of several grasses, including some of our common cereals, after-ripen in dry storage. The period needed varies with the species from a few days to several months. It is generally considered to be longest in oats, shorter in barley and wheat, and shortest in rye. Winter cereals require a shorter period than spring cereals, early-ripening shorter than late-ripening varieties. Also, for all varieties, it has been generally stated that the period is shorter in dry than in wet seasons.

Brown *et al.* (1948) have presented data on the effect in oats, barley, and sorghum of storage conditions on after-ripening, as well as their germination response to different temperatures and the varietal differences in dormancy. They found that the seeds of most cereals after-ripen in 1 to 6 months when stored at 104° F. Freshly harvested seeds of oats and barley, on the other hand, kept their dormancy for a period of three years at a temperature of 36° F. That barley dormancy is a genetic characteristic was demonstrated when varieties from a world collection showed the same relative dormancy when grown under different climatic conditions and in different years. The 111 most dormant varieties were found to be restricted geographically, coming from the Near East and North Africa, while the least dormant varieties came from Abyssinia. The idea of dormancy of cereals as hereditary is in direct contrast with the premise that dry or wet growing seasons determine the dormancy.

Lettuce, *Lactuca sativa* L., seeds are among those of economic importance which are dormant when they are freshly harvested, and which after-ripen in dry storage. The dormancy in this case as in all other seeds included in this section is exhibited as failure to germinate under certain conditions. In the case of lettuce, it is possible to germinate the fresh seeds by furnishing a temperature of 20° C. or below. The degree of dormancy depends not only upon the length of the dry storage period but upon the variety as well (Garman and Barton 1946). This is shown in Table XIII. It is evident from the data that seeds of the lettuce varieties, White Boston, Grand Rapids, Iceberg, and Black-seeded Simpson, are never dormant in the sense that they will not germinate if suitable temperatures are supplied. White Boston is the most dormant as measured by its failure to germinate at both 25° and 30° C. and reduced germination even at 20° C. up to four weeks of dry storage. Iceberg, on the other hand, germinated well at all temperatures except 30° C., and after 16 weeks' storage gave 38 per cent germination at that temperature. Grand Rapids and Black-seeded Simpson varieties were somewhat intermediate in their germination requirements. Some inconsistencies in germination are apparent, *i.e.*, the comparatively low germination of seeds of White Boston at 20° C. and 15° to 30° C., after one week of dry storage and lack of uniformity in the germination behavior of Black-seeded Simpson seeds. However, the general trend in the germination of the four varieties is toward a greater tolerance of high temperatures for germination with increased time in dry storage. Presoaking lettuce seeds in a 0.5 or 1.0 per cent thiourea solution for 16 hours at 20° C. resulted in stimulation of germination at 30° C., thus replacing the need for a period of dry storage.

Certain winter annuals growing in desert regions require comparatively low temperatures or combinations of low with moderately high temperatures for germination even after dry storage for three months or longer (Barton 1936). However, they may fail completely to germinate when they are fresh. Not only does the germination percentage improve with dry storage, but there is an extension of the germination temperature range. The combination of low temperature requirement for germination with a degree of dormancy of fresh seeds prevents their germination during the first summer rainy season that the seeds lie on the ground. This rainy season is accompanied by high temperatures which would kill the seedlings. By the advent of the next favorable winter rainy season the germination temperature range has been broadened somewhat and the dormancy has disappeared in dry storage.

Seeds of *Impatiens balsamina* are also dormant when freshly harvested and need from four to six months of dry storage at room temperature for after-ripening (Kroeger 1941).

Among the weed seeds which have been shown to be dormant when freshly harvested are those of *Amaranthus retroflexus* and *Rumex obtusifolius* (Barton 1945). Fresh seeds of the former germinate at 30° C., and those of the latter at 20° C. Samples held dry gradually change in their capacity for germination so that, after two or three months, they will germinate over a wide range of temperatures including 20° C. for *Amaranthus* and 30° C. for *Rumex*. Embryos of the fruits of the ragweed, *Ambrosia trifida* L., also after-ripen in dry storage but the process is very slow and unequal in different embryos (Davis 1930). Some may germinate readily after a few months of dry storage while others may still be dormant after one or more years.

These are only a few examples of the many different seeds which after-ripen in dry storage. Other species, together with the length of the dry storage period or other special treatment required to break dormancy, and the reporting investigators are shown in Table XIV.

TABLE XIV: *Some Seeds which after-ripen in Dry Storage indicating special Treatments found effective in Germination of fresh Seeds, Length of the Dry Storage Period necessary for after-ripening (with author and date of the report)*:—

SEED	TREATMENT	DRY STORAGE	AUTHOR	DATE
Ambrosia trifida	5°C. 3 mos.		Davis	1930
Agrostis tenuis	KNO₃; Alt. temp.		Anderson	1944
Aira flexuosa	Light	14–15 mos.	Nelson & MacLagan	1935
Astrebla lappacea	KNO₃	12 mos.	Myers	1942
Asystasia gangetica		135 days	Akamine	1947
(*Avena*)* Oats	Removal of scales 40° C. for 8 days		Harrington	1923
(*Avena*)* Oats		2–6 weeks	Foy	1932
(*Avena*)* Vicland oats	Drying at 35° C.	9 mos.	Crosier	1946
Barbarea verna	Light & KNO₃ at 20°–30°C.	1–2 mos.	Toole & Toole	1940
Brassica campestris		7 mos.	Toole & Toole	1939
Brassica juncea		1 mo.	Toole & Toole	1939
Brassica nigra		7 mos.	Toole & Toole	1939
Cosmos, Orange Flare	29° C. or more	Several mos.	Carleton	1936
Covillea		12 mos.	Runyon	1930
(*Cucurbita*)* Cucumbers, pumpkins, muskmelons, & watermelons	Leave in fruit until overripe	4 weeks	Odland	1938
Cyperus rotundus	H₂SO₄ 15 min.	7+ years	Andrews	1946
Daucus pusillus	Alt. temps.		Barton	1936
Digitaria ischaemum	3°C. 4–8 wks. + 20°–40° C.	1 yr.	Toole & Toole	1941
Digitaria sanguinalis	3°C. 2–4 wks. + 20°–35° C.	7–8 mos.	Toole & Toole	1941
Festuca capillata	5°C. 7 days; KNO₃; light	5 mos.	Kearns & Toole	1939
Festuca elatior var. *arundinacea*	5°C. 7 days	3–4 wks.	Kearns & Toole	1939
Festuca rubra strains	5°C. 7 days + KNO₃	1–2 mos.	Kearns & Toole	1939
(*Gossypium*)* Cotton	Thorough drying	1 mo.	Simpson	1935
Guayule	Puncture seed coat; 4°C. 8 wks.; wash in water 18 hrs., then soak for 2 hrs. in calcium hypochlorite	6 mos.–1 yr.	Benedict & Robinson	1946
(*Hordeum*)* Barley		2–6 wks.	Foy	1932
(*Hordeum*)* Barley	Remove hulls	3–9 mos.	Vines	1947
(*Hordeum*)* Barley	Remove scales; 40° C. 8 days		Harrington	1923

TABLE XIV (continued)

SEED	TREATMENT	DRY STORAGE	AUTHOR	DATE
(Hordeum)* Barley	5° C. 2–4 days		Crosier	1946
Impatiens balsamina	5° C. 2 wks.	4–6 mos.	Kroeger	1941
(Lactuca)* Lettuce	High temp. storage	4 mos.	Wharton & Frazier	1939
Lepidium lasiocarpum	10°–30° C.	12 mos.	Barton	1936
Lepidium virginicum	Light or KNO₃ + 20°–30° C.	2+ wks.	Toole & Toole	1940
Nicotiana rustica	Drying at 15° or 21° C. 30 min.	3–5 mos.	Malskaia	1936
Oenothera odorata	KNO₃	7 mos.	Takiguti	1930a
(Oryza)* Rice		6 wks.	Burgess	1936
Peltandra virginica	Remove pericarp & soak in water		Hart	1928
Perilla ocimoides	Remove coats		Takiguti	1930b
(Phleum)* Timothy	Light & KNO₃ & 20°–30° C.		Toole	1939
(Poa)* Kentucky Blue grass	Store at 40° C.		Hite	1923
(Poa)* Canada Blue grass	Store at 40° C.		Hite	1923
(Sorghastrum)* Johnson grass	Remove hulls & H₂SO₄ 2–3 min.; alt. temp.; 24 hrs. H₂O₂; 50% CO₂	4–5 mos.	Harrington	1917
Sporobolus asper	Prechill 14 days & KNO₃	7 mos.	Toole	1941
Sporobolus cryptandrus	KNO₃ & light; H₂SO₄ 2 min.	4+ yrs.	Toole	1941
Stipa viridula		4 mos.	McAlister	1943
Streptanthus arizonicus	Alt. temp.	1–2 yrs.	Barton	1936
(Trifolium)* Red clover		4–6 mos.	Martin	1945a
(Trifolium)* Subterranean clover	Low temp. 3 days	3 mos.	Woodforde	1935
Trifolium subterraneum		12 mos.	Hills	1944
(Triticum)* Wheat	Prick grain, cool temp.	1–2 mos.	Bytschikhina	1929/30
(Triticum)* Wheat	5° C. 2–4 days		Crosier	1946
(Triticum)* Wheat	40° C. 8 days		Harrington	1923

* Scientific name assigned by Crocker & Barton, common names only appeared in original article.

Light and Dormancy:—The lack of light may prevent the germination of some seeds, while the presence of light may cause others to remain dormant. Seeds of the former type will not sprout if they are covered with soil to a depth which excludes all light and seeds of the latter type remain dormant if a shallow planting allows too much light to reach them. One of the authors has treated this subject very fully in an article published in a two-volume review on the biological effects of radiation (Crocker 1936).

To this work the reader is referred for more complete details, and for a bibliography of literature dealing with this subject.

Among the seeds and fruits whose germination is favored by light are those of many *Loranthaceae,* including *Viscum album,* and all *Gesneriaceae* which have been studied up to the present time, in addition to seeds of many epiphytes and grasses as well as species of *Oenothera* and *Epilobium, Ranunculus sceleratus, Lythrum salicaria,* and *L. hyssopifolia.* Occasionally seeds are found which will not germinate at all without light. *Viscum album* seeds are killed within a few weeks in a dark germinator, while *Areuthobium oxycedri* seeds will endure darkness for a longer period, but will not germinate there. For the most part, however, seeds which are light-favored may have their germination accelerated by light, but light is not absolutely necessary for germination. Kinzel made rather limited studies of 964 species of seeds and found 672 of them favored by light.

There are seeds, on the other hand, which have their germination inhibited by the presence of light. Of the total of 964 species, Kinzel listed 258 as inhibited by light. Several species of *Phacelia* and other *Hydrophyllaceae,* three species of *Nigella,* several species of *Allium,* and other *Liliaceae* are among light-inhibited seeds. As might be expected, there are also seeds and fruits which germinate equally well in light and darkness. The small grains, corn, beans, clover, and many other legumes belong to this class.

Other conditions have been found to substitute for the light requirement for germination in several light-favored seeds. Some of the seeds which are dormant when they are freshly harvested will grow in a light germinator at that time. This response to light disappears with after-ripening in dry storage. Lettuce seeds as well as *Poa* achenes and achenes or seeds of *Chloris, Ranunculus, Epilobium,* and *Oenothera* have their need for light partially or completely overcome by periods of dry storage. Also, the inhibiting effect of light on *Phacelia* is diminished with dry storage.

The presence of seed or fruit coats or the hulls of grasses sometimes impose the necessity of light for germination. Removing the hulls from *Chloris* achenes removes the need of light, and pricking the coats of *Oenothera* increases germination in the darkness. Similarly, removal or pricking the coats of *Phacelia* and *Nigella* brings about some germination in the light.

Increased oxygen pressure also removes the light effect on germination from both light-favored and light-inhibited seeds.

Nitrate solutions have been found to substitute for the light requirement in a number of light-favored seeds. Nitrites, nitric acid, ammonium salts, and urea are also favorable. Thiourea has been shown to replace light in the germination of lettuce seeds, and weak acids decrease the need for light in the seeds of *Lythrum, Scrophularia, Verbascum,* and *Epilobium.* A daily alternation of temperature has also been shown an effective substitute for light in several cases.

Secondary dormancy can be induced in light-sensitive seeds by placing them in a light germinator if they are light-inhibited, or in a dark germinator if they are light-favored. This has been done for *Chloris* and for

Nigella. However, imbibed light-favored seeds exposed to light, dried, and later put into a dark germinator retain the beneficial effect of the original light exposure. This latent light effect has been exhibited by seeds of *Ranunculus sceleratus* and achenes of *Chloris,* and may account, at least in part, for the great variation in the sensitivity of different collections of the same species of light-favored seeds. The light exposure of the seeds during ripening in the capsules would vary with the weather, the rate of drying of seeds in the capsules, and the position of the capsule on the plant.

A great deal more chemical, microchemical, and physiological work needs to be done to determine the explanation for light effects on seeds. Most of the theories which have been advanced to account for this phenomenon have assumed that the action of the light is upon the living tissue —either endosperm or embryo, but some of them postulate effects on the non-living coats. It is probable that the effect may be on one or all of these seed parts in different species. McIlvaine and Popp (1940), MacLachlan (1936), and Murakami (1940) have shown that enzyme content, metabolism, and growth substances have been modified in germinating seeds by certain light rays, but these facts have not explained how light favors or inhibits germination.

Oxygen Deficiency and Dormancy:—The embryo enclosed with seed or fruit structures, or sometimes both, does not have such free access to the oxygen of the surrounding atmosphere as does the growing plant with its intracellular aeration system connected with stomata and lenticels. For this reason, one would expect that a higher oxygen pressure would be required for germination than for growth. Schaible (1900), using bean, cress, savory, and *Hydrangea* demonstrated that the oxygen content of the air was far above that needed for normal growth of the plants, but it was not far above that needed for germination. This is due, no doubt, to the necessity for passage through the seed or fruit coats which slows down the rate at which oxygen can reach the embryo. A number of other researches could be cited to show the low permeability of the seed coats to oxygen. The question under consideration at this point is whether this restriction of oxygen supply has any relation to dormancy in the seed.

Perhaps the best example of seed coats restricting the oxygen supply to the embryo below the minimum needed for germination is the cocklebur. The fruit of this plant contains two seeds, an upper and a lower, which differ in size and shape. The "upper" seed borne higher up in the bur is smaller, and convex on its outer face and concave on the inner face. The "lower" seed is borne lower in the bur, and is concave on the outer face and convex on the inner face. The lower seed germinates the first season after maturing and the upper seed does not germinate until the second or later season. Crocker (1906) found that both seeds would germinate the first season after maturation if the seed-bed temperature rose as high as 33° C. at a time when there was an adequate supply of water and air, and that the failure of the upper seed to germinate at lower temperatures was due to the seed coat which reduced the oxygen supply to the embryo below the minimum required for germination. The oxygen supply to the embryo of the lower seed was also reduced in the same way. Both seeds germinated at a lower temperature when the coats were removed, but the effect was more pronounced for the upper seed. The question arises as to why the upper seed germinated during the second or later seasons. Crocker suggested that there was a slow decomposition of the impermeable membrane of the seed coat by the microorganisms in the soil. We shall see in later descriptions of seed dormancy that these organisms play a definite role in eliminating seed coat factors.

More detailed work was done on the cocklebur later by Shull (1911, 1914) and by Thornton (1935). Thornton used full atmospheric pressure, varied the percentages of oxygen, and determined the germination of excised embryos and intact seeds at 21° and 30° C. He observed that complete germination of the lower embryos occurred at percentages of oxygen which gave no germination of the upper embryos. The higher temperature reduced the oxygen requirement in both cases. Intact seeds needed higher oxygen concentrations for germinations than excised embryos. The embryos of the upper seeds gave 100 per cent germination in 1.5 per cent oxygen at 21° C., and in 0.9 per cent at 30° C. In all cases the minimum oxygen pressure needed for the upper embryo was higher than that for the lower. Here is a case where oxygen availability is definitely linked with dormancy.

Dormant wild oats and other cereals have also been forced to germinate by increased oxygen pressure (Atwood 1914; Johnson 1935; Harrington 1923). A portion of the seed coat developed from the nucellus has been found to restrict the oxygen supply to the embryos of seeds of American basswood (Spaeth 1932) and potato (Stier 1938). Considering the relatively few cases of this kind which have been reported, it is doubtful that a limited oxygen supply plays any considerable part in dormancy of seeds.

From reports in the literature, it seems that most of the emphasis on oxygen relationships has been from the point of view of the beneficial effect of an increased oxygen supply. It may be, however, that too much oxygen will prevent, or at least retard, germination (See chapter on Water Relations).

It will be remembered from the section on "Secondary Dormancy" above that oxygen and carbon dioxide supply were involved.

Hard Seed Coats and Dormancy:—Quite apart from the role of impermeable coats in restricting the gaseous exchange as discussed in the preceding section, the seed coverings may prevent the absorption of water and thus limit germination. The seeds of many leguminous plants possess such coats. From the point of view of continuance of the species, this is a very desirable trait. Not only do such seeds remain viable for long periods of time, but, under natural conditions, individual seeds become permeable at different periods after harvest so that any one lot of seeds is capable of producing seedlings over a period of several years. However, this same character has made it difficult to obtain reliable tests of the germination capacity of a given lot of seeds and to secure good commercial seedling stands. In addition to the economic importance of many legumes, the scientific facts to be discovered in permeability studies have led to much investigation. Although *Leguminosae* are most commonly thought of in this respect, seeds of *Malvaceae, Cannaceae, Geraniaceae, Chenopodiaceae, Convallariaceae, Convolvulaceae, Solanaceae,* and other families have species that bear hard seeds.

Hard-coatedness has been shown in some instances to be a genetic factor, but environmental conditions also influence the per cent of hard seeds which appears in any one crop. Collections of white sweet clover vary as much as 98 per cent in the number of hard seeds produced in different years from the same plants. In this plant hard or soft strains can be produced by selection and inbreeding (White and Stevenson 1948). The same can be done for hairy vetch (Hübner 1938). However, James (1949a) was unable to get any evidence of the inheritance of impermeability in crimson clover seeds. In the first generation, selfed parents with a difference of 60.3 per cent in seed coat permeability produced offspring with a difference of only 0.3 per cent. James (1949b) then turned to a study of environmental factors as affecting the production of hard seed in crimson clover, and found a correlation between sequence of flowering and amount of small seed produced, and between seed size and permeability. When conditions favored the production of small seed the crop was hard. Also an extra supply of calcium increased the number of impermeable seeds. Reduction of light intensity and supply of moisture were without effect on the seed coats.

Among the known methods devised for making the hard coats permeable are mechanical scarification, concentrated sulfuric acid treatment, boiling water, and special temperature treatments. The weather factors effective in opening the coats of sweet clover, *Melilotus*, have been studied by Martin (1945b). He found that, in natural seeding in the field or in dry storage over winter in unheated open buildings in Iowa, 80 to 100 per cent of the hard seeds softened by the middle of the following April. In spite of the fact that practically all of the opening of the seed coats to the absorption of water occurred in the interval from March 20 to April 20, a previous exposure of two months or more to fluctuations of temperature near the freezing point was required for effective softening. A constant temperature of 10° C. as well as higher fluctuating temperatures were ineffective in making the seed coats permeable. It has been demonstrated that a fall planting out-of-doors in the region of Yonkers, N. Y. results in 41 per cent seedling production the following spring of hard sweet clover seeds which do not germinate when planted in the spring (Barton 1947).

Freezing has been found to reduce the number of impermeable alfalfa seeds (Midgley 1926). After the first freezing, however, subsequent freezing and thawing had little effect. Also the intensity of the freezing was without effect within the range of 0° to —20° C. Busse (1930) reported that freezing air-dry impermeable seeds of sweet clover and alfalfa in liquid air (—190° C.) made them permeable. Sweet clover seeds were kept in liquid air for 175 days without injury. Cooling to —80° C. softened some of the impermeable alfalfa seed but had little effect on sweet clover seeds. Busse attributed the increased germination after freezing to formation of very tiny cracks in the impermeable membrane. The very low freezing temperature required for rendering hard sweet clover seeds capable of moisture absorption explains the ineffectiveness of freezing and thawing in soil plantings under natural weather conditions. Impermeable seeds of the white sweet clover have been made to absorb water by plunging them in liquid nitrogen (—195.8° C.) (Barton 1947). Four dips of 30 seconds each into the liquid were more effective than one dip of 1 or 5 minutes' duration. One minute was allowed to elapse between the dips. If the seeds were plunged into water at room temperature before and after each dip, they gave 97 per cent germination when placed subsequently on filter paper moistened with water. Seeds dipped four times without being plunged into water gave 38 per cent germination, and untreated hard seeds failed to germinate. Liquid nitrogen treatment, even when extended to 15 minutes' duration, had no effect on impermeable seeds of *Gleditsia triacanthos*. This may be related to morphological differences as will be discussed below.

In 1932, Hamly described a new method for making hard seeds of sweet clover permeable. This consisted in shaking the seeds for 10 minutes at three oscillations per second in a 500 cc. corked Florence flask. Special mechanical impactors were also used. This treatment caused the formation of a strophiolar cleft through which water could enter. Hamly stated that the permeability of naturally soft seeds also occurred through the opening of a cleft at the strophiole. Scarification and sulfuric acid treatment, on the other hand, produced unlocalized permeable areas in the hard seed coat. The permeable areas of the coats were determined by osmic acid staining. This shaking method was later applied by Hutton and Porter (1937) for several different species of legumes and found effective.

Barton (1947) also tried this method and compared its effectiveness for members of three different subfamilies of the family *Leguminosae*. It was found that seeds of the *Papilionoideae* were made permeable by shaking in a glass bottle for 20 minutes, but seeds of the *Caesalpinioideae*, with one exception, were not affected by shaking. The latter subfamily responded to soaking in absolute alcohol with transfer to water immediately after removal from the alcohol, which treatment was without effect on the *Papilionoideae*. *Mimosoideae* occupied an intermediate position, some being made permeable by shaking and some by alcohol soaking. Table XV contains data on effects on seeds of alcohol soaking and shaking as compared with the filed and intact seeds used as controls. The species have been arranged according to their subfamily rela-

TABLE XV: *Percentage of Seeds swelling in Water following various Treatments:—*

Species	Absolute Ethyl Alcohol, 72 Hrs.	Shaking 20 min.	Filed	Intact
Mimosoideae				
Acacia aneura	29	75	100	18
" *constricta*	88	20	100	9
" *greggii*	100	100	100	7
" *hakeoides*	10	70	100	0
" *linifolia*	46	6	93	2
" *pycnantha*	16	30	100	18
" *saligna*	34	39	98	14
Leucaena pulverulenta	14	3	100	3
Prosopis velutina	74	100	100	30
Papilionoideae				
Cladrastis lutea	10	82	100	6
" *amurensis*	26	100	100	21
Cytisus scoparius	22	45	99	2
Melilotus alba	0	86	100	1
Robinia pseudo-acacia	58	98	99	56
Caesalpinioideae				
Cassia artemisoides	57	3	100	2
" *leptocarpa*	97	37	100	10
Cercidium floridum	100	12	100	2
Gleditsia triacanthos	80	5	100	5
Gymnocladus dioica	92	4	100	0
Parkinsonia aculeata	100	8	100	2
" *microphylla*	100	90	100	10
Cercis chinensis	98	10	100	6

tionships. When one compares the *Papilionoideae* and the *Caesalpinioideae*, it becomes evident immediately that the seeds reacted as a group. Seeds of the members of the *Papilionoideae* (*Cladrastis, Cytisus, Melilotus,* and *Robinia*) were made permeable by shaking. None of these seeds gave more swelling after soaking in absolute ethyl alcohol for 72 hours than the corresponding intact controls. Seeds of the *Caesalpinioideae* subfamily were made permeable by the alcohol soaking but not by the shaking. An exception was seeds of *Parkinsonia microphylla*, 90 per cent of which became swollen after shaking for 20 minutes.

The differential responses of these two subfamilies to the two treatments indicate two types of causes of failure to absorb water. One, characteristic of the *Papilionoideae*, is the strophiolar cleft described by Hamly (1932). The five species of legumes for which Hutton and Porter (1937) found shaking effective also belonged to this same subfamily. Verschaffelt (1912) working chiefly with seeds of *Gleditsia triacanthos* concluded that the alcohol soaking permitted subsequent absorption of water by making a path through the coats which the water could follow. The alcohol was able to enter the integument in the hilum region through interstices through which water could not ordinarily pass. He showed that water followed the path of the penetrated alcohol by using aqueous solutions of dyes. This eliminated the consideration of a leaching out of a waterproofing substance, which was thought by Shaw (1929) to be present in the American lotus seeds.

The cuticle surrounding the seeds has received some consideration as the hindrance to water absorption. White (1908) believed that the cuticular layer over the palisade cells or the coats determined the impermeability of small leguminous seeds, while in the larger leguminous seeds the cuticle and a portion of the palisade cells combined to give the effect. Pectic substances change into water-resistant substances as the seeds of the Kentucky coffee tree harden in ripening according to Raleigh (1930).

A rather extensive study of the testa and its relation to germination in some members of the *Papilionoideae* has been made by Watson (1948). He found that no structure which prevents the absorption of water was present in every species with a low percentage of germination, and so was not able to make any definite conclusions as to the relation between structure and impermeability.

In spite of the length of time the hard seed coat phenomenon has been recognized and the amount of work which has been done on it, we obviously need much more research to determine its cause.

The possibility of dormant embryos, in addition to impermeable coats in some kinds of legumes should not be overlooked. Such seeds would need coat treatment followed by moist treatment at low temperatures to break the dormancy of the embryo. This has already been demonstrated for *Cercis canadensis* L. (Afanasiev 1944) and is suspected for certain crops of alfalfa (*Medicago sativa* L.) grown in Australia and kudzu (*Pueraria phaseoloides*) grown in Puerto Rico. If such a dormancy is found to exist it may be the type which is overcome by a period of dry storage.

References:—

Afanasiev, M., 1944: A study of dormancy and germination of seeds of *Cercis canadensis* (Jour. Agric. Res. 69:405-420).

Akamine, E. K., 1947: Germination of *Asystasia Gangetica* L. seed with special reference to the effect of age on the temperature requirement for germination (Plant Physiol. 22:603-607).

Andersen, A. M., 1944: Germination of freshly harvested seed of Western grown Astoria bentgrass (Proc. Assoc. Off. Seed Anal. 1943/44:138-146).

Andrews, F. W., 1946: A study of nut grass (*Cyperus rotundus* L.) in the cotton soil of the Gezira. II. The perpetuation of the plant by means of seed (Ann. Bot. n. s. 10:15-30).

Atwood, W. M., 1914: A physiological study of the germination of *Avena fatua* (Bot. Gaz. 57:386-414).

Barton, L. V., 1936: Germination of some desert seeds (Contrib. Boyce Thompson Inst. 8:7-11).

————, 1945: Respiration and germination studies of seeds in moist storage (Ann. N. Y. Acad. Sci. 46:185-208).

————, 1947: Special studies on seed coat impermeability (Contrib. Boyce Thompson Inst. 14:355-362).

Barton, L. V., & W. Crocker, 1948: Twenty years of seed research at Boyce Thompson Institute for Plant Research, Inc. (148 pp., Faber and Faber Limited, London).

Barton, L. V., & M. L. Solt, 1948: Growth inhibitors in seeds (Contrib. Boyce Thompson Inst. 15:259-278).

Benedict, H. M., & J. Robinson, 1946: Studies on the germination of guayule seed (U.S.D.A. Tech. Bull. 921, 48 pp.).

Brown, E., T. R. Stanton, G. A. Wiebe & J. H. Martin, 1948: Dormancy and the effect of storage on oats, barley, and sorghum (U.S.D.A. Tech. Bull. 953, 30 pp.).

Burgess, C. H., 1936: A note on the germination of padi (Malayan Agric. Jour. 24: 541-542).

Busse, W. F., 1930: Effect of low temperatures on germination of impermeable seeds (Bot. Gaz. 89:169-179).

Bytschikhina, E. A., 1929/30: Winter wheats of Ukraina and their after-ripening (Bull. Appl. Bot., Genet., & Plant-Breed. 23:299-347).

Carleton, R. M., 1936: Seeds of difficult germination (Hort. 14(3):40).

Crocker, W., 1906: Role of seed coats in delayed germination (Bot. Gaz. 42:265-291).

————, 1916: Mechanics of dormancy in seeds (Amer. Jour. Bot. 3:99-120).

————, 1936: Effect of the visible spectrum upon the germination of seeds and fruits (*In* Duggar, B. M., editor, Biological effects of radiation 2:791-827, McGraw-Hill Book Co., New York).

————, 1948: Growth of plants. Twenty years' research at Boyce Thompson Institute (459 pp., Reinhold Publishing Corp., New York).

Crosier, W., 1946: Germinating freshly harvested cereals (Farm Res. 12(4):4-5).

Davis, W. E., 1930: Primary dormancy, after-ripening, and development of secondary dormancy in embryos of *Ambrosia trifida* (Amer. Jour. Bot. 17:58-76; *also in* Contrib. Boyce Thompson Inst. 2:285-303. 1930).

Evenari, M., 1949: Germination inhibitors (Bot. Rev. 15:153-194).

Evenari, M., E. Konis & S. B. Ullman, 1942: The inhibition of germination (Chron. Bot. 7:149-150).

Foy, N. R., 1932: Delayed germination in cereals (New Zealand Jour. Agric. 44: 129).

Garman, H. R., & L. V. Barton, 1946: Response of lettuce seeds to thiourea treatments as affected by variety and age (Contrib. Boyce Thompson Inst. 14:229-241).

Hamly, D. H., 1932: Softening of the seeds of *Melilotus alba* (Bot. Gaz. 93:345-375).

Harrington, G. T., 1917: Further studies of the germination of Johnson grass seeds (Proc. Assoc. Off. Seed Anal. N. Amer. 9/10(1916/17):71-76).

————, 1923: Forcing the germination of freshly harvested wheat and other cereals (Jour. Agric. Res. 23:79-100).

Hart, H. T., 1928: Delayed germination in seeds of Peltandra virginica and Celastrus scandens (Puget Sound Biol. Sta. Publ. 6:255-261).

Hills, K. L., 1944: Dormancy and hardseededness in T. subterraneum. 2. The progress of after-harvest ripening (Austral. Counc. Sci. & Indus. Res. Jour. 17:186-190).

Hite, B. C., 1923: Effect of storage on the germination of blue-grass seed (Proc. Assoc. Off. Seed Anal. N. Amer. 14/15:97).

Hübner, R., 1938: Untersuchungen über die Hartschaligkeit der Zottelwicke und ihre Behebung auf züchterischem Wege (Landw. Jahrb. 85:751-789).

Hutton, M. E.-J., & R. H. Porter, 1937: Seed impermeability and viability of native and introduced species of Leguminosae (Iowa State Coll. Jour. Sci. 12:5-24).

James, E., 1949a: The effect of inbreeding on crimson clover seed-coat permeability (Agron. Jour. 41:261-266).

————, 1949b: Some factors affecting the production of hard seed in crimson clover (Assoc. Southern Agric. Workers Proc. 1949:52-53).

Johnson, L. P. V., 1935: General preliminary studies on the physiology of delayed germination in Avena fatua (Canad. Jour. Res., Sec. C, 13:283-300).

Kearns, V., & E. H. Toole, 1939: Temperature and other factors affecting the germination of fescue seed (U.S.D.A. Tech. Bull. 638, 35 pp.).

Kidd, F., 1914: The controlling influence of carbon dioxide in the maturation, dormancy and germination of seeds. Part II (Proc. Roy. Soc. London, B, 87:609-625).

Köckemann, A., 1936: Zur Frage der keimungshemmenden Substanzen in fleischigen Früchten (Bot. Centralbl. 55:191-196).

Kroeger, G. S., 1941: Dormancy in seeds of Impatiens balsamina L. (Contrib. Boyce Thompson Inst. 12:203-212).

McAlister, D. F., 1943: The effect of maturity on the viability and longevity of the seeds of western range and pasture grasses (Amer. Soc. Agron. Jour. 35:442-453).

McIlvaine, H. R. C., & H. W. Popp, 1940: Further studies on growth substances in relation to the mechanism of the action of radiation on plants (Jour. Agric. Res. 60:207-215).

MacLachlan, P. L., 1936: Fat metabolism in plants with special reference to sterols (Jour. Biol. Chem. 113:197-204).

Malskaia, A. V., 1936: The before-harvesting maturation and the after-harvesting ripening of Makhorka (Nicotiana rustica L.) seeds (Krasnodar Inst. for Tobacco Indus. Bull. 132:331-332).

Mangelsdorf, P. C., 1923: The inheritance of defective seeds in maize (Jour. Hered. 14:119-125).

————, 1926: The genetics and morphology of some endosperm characters in maize (Conn. [New Haven] Agric. Exp. Sta. Bull. 279:509-614).

Martin, J. N., 1945a: Changes in the germination of red clover seed in storage (Iowa Acad. Sci. Proc. 51(1944):229-233).

————, 1945b: Germination studies of sweet clover seed (Iowa State Coll. Jour. Sci. 19:289-300).

Midgley, A. R., 1926: Effect of alternate freezing and thawing on the impermeability of alfalfa and dodder seeds (Amer. Soc. Agron. Jour. 18:1087-1098).

Murakami, R., 1940: The influence of monochromatic lights on the action of enzymes (Jour. Agric. Chem. Soc. Japan 16:15; abstr. in Biol. Abstr. 16:469, 1942).

Myers, A., 1942: Germination of seed of curly Mitchell grass (Astrebla lappacea Domin.) (Austral. Inst. Agric. Sci. Jour. 8:31-32).

Nelson, A., & J. F. A. MacLagan, 1935: Factors in the germination of Aira Flexuosa (Edinburgh Roy. Bot. Gard. Notes 18:251-266).

Odland, M. L., 1938: Observations on dormancy in vegetable seed (Proc. Amer. Soc. Hort. Sci. 35(1937):562-565).

Pope, M. N., & E. Brown, 1943: Induced vivipary in three varieties of barley possessing extreme dormancy (Amer. Soc. Agron. Jour. 35:161-163).

Raleigh, G. J., 1930: Chemical conditions in maturation, dormancy, and germination of seeds of Gymnocladus dioica (Bot. Gaz. 89:273-294).

Runyon, E. H., 1930: Germination and establishment of Covillea (Carnegie Inst. Wash. Yearbook 29:225-226).

Schaible, F., 1900: Physiologische Experimente über das Wachstum und die Keimung einiger Pflanzen unter vermindertem Luftdruck (Beitr. Wiss. Bot. 4:93-148; abstr. in Bot. Centralbl. 82:52-54).

Shaw, M. F., 1929: A microchemical study of the fruit coat of Nelumbo lutea (Amer. Jour. Bot. 16:259-276).

Shuck, A. L., 1935: The formation of a growth inhibiting substance in germinating lettuce seeds (Proc. Internat. Seed Test. Assoc. 7:9-14).

Shull, C. A., 1911: The oxygen minimum and the germination of Xanthium seeds (Bot. Gaz. 52:453-477).

————, 1914: The role of oxygen in germination (Bot. Gaz. 57:64-69).

Simpson, D. M., 1935: Dormancy and maturity of cottonseed (Jour. Agric. Res. 50: 429-434).

Spaeth, J. N., 1932: Dormancy in seeds of basswood, Tilia americana L. (Amer. Jour. Bot. 19:835).

Stier, H. L., 1938: The effect of certain seed treatments on the germination of recently harvested potato seeds (Proc. Amer. Soc. Hort. Sci. 35(1937):601-605).

Stout, M., & B. Tolman, 1941: Factors affecting the germination of sugarbeet and other seeds with special reference to the toxic effects of ammonia (Jour. Agric. Res. 63:687-713).

Takiguti, Y., 1930a: On the germination of seeds of Oenothera (Agric. & Hort. 5: 748-754; abstr. in Japan. Jour. Bot. 5:80, 1931).

————, 1930b: On the germination of seeds of Perilla ocimoides (Proc. Crop Sci. Soc. Japan 2:199-200; abstr. in Japan. Jour. Bot. 5:81, 1931).

Thornton, N. C., 1935: Factors influencing germination and development of dormancy in cocklebur seeds (Contrib. Boyce Thompson Inst. 7:477-496).

Toole, E. H., 1939: Observations on the germination of freshly harvested timothy seed (Proc. Internat. Seed Test. Assoc. 11:119-139).

Toole, E. H., & V. K. Toole, 1939: Germination of some Brassica types at different temperatures (Proc. Internat. Seed Test. Assoc. 11:51-56).

————, ————, 1940: Notes on the germination of seeds of Barbarea verna and Lepidium virginicum (Proc. Internat. Seed Test. Assoc. 12:32-38).

————, ————, 1941: Progress of germination of seed of Digitaria as influenced by germination temperature and other factors (Jour. Agric. Res. 63:65-90).

Toole, V. K., 1941: Factors affecting the germination of various dropseed grasses (Sporobolus spp.) (Jour. Agric. Res. 62:691-715).

Verschaffelt, E., 1912: Le traitement chimique des graines à imbibition tardive (Rec. Trav. Bot. Néerland. 9:401-435).

Vines, A., 1947: Studies on the germination of barley grains (Austral. Jour. Exp. Biol. & Med. Sci. 25:119-126).

Watson, D. P., 1948: Structure of the testa and its relation to germination in the Papilionaceae tribes Trifoliae and Loteae (Ann. Bot. n. s. 12:385-409).

Wharton, M. F., & W. A. Frazier, 1939: Effect of certain storage treatments on field and laboratory germination of seeds of Imperial 152 and Imperial 615 lettuce (Proc. Amer. Soc. Hort. Sci. 36(1938):680-686).

White, J., 1908: The occurrence of an impermeable cuticle on the exterior of certain seeds (Proc. Roy. Soc. Victoria 21(Pt. 1):203-210).

White, W. J., & T. M. Stevenson, 1948: Permeable seeded strains of sweet clover (Melilotus alba), their development and nature (Sci. Agric. 28:206-222).

Woodforde, A. H., 1935: Dormancy in subterranean clover seed (Tasmanian Jour. Agric. 6:126-127).

Chapter X

DORMANCY IN SEEDS, II

Effect of Moist Low-Temperature Pretreatment:—Perhaps no other method for breaking dormancy has been more widely used than that of planting the seeds in some moist medium and placing them at a low temperature, usually between 1° and 10° C., for a period of several weeks. Under these conditions the seeds after-ripen so that they germinate almost immediately upon transfer to a higher temperature. By after-ripening we mean the changes which take place in the seed making it ready to sprout. We have already seen that this process may take place in dry storage. For many temperate-zone forms, however, complete after-ripening requires a moist medium and a low temperature. The term "stratification" has been in use for a long time to describe this process. This came from the practice of nurserymen to alternate layers of seeds with a moist medium, such as sand, for winter treatment of these forms. The same term has been carried over to apply to any moist, low-temperature pretreatment, including mixing of the seeds with any medium, as granulated peat moss or vermiculite, for example, as well as to regular planting in soil, so long as the temperature requirement is met.

In most cases of seeds which respond to this treatment, dormancy is due to the embryo, though there are some cases where there is a combination of a hard coat and a dormant embryo. These latter will be discussed below. At the time of maturity of the seed, the embryo may be an undifferentiated mass of cells, which grows and develops during the period at low temperature. This is typical of seeds of the American holly, *Ilex opaca* Ait. Growth of the embryo, even to the full length of the seed, however, does not insure germination. The embryo of the European ash, *Fraxinus excelsior,* has already reached considerable size by the time the fruit falls from the tree, but it must grow to the full length of the seed before germination will proceed. Furthermore, there seems to be no special temperature requirement for this growth since it has been demonstrated to take place in the greenhouse as well as in a coldframe exposed to the low temperatures of winter in Yonkers, N.Y. In spite of this fact, seeds kept continuously in the greenhouse failed to develop seedlings while those planted in the fall and wintered out-of-doors produced good seedling stands by the following June. In this case, the low temperature brought about other changes necessary for after-ripening which were not effected by the higher greenhouse temperature.

After-ripening changes also may, and usually do, include chemical changes within the embryo and in the endosperm or stored food material in the seed. These are discussed fully in the chapters on chemical composition and chemical changes during germination and storage.

In the temperate zone nature has supplied the seeds with moist low-temperature pretreatment. They fall to the ground in the autumn and are kept moist over winter by a snow mulch, moist leaves, or other material.

Many of the reports in the literature dealing with this subject describe the effect of fall planting on various seeds. Heit (1945), for example, lists *Acer negundo, A. platanoides, A. saccharum, Fraxinus americana, F. pennsylvanica, Quercus borealis,* and *Q. velutina* as seeds which should be planted in the autumn in the vicinity of Geneva, N.Y. *Liriodendron tulipifera, Prunus serotina, Quercus alba,* and *Tilia americana* should also be planted in the fall, but these should be mulched heavily to prevent freezing. Heit recommends that the fruit of *Sorbus* spp. be macerated and the seeds sown before October 15, and that the husks of nuts (*Carya glabra, C. ovata, C. cordiformis, Juglans cinerea,* and *J. nigra*) be removed before planting before October 15 and mulching over winter. In this publication, no specific data as to temperature and time required for after-ripening or the percentage of seedling production obtained is given. It is of value, however, as a guide to planting these species.

Among many other published accounts which state the advantages of fall planting without giving any specific data are those of Jensen (1937), who recommended this procedure for *Aesculus* (buckeye), *Alnus* (alder), *Benzoin* (spice bush), *Caragana* (pea-shrub), *Carpinus* (hornbeam), *Celtis* (hackberry), *Chionanthus* (fringe tree), *Cornus* (dogwood), *Corylus* (hazelnut), *Fraxinus* (ash), *Ilex* (holly), *Juglans* (walnut), *Juniperus* (cedar), *Ligustrum* (privet), *Liriodendron* (tulip tree), *Prunus* (plum), *Rosa* (rose), *Syringa* (lilac), *Taxodium* (bald cypress), and *Tilia* (linden), and of Rose (1919), who classed *Rubus, Sambucus,* and *Tilia* seeds in this category.

Some authors mention the alternative of stratifying the seeds over winter and planting them in their permanent location in the spring. Carleton (1937) described the refrigerator as a garden tool. He mixed seeds with moist peat moss and brick dust and placed them in a refrigerator until they showed signs of germination, when they were removed and planted. The seeds responding favorably to such treatment were *Aconitum,* Hardy *Aster, Adonis vernalis, Anemone, Asperula odorata, Clematis, Dictamnus, Dodecatheon, Gentiana, Helleborus niger, Humulus, Incarvillea, Iris, Lilium, Paeonia, Phlox decussata, Primula,* and *Saxifraga.*

Nichols (1934) studied the influence of winter temperatures on seeds of some native American plants. He found that 23 species germinated only after a period of 71 to 112 days of low temperature. Forty-five other species germinated better with than without refrigeration. Of these, 30 species gave at least five times and 15 species at least twice the germination of untreated seeds.

The germination of some untreated seeds with fleshy fruits was the subject of investigation by Adams (1927). Plantings were made out-of-doors in the fall, but most of the seeds proved difficult, requiring 605 to 645 days to germinate. Some of these have been shown since to require a high temperature preceding the low, as *Symphoricarpos racemosus* Michx., or two periods of low temperature with an intervening high temperature period, as *Smilacina racemosa* (L.) Desf. Of the 17 species on which Adams reported only four, *Aralia racemosa* L., *Berberis vulgaris* L., and two species of *Ribes,* indicated that one cold period was sufficient to bring about sprouting. Seedlings were produced in 202 to 299 days.

The seeds of certain sand-hill plants in Nebraska were planted on the north side of a building in February (Tolstead 1941). Germination began about the middle of March for 13 different species, indicating a low temperature requirement of about 6 weeks.

Aquatic plants also are benefited by stratification. In this case the treatment is given in water. Muenscher (1936) found that 24 species of water plants germinated well after 5 to 7 months in water at 1° to 3° C.

At Boyce Thompson Institute many seeds have been tested for their reaction to low-temperature pretreatment. Ninety-two of these with the special time and temperature needed for after-ripening have been listed in a book by Crocker (1948). Essentially the same list has been published in two other instances (Barton and Crocker 1948; Barton 1939). To these publications the reader is referred for details. From the literature published from other laboratories, however, effective low-temperature pretreatments together with the author and the year in which the reports appeared are presented for several different species of plants in Table XVI. In cases where the temperature was expressed in degree Fahrenheit in the original data, it has been changed. In some instances the seeds exhibited some special germination requirement in addition to the low-temperature pretreatment. For example, *Acer negundo* seeds required a daily alternation of 10° to 25° C. after pretreatment for germination. At 20° to 30° C. only 12 per cent germinated. *Juniperus* spp. required low temperature for germination as well as for stratification, with 15° C. the best subsequent temperature for seedling development. Nine varieties of peach were found to differ greatly in their stratification temperature requirement, and some crops of *Sambucus canadensis* failed to exhibit any dormancy.

TABLE XVI: *Effect of moist Low Temperature Pretreatment on the Germination of Seeds:—*

| | TREATMENT | | | | |
SPECIES	TEMP. (°C.)	TIME (mos.)	% GERM.	YEAR	AUTHOR
Abies concolor	5	3	44	1936	Mirov
Acer negundo	5	3	67	1941	Roe
Acer saccharum Marsh.	5	1–2.5	—	1920	Jones
(*Aleurites*) Tung (shelled kernels)	5–19	2	78	1942	Sharpe & Merrill
Amelanchier alnifolia	Refrig.	7	Approx. 95	1937	Hargrave
Atropa belladonna	3–5	1	91	1941	Heit
Betula populifolia Marsh.	0–10	2	64	1926	Weiss
(*Buchloë*) Buffalo grass	5	1.5	Approx. 90	1941	Musil
(*Celtis* sp.) Hackberry	1–5	—	73	1940	Afanasiev
Cornus florida	0–10	3–4	82	1927	Davis
Crataegus mollis	5–6	2.5–3.0*	90–98	1912	Davis & Rose
Echinocystis lobata (Michx.) T. and G.	5–10	0.5–6	95–100	1940	Choate
Elaeagnus angustifolia	5	3	78	1935	Anon.
Fraxinus pennsylvanica lanceolata	5	3	45	1935	Anon.
Juniperus spp.	5	3.5	—	1921	Pack
Juniperus virginiana	5	2.5	77	1942	Afanasiev & Cress
Libocedrus decurrens	5	3	76	1936	Mirov
(*Maclura* sp.) Osage orange	1–5	4	98	1940	Afanasiev
Morus alba tartarica	5	2	80	1935	Anon.
Pinus cembroides var. *monophylla*	On ice	1	90	1931	Johnstone & Clare
Pinus coulteri	On ice	1	100	1931	Johnstone & Clare
Pinus echinata	5	3	37	1942	McLintock
Pinus lambertiana	5	3	89	1936	Mirov
Pinus monophylla	5	3	49	1936	Mirov
Pinus rigida	5	3	42	1942	McLintock
Pinus sabiniana	On ice	1.5	80	1931	Johnstone & Clare
Pinus sabiniana	5	3	86	1936	Mirov
Pinus strobus L.	8–10	1	87	1934	Baldwin
Pinus torreyana	On ice	1	69	1931	Johnstone & Clare
Pinus torreyana	5	3	64	1936	Mirov
Pinus tuberculata	On ice	1	80	1931	Johnstone & Clare

TABLE XVI (*continued*)

SPECIES	TREATMENT TEMP. (°C.)	TIME (mos.)	% GERM.	YEAR	AUTHOR
Pinus virginiana	5	3	45	1942	McLintock
Polygonum acre	3	1	75	1935	Ransom
Polygonum amphibium L.	2	7.5	73	1944	Justice
Polygonum aviculare	3	5	100	1935	Ransom
Polygonum coccineum Muhl.	2	8.5	64	1944	Justice
Polygonum hydropiperoides Michx.	10	5	70	1944	Justice
Polygonum lapathifolium	3	1	88	1935	Ransom
Polygonum pennsylvanicum	6–9	5	84	1935	Ransom
Polygonum scandens	3	2.5	78	1935	Ransom
Polygonum virginianum	3	3	88	1935	Ransom
Polygonum (21 species)	2–4	0.5–6	—	1941	Justice
Prunus americana	5	5	100	1941	Roe
Prunus pennsylvanica	Refrig.	9	34	1937	Hargrave
(*Prunus* sp.) Wild plum	1–5	3	90	1940	Afanasiev
(*Prunus* sp.) Mahaleb cherry	3	3	89	1934	Haut
(*Prunus* sp.) Mazzard cherry	3	3.5	79	1934	Haut
(*Prunus* sp.) Late Crawford Peach	3	2.5	86	1934	Haut
(*Prunus* sp.) Peach	3–5	2.5	52–93	1941	Scott & Waugh
(*Prunus* sp.) Peach	3–5	0.5–3	40–100	1945	Carlson & Tukey
Pyrus baccata	5	4	0.4–7.5	1940	Davis
(*Pyrus* sp.) apple	5–10 Fluctuation	2.5	50+	1923	Harrington & Hite
(*Pyrus* sp.) McIntosh Apple	3	2	91	1934	Haut
(*Pyrus* sp.) Kieffer pear	3	1.5	89	1934	Haut
Quercus borealis maxima	5	3	100	1935	Aikman
Quercus macrocarpa	5	0.5–3	100	1935	Aikman
Quercus velutina	5	3	100	1935	Aikman
Sambucus canadensis	0–5	3–3.5	87	1927	Davis
Scirpus (8 spp.)	2–4	6	63–100	1944	Isely
Tilia americana	0–2, 10–12	3.5, 0.5	56–82	1919	Rose
Tsuga canadensis (L.) Carr.	10	1.5	60	1930	Baldwin
(*Ulmus* sp.) Slippery elm	1–5	1.5	90+	1940	Afanasiev

* With carpels removed.

There is no doubt about the favorable effects of moist low-temperature pretreatment for many kinds of seeds. The advantage may be only one of increased speed of germination with resulting uniform stands of seedlings or it may mean the difference between good germination and none at all.

Two-Year Seeds:—Seeds, which in nursery practice as well as in nature do not produce seedlings until the second spring after their maturation, are often spoken of as two-year seeds. Studies at Boyce Thompson Institute have shown these seeds to fall into three physiological groups.

1) Seeds possessing both impermeable seed coats and dormant embryos. Here, the coats must first be disintegrated by mechanical abrasion or scarification, acid treatment,

or soil microorganisms to permit absorption of water, after which a period at low temperature will after-ripen the embryos.

2) Seeds which will produce roots in the soil during a period of warm temperature, but which must then have a period at low temperature to after-ripen the dormant epicotyl before the green shoot will be formed.

3) Seeds which require pretreatment in a moist medium at low temperature to induce root growth, followed by a period at higher temperature to grow the root system, after which a second period at low temperature is necessary to break the dormancy of the epicotyl. Seeds in this category may be said to possess a double dormancy.

Each of these groups will be described briefly below. For a more complete discussion *see* Barton and Crocker (1948) and Crocker (1948).

Germination of seeds possessing both impermeable coats and dormant embryos.—*Cotoneaster* species which have proved difficult to germinate will serve as the first example of this type of dormancy. Since the dormancy is broken at low temperature only if the seed has been able to absorb water, it follows that a coat treatment must be given before low temperature stratification. This may be done by soaking in concentrated sulfuric acid for two and one-half hours in the case of *Cotoneaster divaricata* Rehd. & Wils. After this treatment, the seeds must be placed at about 5° C. in a moist medium for two and one-half months for after-ripening. Upon removal from the low temperature to a greenhouse seedlings will appear promptly above the surface of the soil. It has been shown now, for several different species, that a period at a temperature of about 25° C. in a moist medium causes disintegration of the seed coats, making them permeable. This makes it possible to bring about the germination of these seeds by selecting the proper time of year for planting in a temperate region. Late spring or early summer planting out-of-doors is effective. Following planting, the seeds are exposed to the warm weather of summer, during which time soil microorganisms attack the seed coats, breaking them down. The cold weather of the autumn and winter then after-ripen the embryos and seedlings appear above the ground the next spring.

Other forms besides *Cotoneaster divaricata* which fall in this category are *C. horizontalis, Aralia racemosa* L., *Arctostaphylos uva-ursi* (L.) Spreng., *Cornus canadensis* L., *Crataegus crus-galli* L., *C. flava* Ait., *C. oxyacantha* L., *C. punctata* Jacq., *C. rotundifolia* Moench., *Halesia carolina* L., *Rhodotypos kerrioides* Sieb. & Zucc., *Symphoricarpos orbiculatus* Moench., *S. racemosus* Michx., *Taxus cuspidata* Sieb. & Zucc., and *Tilia americana* L. In some of these instances, some germination may be obtained with pretreatment at low temperature only, but much better with high temperature preceding the low. In the case of *Arctostaphylos*, neither high temperature nor sulfuric acid alone was sufficient to overcome the coat effects, but the best results were secured when these two treatments were used together.

Recent work (Barton 1951) has shown that failure to obtain complete germination of *Juniperus virginiana* seeds after low temperature pretreatment is due to the presence of impermeable seed coats in a large percentage of the seeds.

Epicotyl Dormancy:—This type of dormancy, first reported in 1933 for seeds of the tree peony, *Paeonia suffruticosa* Andr., is expressed by the failure of the shoot bud to develop after the root has already started to grow at ordinary greenhouse temperatures. The epicotyl must be given low-temperature treatment after the seed has germinated to form a root. This may be accomplished by planting the germinated seeds in soil in pots and placing the pots in a cold room (from 1° to 10° C.) for two to three months. The soil must be kept moist during this period, at the end of which the pots should be transferred to a greenhouse where the green shoots will appear in a few days.

Since these seeds require a high temperature for root production followed by a low temperature to after-ripen the shoot bud, the practical method of getting seedlings is the same as for seeds of the preceding category, *i.e.*, spring or early summer planting. The changes brought about by the initial high temperature period, however, are different in the two classes. In one instance the condition for the germination of the seed and the growth of the root system necessary before the epicotyl will after-ripen at low temperature is provided, and in the other the growth of microorganisms which make the seed coats permeable is favored.

Besides the tree peony and the herbaceous peony, epicotyl dormancy has been shown to be characteristic of *Asarum canadense* L., *Lilium auratum* Lindl., *L. canadense* L., *L. japonicum* Thunb., *L. rubellum* Baker, *L. superbum* L., *L. szovitsianum* Fisch. & Lall., *Viburnum acerifolium* L., *V. dentatum* L., *V. dilatatum* Thunb., *V. opulus* L., and *V. prunifolium* L.

A combination of root and epicotyl dormancy.—Some seeds have a more complicated type of dormancy than any of those described above, necessitating two separate periods in a moist medium. The first period is to after-ripen the root. This should be followed by a period at high temperature to bring about germination and some growth of the root. A second period at low temperature after-ripens the epicotyl, and during a second period at high temperature green shoots are formed.

Complete double dormancy of this type has been demonstrated for seeds of *Trillium grandiflorum* (Michx.) Salisb. Only an occasional seed germinated to form a root without low-temperature pretreatment and a separate period at low temperature was required to after-ripen the shoot. *Trillium erectum* L. seeds were found to have a similar behavior. *Convallaria majalis* L., *Sanguinaria canadensis* L., *Smilacina racemosa* (L.) Desf., and *Polygonatum commutatum* (R. & S.) Dietr. differ from the two species of *Trillium* in that the roots are only partially dormant. Some germination to form roots takes place without low temperature after-ripening but the percentage is increased by such pretreatment. All of these forms have dormant epicotyls.

Dwarfs from Non-After-Ripened Seeds:—We have seen how dormant embryos may be after-ripened by low-temperature pretreatment so that when they are planted in soil they will germinate and produce normal plants. When certain of these embryos are excised from all enveloping structures and are grown without after-ripening they produce seedlings which develop a characteristic dwarfed appearance. Instead of internodes of normal length, there seems to be no growth of the stem between the nodes. These are physiologic dwarfs which may start to grow normally after a certain time has elapsed or after exposure to low temperature in the seedling stage.

Dwarfish plants have been produced by this treatment, *i.e.*, excision of the embryos without after-ripening, for the peach, *Prunus persica* (L.) Stokes, the Japanese rose tree, *Rhodotypos kerrioides*, the apple, *Pyrus malus* L., and a species of hawthorn, *Crataegus* L. It is worthy of note that excised embryos of the cocklebur, *Xanthium canadense* Mill., in which dormancy has been induced by certain gas or temperature treatments have also been found to form seedlings which show dwarfing effects and slow growth for two to five weeks after which growth is normal.

It is likely that the production of dwarfs from dormant embryos and the epicotyl dormancy described above are very closely related phenomena. In both cases root growth is normal without pretreatment at low temperature, but the development and growth of the shoot is dependent upon certain changes which can be brought about easily at low temperatures but which do not take place at all, or proceed slowly, at ordinary growing temperatures. Further investigations along these lines will doubtless bring us much nearer to a correct interpretation of the whole dormancy problem.

Rapid Viability Tests:—A brief discussion of these methods is presented here under the general topic of "Dormancy," because of the relation of the method to the determination of the germination capacity of dormant seeds.

Before non-dormant seeds, such as those of common flowers and vegetables, are put on the market, and, in many cases again before they are planted, they are tested so that the grower may know what germination to expect, and adjust his seeding rate accordingly. This is a fairly simple process, for these seeds are quick germinators. Even grain seeds which may be dormant when freshly harvested offer no particular difficulty, for their germination ability may be ascertained under controlled laboratory conditions within a short time.

An attempt has been made by Waller (1901) to determine the vitality of *Phaseolus* seeds by an electrical method. After soaking in water, the beans were split and the radicle broken off and placed between clay pads of the electrodes. Stimulus was then supplied by an induction coil and the shock deflection was measured on a galvanometer. A much greater deflection was secured with fresh, vigorous seeds than with older and less vigorous seeds, and no response was obtained with non-viable seeds. The same effects measured on the entire seed were less accurate and much more difficult. The same method was employed later by Fraser (1916), who used barley embryos and confirmed the general results of Waller. Fraser believed that there was a possibility that the electrical response could select seeds of high and low vitality as well as live and dead ones. The literature down to the present time fails to reveal any continuation of this line of attack on the problem.

From time to time, methods of staining grains to distinguish between good and poor quality have been devised. One of the earliest of these methods was that of Dimitriewicz (1876), who found that sections of good grains turned a deep rose color in sulfuric acid in five minutes, while sections of poor seeds required 15 minutes. Indigo carmine has been found to penetrate dead embryos much more readily than live ones. Seeds have been treated with chemicals, the reduction of which by the respiratory activity of the seed has resulted in color changes which indicate viability. Soaking in para- or ortho-dinitrobenzene solutions for 20 hours, followed by ammonia for one hour, gives an orange color to live seeds. Selenium and tellurium compounds upon reduction in the seeds impart a yellow color in the first case and a purple color in the second. More recently, less toxic tetrazolium salts have been recommended. They are reduced by the seed to red formazanes.

In a recent paper from this laboratory (Flemion and Poole 1948), 2,3,5-triphenyltetrazolium chloride was used in a series of tests with 100 different seed lots representing 17 plant families and 58 species. In spite of the fact that dead embryos rarely stained while viable embryos become colored, the various types and degrees of staining secured were difficult to interpret. Tetrazolium chloride has also been used by Bennett and Loomis (1949) to determine the extent of freezing injury in seed corn. However, for fair accuracy, germination had to be moderately high and the corn had to be stored for some time after freezing. Even when these conditions were met, no satisfactory estimate of the percentage of abnormal seedlings could be made.

A more reliable method has been found to consist in excision of the embryos and observation of their behavior on moist filter paper in the diffuse light of the laboratory. This method has been described in detail in several publications from the Institute and its reliability has been determined (Flemion 1948). It is not quite as rapid as the staining method, requiring two to seven days instead of 25 hours for the tetrazolium test, but its greater accuracy makes it desirable. Many of the seeds used in these quick determinations of viability would take from six weeks to six months of special treatment for germination to take place. For a complete account of rapid viability tests of all types, see the literature cited in the last three references.

References:—

Adams, J., 1927: The germination of the seeds of some plants with fleshy fruits (Amer. Jour. Bot. 14:415-428).

Afanasiev, 1940: New seed-handling methods facilitate growing native trees (Okla. Agric. Exp. Sta. Biennial Rept. 1938/40:124-126).

Afanasiev, M., & M. Cress, 1942: Producing seedlings of eastern red cedar (*Juniperus virginiana* L.) (Okla. Agric. Exp. Sta. Bull. 256, 21 pp.).

Aikman, J. M., 1935: The effect of low temperature on the germination and survival of native oaks (Proc. Iowa Acad. Sci. 41(1934):89-93; abstr. in Biol. Abstr. 10:21879, 1936).

Baldwin, H. I., 1930: The effect of after-ripening treatment on the germination of Eastern hemlock seed (Jour. Forest. 28:853-857).

————, 1934: Effect of after-ripening treatment on germination of white pine seeds of different ages (Bot. Gaz. 96:372-376).

Barton, L. V., 1939: Experiments at Boyce Thompson Institute on germination and dormancy in seeds (Sci. Hort. 7:186-193).

————, 1951: Germination of seeds of *Juniperus virginiana* L. (Contrib. Boyce Thompson Inst. 16:387-393).

Barton, L. V., & W. Crocker, 1948: Twenty years of seed research at Boyce Thompson Institute for Plant Research, Inc. (148 pp., Faber & Faber Ltd., London).

Bennett, N., & W. E. Loomis, 1949: Tetrazolium chloride as a test reagent for freezing injury of seed corn (Plant Physiol. 24:162-174).

Carleton, R. M., 1937: The refrigerator as a garden tool (Hort. 15:412).

Carlson, R. F., & H. B. Tukey, 1945: Differences in after-ripening requirements of several sources and varieties of peach seed (Proc. Amer. Soc. Hort. Sci. 46:199-202).

Choate, H. A., 1940: Dormancy and germination in seeds of *Echinocystis lobata* (Amer. Jour. Bot. 27:156-160).

Crocker, W., 1948: Growth of plants. Twenty years' research at Boyce Thompson Institute (459 pp., Reinhold Publ. Corp., New York).

Davis, L. L., 1940: Germination and growth of crab-apple seedlings (*Pyrus baccata*) as influenced by fungicidal treatment (Proc. Amer. Soc. Hort. Sci. 37(1939):359-360).

Davis, O. H., 1927: Germination and early growth of *Cornus florida, Sambucus canadensis,* and *Berberis thunbergii* (Bot. Gaz. 84:225-263).

Davis, W. E., & R. C. Rose, 1912: The effect of external conditions upon the after-ripening of the seeds of *Crataegus mollis* (Bot. Gaz. 54:49-62).

Dimitriewicz, N., 1876: Ueber die Methoden der Samenprüfung landwirtschaftlicher Culturpflanzen (Inaug.-Diss. Univ. Leipzig, 40 pp.).

Flemion, F., 1948: Reliability of the excised embryo method as a rapid test for determining the germinative capacity of dormant seeds (Contrib. Boyce Thompson Inst. 15:229-241).

Flemion, F., & H. Poole, 1948: Seed viability tests with 2,3,5-triphenyltetrazolium chloride (Contrib. Boyce Thompson Inst. 15:243-258).

Fraser, M. T., 1916: Parallel tests of seeds by germination and by electrical response (preliminary experiments) (Ann. Bot. 30:181-189).

Hargrave, P. D., 1937: Seed germination of the Saskatoon and Pincherry (Sci. Agric. 17:736-739).

Harrington, G. T., & B. C. Hite, 1923: After-ripening and germination of apple seeds (Jour. Agric. Res. 23:153-161).

Haut, I. C., 1934: The effect of various low temperatures upon the after-ripening of fruit tree seeds (Proc. Amer. Soc. Hort. Sci. 30(1933):365-367).

Heit, C. E., 1941: Laboratory germination of belladonna (*Atropa belladonna*) seed (Proc. Assoc. Off. Seed Anal. N. Amer. 33:84-87).

————, 1945: Fall planting of hardwood tree seed (Farm Res. [Geneva] 11(3):14, 15).

Isely, D., 1944: A study of conditions that affect the germination of *Scirpus* seeds (New York [Cornell] Agric. Exp. Sta. Mem. 257:1-28; *abstr. in* Biol. Abstr. 19:7337, 1945).

J[ensen], L. P., 1937: Growing woody plants from seeds (Mo. Bot. Gard. Bull. 25:53-58).

Johnstone, G. R., & T. S. Clare, 1931: Hastening the germination of western pine seeds (Jour. Forest. 29:895-906).

Jones, H. A., 1920: Physiological study of maple seeds (Bot. Gaz. 69:127-152).

Justice, O. L., 1941: A study of dormancy in seeds of *Polygonum* (New York [Cornell] Agric. Exp. Sta. Mem. 235, 43 pp.).

————, 1944: Viability and dormancy in seeds of *Polygonum amphibium* L., *P. coccineum* Muhl., and *P. hydropiperoides* Michx. (Amer. Jour. Bot. 31:369-377).

McLintock, T. F., 1942: Stratification as a means of improving results of direct seeding of pines (Jour. Forest. 40:724-728).

Mirov, N. T., 1936: A note on germination methods for coniferous species (Jour. Forest. 34:719-723; *abstr. in* Exp. Sta. Rec. 75:785, 1936).

Muenscher, W. C., 1936: Storage and germination of seeds of aquatic plants (New York [Cornell] Agric. Exp. Sta. Bull. 652, 17 pp.).

Musil, A. F., 1941: The pretreatment of buffalo grass for field planting (Proc. Assoc. Off. Seed Anal. N. Amer. 33:76-82).

Nichols, G. E., 1934: The influence of exposure to winter temperatures upon seed germination in various native American plants (Ecology 15:364-373).

Pack, D. A., 1921: After-ripening and germination of *Juniperus* seeds (Bot. Gaz. 71:32-60).

Ransom, E. R., 1935: The inter-relations of catalase, respiration, after-ripening, and germination in some dormant seeds of the *Polygonaceae* (Amer. Jour. Bot. 22:815-825).

Roe, E. I., 1941: Effect of temperature on seed germination (Jour. Forest. 39:413-414).

Rose, R. C., 1919: After-ripening and germination of seeds of *Tilia, Sambucus,* and *Rubus* (Bot. Gaz. 67:281-308).

Scott, D. H., & J. G. Waugh, 1941: Treatment of peach seed as affecting germination and growth of seedlings in the greenhouse (Proc. Amer. Soc. Hort. Sci. 38:291-298).

Sharpe, R. H., & S. Merrill, Jr., 1942: Effect of stratification and time of planting on germination of tung seed (Proc. Amer. Soc. Hort. Sci. 40:286-291).

Tolstead, W. L., 1941: Germination habits of certain sand-hill plants in Nebraska (Ecology 22:393-397).

Waller, A. D., 1901: An attempt to estimate the vitality of seeds by an electrical method (Roy. Soc. Proc. 68:79-92).

Weiss, F., 1926: Seed germination in the gray birch, *Betula populifolia* (Amer. Jour. Bot. 13:737-742).

Anon., 1935: Seed treatments for shelterbelt species (Forest Res. Digest, p. 6-7).

Chapter XI

STORAGE AND LIFE SPAN OF SEEDS

Life Span vs. Storage:—The length of life of seeds has been of interest from very early times. There have been, and still are, published accounts of the sprouting of wheat which has lain in some Egyptian tomb for hundreds of years in spite of perennial denials of this possibility by authorities. Early work on seed longevity was done on old seeds from herbaria or other incidental collections, and much valuable information was secured from these sources. Becquerel (1932, 1934), for example, tested seeds from a storage room in the National Museum of Paris. These seeds had been collected from 1819 to 1853 and were tested in 1906 and again in 1934. He determined the longevity of 13 species at 55 to 158 years, and estimated the probable life span of *Mimosa glomerata* Forsk., *Astragalus massiliensis* Lam., *Dioclea pauciflora* Rusby, *Leucaena leucocephala* Linn., and *Cassia bicapsularis* Linn. at 221, 100, 121, 155, and 199 years respectively. All of these seeds belong to the family *Leguminosae,* as did the remainder of the 13 species with the exception of *Lavatera (Malvaceae)* and *Stachys (Labiatae).* It is well-known that members of the *Leguminosae* family possess impermeable coats, which, no doubt, accounts for their long life.

Other reports on the viability of many different sorts of old seeds from various sources have been made by Turner (1933), Schjelderup-Ebbe (1936), and Ewart (1908). Ewart divided seeds into three classes on the basis of their longevity under what he called optimum conditions. Microbiotic seeds were those with a longevity not exceeding three years; mesobiotic, those with a life span of from three to 15 years; and macrobiotic, those that may live for 15 to 100 years or more. This classification is dependent, of course, upon the knowledge of the optimum conditions of storage for each kind of seed. It is doubtful whether these are known for any type, for new data are constantly showing possibilities of lengthening the life of many seeds by control of the conditions under which they are stored.

Thus life span becomes a relative term and the actual age of any given seed lot does not determine the germination capacity, which depends rather upon the genetical constitution, especially upon the presence or absence of an impermeable seed coat, and the environmental conditions under which it is placed.

The oldest known viable seeds found in their natural surroundings are those of the Indian lotus, *Nelumbo nucifera* Gaertn. (Ohga 1926). These particular seeds were found in a naturally drained lake bed in Manchuria and were thought to have been buried there for at least 160 years and probably more than 250 years. With the new radioactive carbon measurement of age, Libby (1951) has examined some of these same old *Nelumbo* seeds and has found that they are 1040 ± 210 years old. These old seeds possess impervious coats which must be broken before germination can proceed to form healthy, vigorous seedlings.

Short-Lived Seeds:—There are many seeds, including both temperate zone and tropical forms, which deteriorate rapidly when exposed to open air. Thus, if suitable germination conditions do not prevail almost immediately after maturation of the seeds, they are lost. This behavior has been reported for seeds of the river maple, wild rice, oaks, beeches, horse chestnuts, walnuts, hickories, chestnuts, willows, poplars, and elms (Crocker 1938). At first it was assumed that desiccation caused the death of these seeds, but this has been disproved in some cases. For example, it has been shown in some willow species that vitality of the seeds is lost completely within a week when they are exposed to open air, but they live for at least 360 days in an ice chest in an atmosphere with a relative humidity of only 13 per cent, which is considerably lower than the average humidity of the air at the time the seeds are mature. The deterioration of poplar seeds in open air has been attributed to the injurious action of oxygen and to higher temperatures. Seeds of the American elm which were thought formerly to be killed by drying will retain full vitality for at least nine years in sealed containers at temperatures as low as 5° C. and —5° C., with the moisture content reduced to about 3 per cent (Barton 1939*b*; also unpublished data).

Certain citrus seeds (grapefruit, sweet orange, sour orange, and rough lemon) apparently endure only partial drying in the air (Barton 1943). It is likely, however, that the rate and the temperature of drying as well as the degree may be important. Also, it has been pointed out by Childs (1948) that the growth of fungi and bacteria on moist citrus seeds in storage is an important factor in their deterioration.

Tropical seeds known to degenerate rapidly in open air storage are sugarcane and *Hevea brasiliensis*. The former can be kept longer by taking seeds from air-dried heads, placing them in cans with 9 grams of calcium chloride to 1 liter of space, displacing the air with carbon dioxide, hermetically sealing, and storing at the freezing point, while the latter remain viable for longer periods in containers with 40 to 45 per cent carbon dioxide (Crocker 1938).

Seeds of maga, *Montezuma speciosissima* Moc. & Sessé, another tropical plant, lose their ability to germinate upon storage in open air. Using seeds sent to Yonkers, N.Y. by air mail from Puerto Rico, it was found that deterioration was significant within two weeks under ordinary storage conditions (Barton 1945*b*). With moisture contents as high as 50 per cent of the dry weight, these seeds could be kept for a month in sealed storage at 5° C. Drying in the laboratory to approximately 12 per cent moisture reduced the germination capacity by one-half, but permitted retention of this germination capacity at —4°, 5°, or 20° C. for at least six months and possibly longer.

It is evident from the above discussion that seeds which lose their germination ability rapidly in open-air storage are not necessarily injured by drying. There are several other factors which may be involved, which certainly should not be overlooked in a study of these phenomena. To secure accurate information on the effect of the several environmental factors responsible for degeneration of seeds in storage, it is necessary to study the response of each species to a wide range of intensity of the variables, singly and in combination. A beginning has been made and will be discussed below under "Storage of Seeds."

Longevity of Seeds in Soil:—Every gardener knows how difficult it is to get rid of weeds even though he is careful to eradicate all seedlings as they appear and to make every effort to prevent the introduction of new weed seeds. This is due, of course, to the long life span of many seeds buried in the soil. There are many reports of seeds which will germinate after 10 or more years of dormancy in the soil. These reports have been based, for the most part, on the appearance of plants not common to the region, usually on newly excavated or plowed soil. There have been cases, however, where the seeds were buried and then dug up for testing at intervals.

One of these was a project of the Seed Testing Laboratory of the United States Department of Agriculture started by Duvel in 1902 (Crocker 1938). One hundred and seven species representing both wild and cultivated plants were buried in 32 sets in sterile soil in flower pots with porous clay covers at depths of 8, 22, and 42 inches. Germination tests have been reported after burial for 1, 3, 6, 10, 16, and 20 years. The results of the 20-year test showed that depth of burial had little effect on life span. Most of the seeds of cultivated plants died after one year in the soil, but timothy, Kentucky blue grass, beet, bush clover, three species of clover, tobacco, celery, and black locust gave some germination after 20 years. Seeds of wild plants, on the other hand, were found to be especially resistant to deterioration in the soil and many retained high germination capacity after 20 years in the soil. A similar experiment was started as early as 1879 by Beal (Crocker 1938). In this case seeds of 20 different wild species were mixed with sand and buried in uncorked pint bottles, the mouths of which were tilted downward to prevent filling with water. After 20 years, seeds of 11 species were still alive; after 40 years, 8 species, including *Amaranthus retroflexus*, *Ambrosia elatior*, *Brassica nigra*, *Lepidium virginicum*, *Oenothera biennis*, *Plantago major*, *Portulaca oleracea*, and *Rumex crispus*; and after 60 years, only *Oenothera biennis* and *Rumex crispus*.

One of the remarkable things about the longevity of weed seeds in the soil is that most of them do not have impermeable coats. This means that they become fully imbibed with water shortly after falling on the ground and remain in that condition until their requirements for germination, which may be light, or alternating temperature, mechanical disturbance or abrasion or some other unknown factor, are met. Furthermore, it has been shown by Kjaer (1940) that some weed seeds actually remain viable longer in the soil than they do in dry storage in the laboratory. This report includes tests up to the five-year period only. It will be interesting to see what future tests of these same seeds disclose as to the nature of this phenomenon. Other evidence of the superiority of moist soil over dry storage at room temperature is to be found in various reports, especially those of Ewart, Beal, and the United States Department of Agriculture (Crocker 1948, p. 40).

In an effort to obtain more definite information on the behavior of these seeds, *Amaranthus retroflexus* L. seeds were collected in 1942 and 1943 and were placed in germinators at 20° C. (Barton 1945a). Some of them have remained dormant for more than six years, while others have germinated from time to time for no apparent cause (*see* Table XII). The seeds could be induced to germinate at any time by raising the temperature to 35° C., rubbing them in the palm of the hand with the finger and replacing at 20° C., partial desiccation, or alternating temperature. Dormancy induced on the moist medium at 20° C. resulted in a decreased respiration rate (*see* chapter on Respiration). A recent report on physiological studies of weed seed germination (Bibbey 1948) has shown primary and secondary dormancy, as well as sensitivity to oxygen and carbon dioxide pressures to be factors in the life span of *Thlaspi arvense* L., *Brassica arvensis* L., *Avena fatua* L., and *Melilotus alba* Desr. in the soil. When the explanation for the behavior of buried weed seeds is found, it will mark a significant advance in our knowledge of seed physiology.

The reader is referred to a review article by Crocker (1938) entitled "Life-Span of Seeds," for a more comprehensive treatment of the historical phases of the subject.

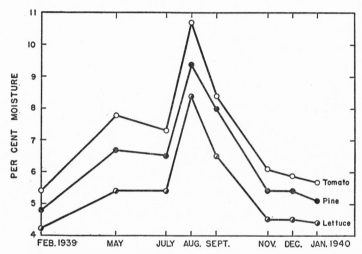

FIGURE 2.—Moisture contents at various times of the year of seeds stored open in the laboratory. Moisture expressed as percentage of dry weight of seeds. Duplicates of approximately 2 grams each used for each test.

Storage of Seeds:—Much work has been done and reports published on the effects of different storage conditions upon the retention of viability by different kinds of seeds. For a discussion of the literature, the reader is referred to a review article by Crocker (1938), as well as to two books which contain chapters on the subject (Crocker 1948; Barton and Crocker 1948). As mentioned previously, each kind may give a different response which must be determined experimentally. However, there are certain general conclusions which may be drawn as a result of the combined work of many investigators in the field.

Whereas there are many seeds which do not tolerate drying or perish quickly from other causes when exposed to the open air (*see above*), the majority of seeds are benefited by drying. In fact, low moisture content is one of the requirements for increasing the life span of many seeds. Temperature and gaseous exchange during the storage period are also of prime importance. In general, it has been found that a combination of low relative humidity and low temperature furnishes almost ideal storage conditions for periods up to five years. If either the humidity or the temperature is too high, reduction of the oxygen supply favors retention of germination capacity.

The moisture content of so-called "air-dry" seeds varies greatly from one locality to another and in the same locality at different times of the year. This is strikingly illustrated by the amount of moisture taken up by seeds stored in open containers in the laboratory at Yonkers, N.Y. The resulting moisture contents for tomato, pine, and lettuce seeds are shown in Figure 2. Here it will be seen that the moisture present in the seeds in August is approximately twice that present during the winter months when the atmosphere of the laboratory is very dry. The significance of this variation will be seen in data to be presented below, and emphasizes the importance of adjusting the moisture content of the seeds to a known safe level before storage, rather than relying on air drying, unless the relative humidity of the air is known to be low. Also it will be noted from Figure 2 that different seeds absorb different amounts of water at a given relative humidity. As compared with tomato, lettuce seeds retain a relatively small amount of water, while pine seeds occupy an intermediate position. As already noted in Chapter V, Table IX, onion seeds absorb even more water under a given set of conditions than tomato. The amount of water taken up also depends upon the temperature of exposure (Barton 1941). In an atmosphere of 35 per cent relative humidity, a given variety of seeds takes up approximately the same amount of water at 5° and 10° C. and less at 20° and 30° C. At 55 and 76 per cent relative humidities, most moisture was absorbed at 10° C. and least at 30° C. Other workers have found similar effects. Recently Gane (1948) found that grass, pea, and linseed had different water contents after exposure to the same humidity and that for pea meal, there was a decrease in water content as the temperature was raised. The explanation for these phenomena is not known at the present time, but must be sought in the physical and chemical characteristics of the seeds themselves, as well as the physical conditions of the atmosphere surrounding the seeds.

From the many data accumulated in the Seed Laboratory at Boyce Thompson Institute which show effects of moisture content, sealing, and temperature on the keeping quality of seeds in storage, a few have been selected and are presented in Tables XVII and XVIII.

The keeping quality of vegetable seeds under different conditions of storage is a matter of general interest and great economic importance. Various workers are in agreement as to the general beneficial effect of low moisture content and low temperature for extending the life of these seeds. Some of the results obtained at Boyce Thompson Institute are shown in Table XVII. Here, storage in the laboratory is compared with storage in a cold room with an average temperature of approximately −4° C. For each species, the higher moisture content was an actual determination made at the beginning of the experiment and calculated on the basis of the dry weight of the seeds. With this information at hand a given weight of the seeds was mixed with an amount of anhydrous calcium oxide calculated to remove one-half of the original moisture, thus giving the approximate lower moisture contents indicated. Seed samples were also dried to given moisture contents in a desiccator over calcium oxide and then stored in sealed containers. Other lots were mixed with a quantity of the calcium oxide sufficient to remove only one-third of the original moisture from the seeds. Data from these two last moisture contents are not included in the table.

When storage was in the laboratory, a reduction in moisture content was essential to maintenance of viability for periods of five years or longer.

TABLE XVII: *Germination on moist Filter Paper at controlled Temperatures of some Vegetable Seeds after Storage under various Conditions:—*

| | | GERMINATION PERCENTAGES AFTER STORAGE FOR YEARS | | | | | | | | | | | | | |
| | PER CENT | LABORATORY | | | | | | | −4° C. | | | | | | |
SEED	MOISTURE	1	3	5	7	10	15	17	1	3	5	7	10	15	17
Carrot	Open	66	63	53	48	22	0	—	68	73	61	58	60	59	63
67*	10.7	60	25	0	—	—	—	—	67	75	64	67	68	74	67
	5.4	63	64	67	62	64	44	22	69	71	67	67	76	69	73
Eggplant	Open	81	82	78	58	27	0	—	82	84	77	90	76	—	—
86*	10.4	86	83	72	52	4	0	—	85	85	89	86	79	—	—
	5.2	93	89	87	66	79	73	71	82	82	85	86	84	89	85
Lettuce	Open	95	76	0	—	—	—	—	94	94	93	92	93	93	89
98*	8.2	92	85	0	—	—	—	—	95	93	93	95	96	89	83
	4.1	94	88	64	73	73	6	0	91	95	92	94	91	80	74
Onion	Open	62	33	1	—	—	—	—	94	94	93	81	69	—	—
98*	12.5	82	1	0	—	—	—	—	96	97	94	90	71	—	—
	6.3	96	99	89	78	71	0	—	97	97	91	94	92	88	91
Pepper	Open	67	45	12	2	—	—	—	80	73	75	77	59	60	52
73*	10.4	22	2	0	—	—	—	—	75	76	77	73	65	66	—
	5.2	76	66	61	57	20	0	—	43	74	69	66	76	72	70
Tomato	Open	94	89	81	76	27	0	—	92	91	91	91	92	—	—
93*	10.0	91	75	32	7	—	—	—	93	91	95	95	84	—	—
	5.0	90	91	89	92	83	63	—	90	85	94	89	97	94	93

* Per cent germination of fresh seeds.
— Indicates no test was made, either because of loss of germination capacity or exhausted seed supply.

Also onion, lettuce, and pepper seeds were less resistant to an unfavorable environment than carrot, eggplant, and tomato seeds. These tests have also shown that the simple method of mixing a drying agent with the seeds is an effective way to reduce the moisture content. No evidence of injury by contact with calcium oxide was noted in any of the tests. Open storage was less harmful than sealed storage at the higher moisture contents, for the reason that seeds tended to become more dry in open storage, while the excess moisture was held in the seeds in sealed storage. With reduced moisture content, however, it was advantageous to seal the containers to prevent the absorption of more moisture from the atmosphere.

At —4° C. full germination capacity of all seeds has been retained for 17 years, with some seeds still in storage for future tests. At the 10-year and subsequent periods, there was some evidence of deterioration of onion and pepper seeds in open storage at —4° C. There is no doubt that below-freezing temperature offers a very satisfactory condition for retention of viability of vegetable seeds. Unfortunately, no other low temperature was tried in this particular experiment. Other recent data on vegetable seed storage as affected by temperature and relative humidity is to be found in an article by Toole et al. (1948).

TABLE XVIII: *Germination at controlled Temperatures of different Seeds after Storage under various Conditions:—*

SEED + % GERM.	PER CENT MOISTURE	GERMINATION PERCENTAGES AFTER STORAGE FOR YEARS																	
		LABORATORY						5° C.						—4° C.					
		1	3	5	7	10	11–15	1	3	5	7	10	11–15	1	3	5	7	10	11–15
Callistephus	Open	83	0	—	—	—	—	64	0	—	—	—	—	86	86	82	78	74	62
chinensis	7.9	83	0	—	—	—	—	91	89	87	81	71	2	87	91	90	86	72	90
Nees	6.7	83	9	0	—	—	—	90	93	81	80	59	0	88	92	89	90	86	91
88	4.6	90	76	27	0	—	—	91	91	89	82	65	0	87	90	90	89	82	91
Delphinium	Open	11	0	—	—	—	—	3	0	—	—	—	—	44	48	38	24	6	0
(perennial)	Sealed	35	4	0	—	—	—	39	37	33	27	5	0	42	45	42	46	50	40
43																			
Lilium regale	Open	91	1	0	—	—	—	—	16	0	—	—	—	92	92	95	94	93	72
Wilson	9.9	98	1	0	—	—	—	—	—	94	88	59	20	97	92	96	94	93	83
92	4.5	94	92	77	57	0	0	90	92	97	94	91	—	89	91	95	92	98	85
Taraxacum	Open	69	0	—	—	—	—	73	2	0	—	—	—	91	87	86	88	79	60
officinale	7.9	72	0	—	—	—	—	83	82	80	32	7	0	88	90	85	95	86	71
Weber	6.2	80	0	—	—	—	—	92	85	76	41	5	0	92	92	94	88	88	66
91	5.0	74	2	0	—	—	—	91	85	79	54	4	0	82	87	88	89	83	80
	3.9	83	62	4	0	—	—	87	85	81	66	13	0	86	90	92	92	89	83
Ulmus	Open	67	0	—	—	—	—	13	0	—	—	—	—	95	85	61	55	14	8
americana L.	7	86	55	0	—	—	—	91	89	82	79	2	0	77	90	82	74	86	83
89	3	81	81	1	—	—	—	85	90	84	88	62	0	88	83	84	81	79	87
	2	84	77	1	—	—	—	82	70	66	81	39	1	81	87	75	85	78	82

Data in the last column for each storage temperature were secured after 15 years of storage of *Delphinium* and *Lilium;* 13 years' storage of *Callistephus* and *Taraxacum;* and 11 years' storage of *Ulmus.*

Data on the comparative effects of above-freezing and below-freezing temperatures are available for several other kinds of seeds, some of which are shown in Table II. Publications (Barton 1939a, b, and c) have already been made showing detailed results for the early storage periods of the tests shown in Table XVIII. Aster, *Callistephus chinensis* Nees., perennial *Delphinium,* regal lily, *Lilium regale* Wilson, dandelion, *Taraxacum officinale* Weber, and the American elm, *Ulmus americana* L., have been selected to illustrate some of the effects.

A glance is sufficient to show the superiority of low temperatures (5° and —4° C.) over laboratory temperature for maintaining viability. It should be noted here that the rapid deterioration in open storage at 5° C. was due to the moisture laden atmosphere in the room, which emphasizes the necessity for the control of both humidity and temperature. Many people make the mistake of assuming that any low-temperature room is good for keeping seeds viable. Also, it will be seen from Table XVIII that sealed storage is to be preferred over open where the moisture content of the seeds is not high enough to prove detrimental in an enclosed atmosphere. Reduction in moisture content to approximately 4 or 5 per cent of the dry weights of the seeds before sealing was effective in prolonging the life of the seeds, especially at laboratory temperature.

Another striking temperature effect, and one which shows up only after longer periods of storage, is the definite superiority of below freezing (—4° C.) over above freezing (5° C.) for keeping seeds viable. It should be kept in mind that we are dealing here with very dry seeds. Seeds which must be stored with high moisture contents, such as citrus seeds discussed in a previous chapter, are injured by freezing. Data in Table XVIII show that up to five years of storage there were no differences in the germination capacity of seeds stored at five degrees above freezing and four degrees below freezing. However, as the storage period lengthened, the superiority of the below-freezing temperature was demonstrated in all cases. After 11 to 15 years of storage all of the seeds had deteriorated completely, or had their vitality reduced so that they were worthless, at 5° C., but had retained their viability unimpaired in sealed containers at —4° C. There is an indication of the falling off in vigor of seeds stored in open containers at —4° C. for longer than ten years, so it seems that even with the best storage temperature known, it is important to protect the seeds from excessive moisture. In spite of the low temperature the seeds may absorb harmful amounts of water from a moisture-saturated atmosphere. This has been demonstrated for seeds held in the —4° C. room used in these tests.

The advantage of a below-freezing temperature over 5° C. for storing pine seeds has also been demonstrated (Barton 1935). The data on Southern pine seeds contained in this report have been subjected to an extended statistical analysis by Wakeley (1945) who emphasized these findings. Below-freezing temperature may finally prove to be the most practical method of keeping valuable seeds and even of keeping crops of seeds for short periods. More work needs to be done on the relationship between moisture content and different degrees of freezing. New tests have been started at Boyce Thompson Institute using a lower freezing temperature. It is to be hoped that other investigations will add to our knowledge of this subject.

Effect of Chemicals on the Keeping Quality of Seeds in Storage:—

The use of chemicals to treat seeds to reduce the injury by fungal or insect attack during storage has been a subject of experimentation for several years and will be discussed in another chapter (see Effect of Seed Treatment on Viability in Storage). More recently chemicals have been used to preserve the vitality of cottonseed, probably by preventing the formation of deterioration products (Lambou, King and Condon 1948). A concentration of 0.28 per cent and 0.14 per cent of a solution of 4,6-bis-chloromethyl xylene in propylene glycol dipropionate, in the ratio of 1:8 by weight used to treat the seeds before storage maintained germination capacity and growth at a higher level than that of the untreated control. The same treatments caused a significant reduction in the amount of free fatty acids formed in the seeds, thus correlating with the deterioration of the oil in the cotton seeds. Further tests (Condon et al. 1949) have shown certain concentrations of ethylene chlorohydrin, propylene chlorohydrin, and ethylene bromohydrin to inhibit the formation of free fatty acids in flax and cotton seed and to prevent the heating of these seeds when stored in large lots.

Lambou, Condon, Jensen, Andrews and Altschul (1948) have devised a rapid method for the measurement of inhibition by chemicals of deterioration in intact seeds of flax, grain sorghum, rice, and cotton seed. According to the authors, the following steps are involved (p. 85):

1) Conditioning of prime seed to a sufficiently high moisture content to promote rapid heating and deterioration.

2) Treating of a portion of the conditioned seed with the desired quantity of potential inhibitor.

3) Storing samples of the treated and untreated seed in calorimeters for six days under conditions of aeration which will support maximum heating.

4) Recording the temperatures in the seed during the period of storage.

5) Analyzing the seed-oil at the end of the storage period for the percentage of free fatty acids.

This phase of the investigation of the life span of seeds is new and further work may prove of great value. It seems certain that chemical treatments which preserve the germinating power of these oily seeds, also preserve the commercial quality of the oil they produce. It is claimed (Altschul 1949) that some of the chemicals used are relatively non-toxic, and that feeding experiments with meals made from treated cotton seeds, have shown no ill effects.

Keeping Quality of Seeds upon Removal from Storage:—It has been demonstrated that onion, tomato, and eggplant seeds deteriorate rapidly at unfavorable temperatures and humidities upon removal from storage (Barton 1939a, 1941, 1949). Furthermore, it is essential that the seeds maintain full germination capacity under the original storage condition, in order to withstand further storage under unfavorable conditions. The better the storage condition for keeping the seeds viable, the better the chance of survival when they are removed to an unfavorable environment. Other conditions being equal, low temperature has been found to be superior to higher temperatures for the maintenance of germination capacity. However, seeds dried and stored sealed at ordinary room temperature may keep better than those stored open in a room at 5° C. where high humidity prevails, as has been demonstrated repeatedly in this laboratory. In these cases, then, resistance to further storage would be in favor of the original room temperature storage.

The keeping quality of any particular lot of seeds does not depend upon its initial high quality, but upon the storage conditions. Seeds of low germination capacity may be kept successfully for fairly long periods if storage is favorable. On the other hand, seeds in which deterioration has been initiated, even if the germination capacity is still high, are incapable of remaining viable for long periods under adverse storage conditions.

All of these facts point to the necessity of maintaining dehumidified or cold storage rooms if commercially important seeds are to be held over for sale in subsequent years. Responsible seedsmen have come to realize this and have provided the proper facilities. Another problem, that of deterioration upon removal from storage, has presented itself. Seedsmen must

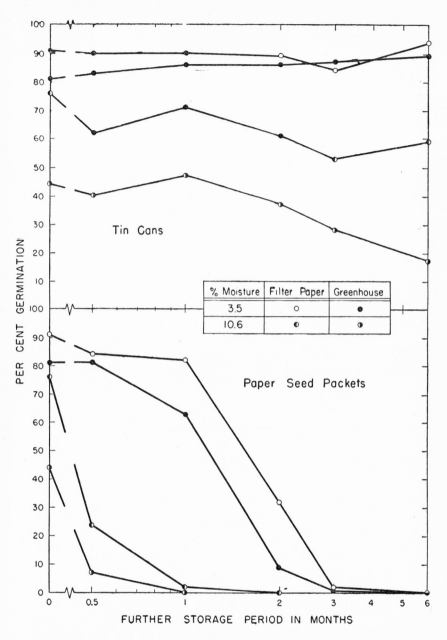

FIGURE 3.—Germination on moist filter paper at 20° C. and in soil in the green-house of onion seeds with moisture contents of 10.6 and 3.5 per cent held for 24 months at 25° C. and then placed in paper seed packets or tin cans for a further storage period of one-half to six months at 30° C. and 76 per cent relative humidity.

packet their seeds for the trade well in advance of the time the consumer buys and plants them. Seeds are usually packeted in Kraft paper envelopes which allow the moisture in the surrounding atmosphere to reach the seeds. Sometimes these packets remain for months in warehouses or retail stores under high temperature or humidity conditions before they are sold.

Detailed tests have been conducted to determine the value of moisture-proof packets for keeping onion seeds which have been removed from their original storage conditions (Barton 1949). Sealed tin cans have been compared with Kraft paper packets as receptacles. Some of the results obtained are pictured graphically in Figure 3. All of these seeds were held for 24 months at 25° C., after which they were removed and a sample tested immediately for ability to germinate on moist filter paper at 20° C. and to produce green seedlings in soil in the greenhouse. These tests (0 further storage) showed a decline in germination ability of the seeds with 10.6 per cent moisture. Further storage of these two-year-old onion seeds at 30° C. and 76 per cent relative humidity revealed the increased tolerance of seeds stored with a small amount of moisture (3.5 per cent) to subsequent unfavorable storage; the efficacy of tin cans for satisfactory keeping after packeting; and the poor performance of weak seeds in the soil as compared to their ability to germinate on moist filter paper. Thus, only those seeds which had had previous dry storage and which had therefore been able to retain more of their initial germination energy, were able to survive six months of packeting, even when air-tight packets were used. Original storage at low temperature brought about similar effects when the moisture content of the seeds was high. Seeds with 10.6 per cent moisture stored for 6 or 24 months at 5° C. were much more tolerant of further storage in paper seed packets than those stored at 25° C. for the same length of time.

The importance of moisture-resistant packets for seeds cannot be overemphasized. Certain metal foils offer promise of a practical material for this purpose.

Effect of Age and Storage Condition of Seeds on Yield:—With the experimental determinations of the storage conditions effective for the maintenance of viability of several types of seeds has come the question of the performance in the field of plants produced from old seeds. From time to time, different authors have dealt with this subject and have variously reported increased or decreased yields as a result of using old seeds (for a review of these papers *see* Barton and Garman 1946). According to the different workers, the yields have been affected by the stand of seedlings obtained, by the dryness or the wetness of the growing season, by lack of soil homogeneity, etc. Advantages of using old seeds have been claimed in the quantity of mung beans produced and the length of sprouts in Indian lotus, while smaller plants and decreased production has been found to parallel increasing age of the seeds of wheat and *Brassica*. Seeds of aster, verbena, pepper, tomato, and lettuce of various ages have been used to determine the effect of age and storage conditions on the yield of plants grown from them. Plants from the different seed lots of each species were arranged in field plantings, so that the yield data could be analyzed statistically. These results showed that old and fresh seeds produced plants of similar quality in the cases of verbena and pepper. Plants grown from nine-year-old seeds of aster flowered earlier than those from fresh seeds, but produced the same total number of flowers during the growing season. Lettuce seed stored for 13 years produced heads of larger weight than fresh lettuce seed. Tomato seeds, stored 13 years in the laboratory and showing a germination capacity of only 6 per cent, produced plants which were inferior in field performance. However, tomato plants from seeds stored 13 years under dry conditions at —4° C. were equal in every respect to those from fresh seeds. This points again to the importance of the storage condition rather than the age of the seed as far as performance is concerned. These results would seem to justify the use of seeds within rather wide age limits.

Causes of Seed Deterioration:—Degeneration of enzymes, disappearance of stored foods, the type of seed coat, loss of ability of the inert proteid molecules to recombine to form the active protoplasmic molecule, gradual coagulation of proteins of the embryo, accumulation of toxic metabolic products, and a gradual degeneration of the nuclei of the cells of the embryo, have been given at various times by different authors as the possible causes of the loss of viability by seeds (Crocker 1948). The last of these has more positive evidence supporting it than any of the others. In some cases, the gradual degeneration of the nuclei of the cells of the embryo might be expected to result in mutations of different kinds before the actual death of the seed. This has actually been found to have occurred in five-year-old seeds of *Crepis tectorum* which produced plants, 80 per cent of which showed cytological mutations in the roots, and many of which were abnormal in appearance. Mutations of various kinds have also been found in plants produced from old seeds of *Datura* and maize. Furthermore, the similarity between chromosome and plant mutations produced artificially by heating and irradiation and those produced by aging indicates that the effects of the three processes may be on the same or similar mechanisms in the seeds.

One might expect that a delicate nuclear mechanism would degenerate with time, but he would hardly be prepared for the remarkable stability of this mechanism in seeds which have remained dormant and fully viable with the capacity to produce normal plants after decades or even after centuries in the soil or in dry storage. If this explanation of the degeneration of seeds is correct, then the best storage conditions for seeds are those which best preserve the complex nuclei and the mitotic mechanism of the cells of the embryo.

References:—

[Altschul, A. M.], 1949: Sweet and unspoiled. Chemical treatment prevents deterioration of cottonseed under storage (Chem. Indus. 64:211).

Barton, L. V., 1935: Storage of some coniferous seeds (Contrib. Boyce Thompson Inst. 7:379-404).

————, 1939a: A further report on the storage of vegetable seeds (Contrib. Boyce Thompson Inst. 10:205-220).

————, 1939*b*: Storage of elm seeds (Contrib. Boyce Thompson Inst. 10:221-233; also unpublished data).

————, 1939*c*: Storage of some flower seeds (Contrib. Boyce Thompson Inst. 10:399-427).

————, 1941: Relation of certain air temperatures and humidities to viability of seeds (Contrib. Boyce Thompson Inst. 12:85-102).

————, 1943: The storage of citrus seeds (Contrib. Boyce Thompson Inst. 13:47-55).

————, 1945*a*: Respiration and germination studies of seeds in moist storage (Ann. New York Acad. Sci. 46:185-208).

————, 1945*b*: A note on the viability of seeds of maga, *Montezuma speciosissima* (Contrib. Boyce Thompson Inst. 13:423-426).

————, 1949: Seed packets and onion seed viability (Contrib. Boyce Thompson Inst. 15:341-352).

Barton, L. V., & W. Crocker, 1948: Twenty years of seed research at Boyce Thompson Institute for Plant Research Inc. (148 pp., Faber & Faber Ltd., London).

Barton, L. V., & H. R. Garman, 1946: Effect of age and storage condition of seeds on the yield of certain plants (Contrib. Boyce Thompson Inst. 14:243-255).

Becquerel, P., 1932: La reviviscence des plantules desséchées soumises aux actions du vide et des très basses températures (Compt. Rend. Acad. Sci. [Paris] 194:2158-2159).

————, 1934: La longévité des graines macrobiotiques (Compt. Rend. Acad. Sci. [Paris] 199:1662-1664).

Bibbey, R. O., 1948: Physiological studies of weed seed germination (Plant Physiol. 23:467-484).

Childs, J. F. L., 1948: A method of maintaining viability of citrus seed in storage (Citrus Indus. 29(12):16-18, 20-21).

Condon, M. Z., M. G. Lambou, J. L. Vignes, J. B. Loe & A. M. Altschul, 1949: Inhibitors of heating and deterioration in seeds. I. Ethylene chlorhydrin and related compounds (Plant Physiol. 24:241-254).

Crocker, W., 1938: Life-span of seeds (Bot. Rev. 4:235-274).

————, 1948: Growth of plants. Twenty years' research at Boyce Thompson Institute (459 pp., Reinhold Publ. Corp., New York).

Ewart, A. J., 1908: On the longevity of seeds (Proc. Roy. Soc. Victoria 21:1-210).

Gane, R., 1948: The water content of the seeds of peas, soybeans, linseed, grass, onion and carrot as a function of temperature and humidity of the atmosphere (Jour. Agric. Sci. [London] 38:81-83).

Kjaer, A., 1940: Germination of buried and dry stored seeds. I. 1934-1939 (Proc. Internat. Seed Test. Assoc. 12:167-190).

Lambou, M. G., M. Z. Condon, E. Jensen, F. R. Andrews & A. M. Altschul, 1948: A rapid method for the measurement of the inhibition of deterioration in intact seeds (Plant Physiol. 23:84-97).

Lambou, M. G., G. S. King & M. Z. Condon, 1948: Effect of chemical treatment prior to storage on viability and growth of cottonseed (Science 108:563-564).

Libby, W. F., 1951: Radiocarbon dates, II. (Science 114:291-296).

Ohga, I., 1926: The germination of century-old and recently harvested Indian lotus fruits, with special reference to the effect of oxygen supply (Amer. Jour. Bot. 13:754-759; *also in* Contrib. Boyce Thompson Inst. 1:289-294. 1926).

Schjelderup-Ebbe, T., 1936: Ueber die Lebensfähigkeit alter Samen (Skrifter Norske Vidensk.-Akad. Oslo, Mat.-Naturvidensk. Kl. 1935: 1-178; *abstr. in* Biol. Abstr. 11:10520. 1937).

Toole, E. H., V. K. Toole & E. A. Gorman, 1948: Vegetable seed storage as affected by temperature and relative humidity (U.S.D.A. Tech. Bull. 972, 24 pp.).

Turner, J. H., 1933: The viability of seeds (Kew Bull. Misc. Inform. 1933:257-269).

Wakeley, P. C., 1945: Office report on an extended analysis of Barton's storage tests of Southern pine seed (U.S.D.A. For. Serv. Southern Forest Exp. Sta., New Orleans, La. [typewritten]).

Chapter XII

METABOLIC AND ENERGY CHANGES IN SEED DEVELOPMENT AND GERMINATION, I

METABOLIC and energy changes in seed development and germination will be treated in three chapters. Chapter XII will deal with metabolic and energy changes during the development and maturation of the seed from the fertilized egg, which involve mainly the synthesis of organic compounds, and chemical and physical changes during after-ripening and vernalization of seeds. Chapter XIII will deal with similar changes during the germination of seeds involving both the hydrolysis of stored substances in the seed and later transportation and synthesis of these substances into the substances of the growing seedling, and the energetics of germination. Chapter XIV will discuss the hydrolytic enzymes involved in seed development and seed germination. The enzymes involved in respiration have been discussed under the chapter dealing with respiration.

Chemical Changes Involved in Seed Development:—Many studies have been made of chemical changes that occur in seeds as they grow from the fertilized egg to maturity. The raw materials that build up the various organic compounds of the seed, of course, must move into the seed from the vegetative portion of the plant, though some may be temporarily stored in the ovary or other organs connected with the flower. The raw material for fat and carbohydrate storage in the seed is soluble sugar. The synthesis of proteins and nucleo-proteins requires in addition nitrates or other nitrogen sources as well as phosphates and sulfates. The mineral content of the seed, of course, moves in from the vegetative portion of the plant. It will be well to consider first the development of seeds rich in carbohydrates and later fatty seeds in which extensive reduction of sugars must occur. In both types we must, of course, consider protein synthesis.

Starchy seeds.—The extensive literature on the development of starchy seeds is discussed by Miller (1938). Because of limited space and since the cereals are of great importance to man, the discussion of the development of wheat and corn grains must suffice for this topic.

Koblet (1940) has followed the chemical changes taking place in developing wheat grains in Switzerland from the 13*th* day after the beginning of bloom until the grains were mature. He used both winter and spring wheats. The two spring wheats, Huron and Marquis, were sown at three periods in the spring about one month apart. The first sowing was made about March 25. The difference in seeding and ripening time enabled the author to estimate the effect of environmental conditions on the amount

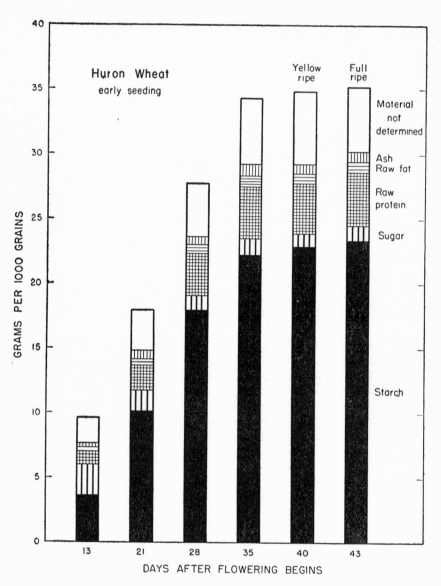

FIGURE 4.—Changes in the total quantity of individual groups of substances. (Courtesy of R. Koblet.)

of various constituents in the grain at the several periods during filling. The dry weight per grain increased up to the yellow-ripe stage after which it remained constant. Total water content per grain rose with growth. It was nearly constant during most rapid growth and fell rapidly in yellow-ripe and full-ripe stages. The percentage of water fell continuously to a critical point of about 40 per cent in strict relation to the dry weight increase. After the yellow-ripe stage drying was determined by the weather and the water loss was slower from the embryo than from the endosperm. All parts of the endosperm lose water at the same rate.

Figure 4, copied from Koblet's article, shows the changes in the amount of the several constituents per 1000 kernels of early sown Huron wheat during development and ripening of the crop. The amount of starch per 1000 grains increases rapidly up to the 35th day, or the milk stage, with practically no increase thereafter. Soluble sugar falls rapidly at first and then more slowly, reaching a minimum per 1000 grains at about the milk-ripe stage. The mature grains contain 2 to 3 per cent soluble sugar, dry weight basis, mainly sucrose. Koblet found that environmental conditions affected the sugar and starch content at various stages by affecting the rate of development. Killing assimilative tissue, or lodging of the crop, reduced the amount of starch stored in the mature grain.

The protein and total nitrogen per 1000 grains increase until the grain is fully ripe. The percentage of total nitrogen, dry weight basis, fell up to the milk-ripe stage and then rose again. The embryo was always richer in nitrogen than the endosperm and the distal end of the endosperm than the proximal end. In the earlier stages of development there is considerable non-protein nitrogen (amino, ammonia, and amide). Later much of the various non-protein nitrogen compounds were made into protein nitrogen. Synthesis of proteins from other organic nitrogen compounds continued up to ripeness of the grain. In the embryo there was little fall in amino nitrogen and amide nitrogen increased. In the ripe embryo 7 per cent of the total nitrogen was in the form of asparagine and glutamine. Both of these compounds bear amino and amide nitrogen. Eckerson (1917) states that the endosperm of wheat just before ripening contains much asparagine, considerable arginine, histidine, and some leucine but no glutamine. On desiccation of the grain, amino acids and most of the asparagine disappear and protein (gluten) is synthesized in the storage cells. Formation of proteins is a condensation process which results from the desiccation of the kernel.

Koblet found that ripe grains from various plots showed considerable difference in protein content and resulting vitreous character of the grains. The grains from fall and early spring seedings were protein-poor and mealy; those from medium late or late spring seedings were protein-rich and glossy. The protein content of the dry grain was strongly influenced by the dry mass going into the grains before the milk stage. This is the period during which the carbohydrates accumulate. The grains from the fall and early spring seedings bore 1.31 to 1.90 per cent nitrogen; late spring seedings 2.20 to 2.54 per cent nitrogen. Time of harvest and weather during ripening exerted only slight influence on protein content and the glossy character. As the literature shows, the nitrogen compounds for grains are drawn largely from nitrogen compounds absorbed by the plant before bloom. The carbohydrates are produced mainly by the plant during formation of the grain. The protein content or hardness of the wheat is determined by the relative supply of carbohydrates and nitrogen compounds during the building of the grain. Leaf surface, amount of illumination, amount of sugar used in respiration by the plant, and many other factors affect the carbohydrate supply. The amount of available nitrogen in the soil and the favorable conditions for its absorption before bloom affect the nitrogen supply.

Koblet studied the proteinase content of the grains during various stages of development but found no relation between the amount of these enzymes and the rate of protein synthesis. This is not surprising because Eckerson found that very active protein synthesis occurred after desiccation set in. The fall in water content would, of course, favor the synthetic action of whatever proteinases were present.

As is seen in Figure 4, the raw fats per 1000 grains increase up to the 35*th* day with about the same amount at the full-ripe stage. The ash shows a similar increase. In the mature stage the ash is 50 per cent P_2O_5, 30 per cent K_2O, 12 to 14 per cent MgO, and 4 to 5 per cent CaO.

Evans (1941) analyzed the corn grain at seven different periods after silking. The first analysis was made on the 15*th* day and the last on the 57*th* day. The results are reported on the percentage dry weight. Table XIX shows the percentage changes in the various fractions as the kernel of corn grows. This does not give a true picture of the total amount of each constituent in each grain of corn as it develops because the total dry weight of the grain is increasing continuously, hence a constituent may fall in percentage with development and still increase in total amount per kernel. An examination of the table shows that starch is the only constituent that increases markedly in percentage dry weight with the growth of the kernel. It is the main storage food. The percentage ether extract rises somewhat, especially in the early stages. Of course, there is an increase in the amount of most constituents per kernel with growth; there is a continual rise in

TABLE XIX: *Composition of Corn Kernels on Dry Matter Basis* (Evans 1941):—

	DAYS AFTER SILKING						
	15	22	29	36	43	50	57
Crude protein (Nx6.25), %	19.28	13.99	11.96	11.82	11.57	11.61	11.59
Starch, %	22.8	58.3	71.0	71.8	71.5	71.8	71.6
Sugars (reducing) as:							
Dextrose, %	5.24	3.49	1.99	0.80	0.75	0.81	0.74
Sucrose, %	3.80	2.82	2.34	2.40	2.35	2.41	2.33
Crude fiber, %	7.2	3.6	2.2	1.7	1.7	1.7	1.7
Ether extract, %	3.78	4.26	5.11	5.19	5.22	5.18	5.17
Ash, %	3.33	2.71	1.99	1.92	1.82	1.78	1.78
Undetermined, %	34.6	10.8	3.4	4.3	5.1	4.7	5.1

organic nitrogen with a late vigorous synthesis of protein, also fat synthesis occurs with kernel growth. Table XX shows the changes in the per cent and nature of the fats during the development of the grain. The fats rise slightly in percentage and greatly in amount per grain. The iodine number of the fats rises while the acid value and the free fatty acid figured as oleic acid fall markedly with development. The significance of the fat changes will be discussed more fully in connection with the development of fatty seeds.

Fatty seeds.—Amongst fatty seeds in which the chemical changes during development have been followed in more or less detail are olive, flax, walnut, almond, sunflower, cotton, pecan, *Macadamia,* and soy. More limited studies of this sort have been made on many other fatty seeds. Some fatty seeds, *Macadamia,* pecan, etc., have a long period of development from fertilization of the flower to maturity of the seed while others, flax, soybean, cotton, etc., have a relatively short period.

The *Macadamia* (Jones 1938; Jones and Shaw 1943) embryo is very rich in oil, bearing at maturity as much as 78.2 per cent oil (Miller and Louis 1941) on dry weight basis. Ninety days after flowering the shell is practically completely developed but embryo enlargement and accumulation of oils, proteins, and other food materials in the kernel has scarcely started. From 90 to 215 days there is a continuous enlargement of the embryo and synthesis and accumulation of food materials. Table XXI shows the low dry weight of the kernel content at the 90-day period and the rapid increase during the 90- to 215-day period. The oils and proteins are synthesized and stored during the period of rapid dry weight increase. The total sugars increase during the early dry weight increase but decrease as maturity is attained. The sugars moving from other parts of the plant furnish the material for oil and other lipid synthesis as well as protein synthesis. The most marked changes in the quality of the oil occur during the 90- to 115-day period. During this period the acid number of the fats drops from 163.9 to 6.56 with a final value of 0.57. This means that the acids are formed first and later combined with glycerol to form oils. During the same period the saponification number falls from 380.6 to 204.2 with a final value of 197.3. Also the soluble acids fall from 23.65 per cent to 1.67 per cent with a final value of 0.26 per cent. These two facts mean short chain fatty acids are synthesized early and later combined into long chain fatty acids. The longer chain fatty acids require less KOH per gram for saponification and are less soluble in water. During this period the iodine number of the fats increases from 64.4 to 75.4 with a final value of 75.2. The fatty acids develop more double bonds or become more unsaturated as the fat

TABLE XX: *Characteristics of Fat from Corn Kernels at different Stages of Maturity* (Evans 1941):—

| | DAYS AFTER SILKING | | | | | | |
	15	22	29	36	43	50	57
Ether extract (dry substance basis), %	3.78	4.26	5.11	5.19	5.22	5.18	5.17
Iodine value (Wijs)	100.8	112.2	123.0	127.7	127.3	126.9	127.1
Acid value	67.2	58.8	54.5	23.5	13.2	13.5	13.4
Free fatty acids as oleic (% ether extract)	33.7	29.6	27.4	11.8	6.7	6.8	6.8

synthesis progresses. Sahasrabuddhe (1933) finds the fatty acids in *Guizotia abyssinica* show like behavior. The fatty acids previous to becoming more unsaturated show many hydroxyl groups. He suggests that the hydroxyl group along with a hydrogen atom on an adjoining carbon atom are removed to produce the unsaturated acid. We have already mentioned dehydration as a method of rendering castor oil more unsaturated. The oil being non-drying has a relatively low degree of unsaturation or relatively low iodine number. This will be evident later when the iodine number is compared with that of linseed oil. As we shall see later, this series of changes represents in general the order of synthesis of fats from carbohydrates in the development of various seeds, including those high as well as those low in oils. This has already been mentioned for cereals that bear little oil.

The mature pecan kernel (embryo) contains over 70 per cent fat on a dry weight basis. Thor and Smith (1935, 1939) report analyses at various stages of development of two varieties of pecans growing in Texas. Separate analyses were made of the shucks, shells, and kernels. Like other investigators in this field they point out that the data must be reported on the change per nut rather than merely on the per cent dry weight basis in order to give a true picture of the development. For example, on the per cent dry weight basis the ash content of the pecan kernel falls markedly during development, while on the basis of content per kernel it rises two- to three-fold.

Like *Macadamia,* the nut of pecan shows two stages of development. The first period extends from early May to late August during which the shell and shuck develop. The second period extends through September, October, and early November during which the nut fills and the embryo develops. Except for fall in moisture content and in total sugar there is little change in the composition of the shell during the second period. During the same period the shuck shows little change in nitrogen content per fruit, a continuous rise in the ash content, and a rise followed by a fall in both moisture and total sugar content. Of greater interest, of course, are the chemical changes involved in the development of the kernel or embryo. The kernel of the Burkett variety showed little oil late in August, followed by a very rapid rise up to early October, after which there was a slight fall. The Stuart variety contained considerable oil in late August, showed a rapid rise during September, after which there was a slower rise to the middle of November. The curves for protein accumulation in the kernels of the two varieties are similar to those for oil but the curves are far less steep because the final protein content in the mature kernel is relatively low. Figured on the basis of total nitrogen it is about 12 per cent in Burkett and about 9.5 in Stuart. These values are high because not all the nitrogen is protein nitrogen. In both varieties the total sugar per kernel rises rather rapidly during September and most of October with a slow rise to maturity. At maturity the total sugar in the embryo is nearly 4 per cent. The authors find that most of the sugars and necessary minerals for building the oils and proteins move in from other parts of the plant during the development of the kernel.

TABLE XXI: *Dry Weight Changes in the Macadamia Fruit* (Jones and Shaw 1943):—

AGE GROUP	TIME AFTER FLOWERING, DAYS	AVERAGE DRY WEIGHT PER EMBRYO, G.	FRESH WEIGHT PER EMBRYO, G.	PERCENTAGE DRY WEIGHT, %
1	90	0.067	1.138	5.0
2	111	0.491	2.806	17.5
3	136	0.992	3.410	29.1
4	185	1.382	2.877	48.0
5	215	1.882	2.781	57.7

Sell *et al.* (1946) find that in the tung fruit reducing and non-reducing sugars move from the hull and shell and serve as building material for the kernel, but that translocation from other parts of the tree is necessary to account for the increased substance of the mature kernel. During the period of embryo or kernel development the draft on sugars is heavy for they not only furnish the carbon-building material for oils and proteins but much sugar is oxidized to furnish the energy for reducing the sugar to oils. The pecan tree must be maintained in good condition to insure proper filling of the kernel; foliage kept on and healthy (Lutz and Hardy 1940) throughout the growing season; sufficient but not an excess of nitrogen fertilizer (Finch and Van Horn 1940); and tree without shading so as to insure high photosynthesis and good water supply. The heavy draft on sugars and to a less extent on nitrogen during filling of the kernel accounts for the importance of the above conditions.

As will be seen from Table II, flax seed is relatively rich in both fats and proteins. Ten samples contain on the average 6.4 per cent moisture and bear an average of 23.5 per cent proteins and 36.4 per cent oil. The percentage of both the protein and fats on the dry weight basis is, of course, higher. The flax seed is of especial interest because it contains a drying oil and is therefore of great industrial importance. Since the iodine number of the oil is a rough measure of the drying quality it too is of interest.

Eyre (1931) determined oil percentage and the iodine number of the oil of flax at 27 stages of development during the 53 days it took for the seeds to grow. Figure 5 taken from his article shows the accumulation of the oil on percentage dry weight basis (not per seed), the accumulation on the per cent wet weight basis, and the increase in iodine number of the oil as it accumulated. As is evident from the figure, there is little synthesis of oil up to the 10th day after flowering. There is a very rapid synthesis between the 10th and 20th day with the maximum per cent reached on about the 25th day. The iodine number continues to rise after the oil reaches the maximum percentage. The author comes to the following conclusions: the acid constituents are formed first; whether the glycerol

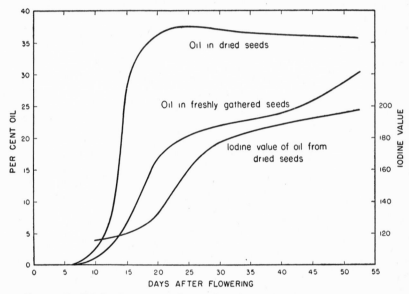

FIGURE 5.—Oil development in flax seeds. (Reproduced from the *Biochemical Journal*.)

is formed at the same time or delayed until later is not clear; the continued increase in the iodine number after maximum percentage of oil formation indicates that the developing unsaturation is a separate process from fat formation; and the early oil formation from carbohydrates is a reduction process while the continued increased unsaturation involves oxidation.

By determining both the iodine and thiocyanogen numbers of 20 different samples of linseed oils and calculating the various types of acids in the oils on the basis of a formula he developed, Painter (1943) found from 0.79 to 1.34 per cent of unsaponifiable materials; 7.3 to 16.3 per cent of saturated acids of the stearic acid type; 11.9 to 40.5 per cent of oleic acid with one double bond; 11.7 to 24.6 per cent of linoleic acid with two double bonds; and 20.5 to 61.8 per cent of linolenic acid with three double bonds in the chains. The iodine number in itself does not determine the drying quality of the oil. A high percentage of linolenic acid is desirable for a good drying oil. Painter *et al.* (1944) show that variations in the climate affect the final percentage of oil in flax of various varieties grown in North Dakota to considerable degree, and that temperature or other unrecognized environmental factors affect greatly the increase in iodine number with progress of filling.

The 1941 crops grown with high temperatures during filling showed an iodine number 20 points below that of the 1942 crop in which the temperatures were lower during filling. The iodine number of the oils in the 1941 crop failed to increase in the midst of the rapid oil accumulation; however, the unsaturated acids per 1000 seeds increased during the entire period of fat accumulation. It was not uncommon for weather conditions during the period of growth to modify the oil content of a variety by 10 per cent and the iodine number by 40 points. A range of 60 points in the iodine number of oils from a single variety was found. When the climatic and varietal factors are additive, the range may be still greater. The authors report a range in the iodine number from 127.8 to 202.8. Gross and Bailey (1937) also find the variety an important determiner of the iodine number.

The points of unsaturation in flax oil have the power to absorb oxygen as well as iodine. Oxygen absorption accounts in part for the drying. The question arises, are the oils oxidized when the seeds are held in storage for considerable periods? Painter and Nesbitt (1943) found that dry, dark storage of intact seeds for two to seven years lowers the iodine number only slightly. The greatest decrease in the iodine number was in samples in which the coats were cracked or had microscopic injuries. Oil from flax seed stored from 1867 to the date of their investigation had a very low iodine number, 111.14. These samples were stored in small cloth bags with full exposure to air. They mention that seeds stored in large bins will have the seed interspaces largely filled with CO_2. Lillevik and Geddes (1943) report the asphyxiation of an elevator worker in the air over a large bin of flax seed. The seeds had not only used up the seed interspace oxygen leaving only CO_2 but had used up much of the oxygen above the seeds so as to cause asphyxiation.

There is much experimental evidence for the synthetic action of the hydrolytic enzymes both in the intact plant organism and *in vitro*. Kretowich *et al.* (1940) showed that the acid value of the ether extract of wheat grains rose or fell as the water content of the stored grains rose or fell. Karon and Altschul (1944) showed similar behavior in cotton seeds. Schreiber (1942) showed that extracts from various fatty seeds synthesized oils from fatty acids and glycerol. An optimum glycerol concentration for the synthesis was 55 to 90 per cent and synthesis reached 48 per cent of the calculated possible maximum. It appears then that lipase synthesizes oils from fatty acid and glycerol in the living cell and *in vitro* when the equilibrium is such as to cause synthesis. The equilibrium is determined by the moisture content of the seeds.

The condensation of fatty acids and glycerol to oils is only the last step in the synthesis of oils. The glycerol and fatty acid synthesis are earlier steps. The formation of glycerol as well as fatty acids from sugars have both had attention and in both, 2-carbon atom chains, acetaldehyde (Haas and Hill 1929) or acetic acid (Rittenberg and Block 1944), have been suggested as intermediate products. Most fatty acids in plant oils have a multiple of 2-carbon atoms in the chain as will be seen in Table VIII, which is in accord with acetaldehyde or acetic acid being involved in the synthesis. Other intermediate products in the synthesis of fatty acids from carbohydrates including pyruvic acid have been considered but space does not permit a fuller discussion of this point. Plants, including developing seeds, as well as animals transform carbohydrates to fats readily. This has already been shown in this chapter for seeds and we know that hogs fed on corn, largely carbohydrates, become fat. In germination seeds convert fats to carbohydrates very extensively. It is a question to what extent animals do the same if at all.

Little is established on the details of protein synthesis. What is known will be discussed under proteases. A brief statement should be made at this point on the reduction of nitrates, the main form in which land plants absorb nitrogen, to amino or amide nitrogen, the forms in which it appears in proteins. Miller (1938, Chap. IX) discusses fully the amount of nitrates found in various plant tissues as affected by internal and external factors, also the effect of various conditions on the reduction of nitrates. Some workers conclude that this reduction is carried on by an enzyme formed in plant tissue, which Eckerson (1931, 1932) called reducase. There is a disagreement as to its thermostability and consequently as to whether it is a true enzyme. *In vitro* reducase is most active in a slightly alkaline solution, pH 7.6, in the presence of formaldehyde, glucose, or fructose and causes the reduction of nitrates to nitrites and ammonia. The optimum temperature for the reduction of nitrates to nitrites is 50° C. Several conditions seem to be required for maximum formation of reducase in plants, such as high insolation and proper supply of various minerals. The amount formed also varies with plant organ and the genus of the plant. We know little about reducase in developing seeds. We must remember that ammonium salts and various amino acids move into the developing seed from other parts of the plant as a possible source of NH_2 groups.

Baly and co-workers believe that the formation of amino compounds is a part of the photosynthetic process starting with carbon dioxide, water, nitrates or nitrites. This scheme of synthesis is described by Gortner (1929, p. 307). As noted above, fatty seeds during their early development contain considerable NH_3 as well as amide and amino nitrogen, all of which decrease as the seed matures. This suggests that amino acids are synthesized in seeds and later condensed into proteins. It is doubtful whether developing seeds bear enough chlorophyll and have sufficient exposure to light to permit photosynthetic synthesis of the amino acids. In the green leaf this is possible.

Chemical Changes Occurring in Seeds During After-Ripening, Vernalization, and Germination:—The little that is known about physical and chemical changes occurring in certain seeds that after-ripen in dry storage is discussed in another chapter. In this section we shall consider chemical changes that occur in seeds during after-ripening or vernalization in a germinator at a low temperature.

Low temperature vernalization of seeds is carried out by holding the seeds in a partially water-saturated condition just above the freezing point for some weeks and many seeds are after-ripened by holding them at a desirable low temperature in a water-saturated condition with good air supply for one to several months. The rate of chemical changes in seeds at such low temperatures is, of course, slow, but the time is so long for completing either process that the changes can be measured by quantitative chemical methods or observed by microscopical staining methods. There is no reason to believe that the chemical changes in low-temperature vernalization and low-temperature after-ripening differ greatly; in vernalization the water absorption is restricted to prevent germination, in the second process the dormancy of the seeds prevents germination until after-ripening has occurred. In vernalization the vegetative period is shortened and reproduction hastened. In after-ripening the seeds most carefully studied are those in which reproduction does not occur until the plant is several years old (*Acer, Sorbus, Juniperus, Prunus, Malus,* etc.), so the hastening of the reproduction is not evident. There are, however, very fundamental and long-lasting changes that take place in rosaceous seeds after-ripened at low temperature (Flemion 1934*a*); the non-after-ripened epicotyls grow for a long time or perhaps permanently as dwarfs if they do not get a period of low temperature, while the after-ripened epicotyls grow with vigor and produce normal plants.

David (1944, 1945, 1947), by use of microscopical staining, studied the changes occurring in the embryo during the vernalization of the wheat grains. The embryos of the grains held at $+2°$ C. for five weeks were compared with those germinated at $23°$ C. for three days. In the embryos at high temperature the assimilative layer, the cotyledon, the top part of the caulicle, and the meristem of the gemmule are always rich in oils. In the same organs of vernalized grains the oil inclusions become smaller and fewer as vernalization progresses. During vernalization the aleurone grains of the parenchyma cells of the cotyledon dissolve and large vacuoles appear in these cells and part of the starch of the cotyledon disappears and starch appears in organs of the embryo that later form the top and roots of the plant or in tissues surrounding these organs. David (1949) later showed by quantitative methods that during vernalization of the wheat grain there is considerable hydrolysis of insoluble carbohydrates in the endosperm with movement of the soluble sugars to the axis organs of the seedling. As a result in the early stages of germination there is much more soluble sugar in the vernalized seedling than in the control seedling and the vernalized endosperm is lower in insoluble carbohydrates than the control endosperm. Sechet (1949) found similar changes in several cereals with low temperature vernalization. In summary, during vernalization readily available materials accumulate that can be used by the growing seedling.

In line with the fat changes found by David, Pack (1925) had earlier found that as juniper seeds after-ripen and finally grow in a germinator at $5°$ C., the lipoid particles in the endosperm and embryo become smaller and more numerous. The largest lipoid particles in the resting seeds were 20 to 30μ in diameter while in the active tissues they became much smaller and were finally so thoroughly dispersed that they were invisible under the microscope. In the development and maturing of *Juniperus* seeds Pack found the reverse occurring as to fat particle size and dispersal. Similar fat changes were observed in sunflower and bean seeds during germination and in hawthorn and peach during low-temperature after-ripening and germination. Pack suggested that the high dispersal of the fats preceded their digestion and transformation to carbohydrates, lipoproteins, and various other lipids, the greater specific surface speeding up the changes just mentioned. He showed that the phosphatides, dry weight basis, more than double during low-temperature after-ripening of *Juniperus* seeds. Lecithins are active emulsifiers and may play a part in fat dispersal. Pack mentions that in contrast to his findings, Czapek and others had claimed that even in resting fatty seeds the fats are so highly dispersed that the particles are not visible under the microscope.

Konovalov and Rogalev (1937) found that during vernalization the proteins of the grains become more soluble and the amide, amine, and ammonium nitrogen show some change. B. Sen (Murneek and Whyte 1948, p. 126) found that (in wheat) diastase and phosphatase, (in mustard) lipase, catalase, and phosphatase, and (in barley) diastase were higher in vernalized than non-vernalized seeds.

The chemical changes occurring in seeds during low-temperature stratification for after-ripening have received more attention than the changes taking place during low-temperature vernalization, but here, too, much more detailed study is needed especially in phases opened up by recent developments in biochemistry.

Pack (1921a and b, 1925) made a rather thorough study, for the time, on the chemical changes occurring in *Juniperus* (*J. virginiana*, *J. communis*, and *J. prostrata*) seeds during after-ripening at low temperatures and early germination. The food reserves in these seeds are mainly proteins and fats with no starch and a low percentage of soluble sugars. These seeds require a low-temperature period in a germinator to prepare them for germination; 5° C. for 90 to 100 days was most effective and 1° or 10° C. was effective but required more time. No seed stimulants or other conditions that favor germination and known at that time would displace the need of low-temperature treatment. Water absorption by the seeds changed little except for a slight drop during later after-ripening, but increased greatly with germination. The embryo and endosperm with the seed coats removed absorbed somewhat more water than the same organs in the intact seeds. In the non-after-ripened seed the pH of the embryo was 8.4 to 8.8 and that of the endosperm 4.4 to 6.0. The embryo became acid during low-temperature treatment reaching a pH of 4.4 to 6.0 after 90 days. The titratable acids showed a measurable increase during after-ripening and a marked increase after germination. Total lipoids decreased measurably with progress in after-ripening and much more with germination, while phosphatides more than doubled

TABLE XXII: *Chemical Composition of Sugar Maple Seeds* (Jones 1920):—

STAGE	SUGAR CALCULATED AS PERCENTAGE TO TOTAL DRY WEIGHT		
	FREE REDUCING SUGAR	SUCROSE (as invert sugar)	POLYSACCHARIDES (as glucose)
Dormant	0.06	6.40	5.21
After-ripened	0.67	4.32	4.66
Beginning germination, radicles about 1 cm.	1.81	2.36	3.43
Seedlings with 2–3 cm. radicle (with integuments)	1.13	1.80	5.91
Seedlings with 5–6 cm. radicles (integuments shed)	0.06	2.62	5.43

during after-ripening, dry weight basis, and fell somewhat with germination. With the decrease in fats went an increase in carbohydrates. They more than doubled during after-ripening and more than doubled again with germination. There was some increase in reducing sugars after hydrolysis with weak acid as well as in direct reducing sugars with after-ripening but both increased much more with germination. Amino nitrogen increased markedly with after-ripening and still more during germination. Catalase increased during after-ripening and was a good measure of the progress of after-ripening. Low-temperature after-ripening of *Juniperus* seeds led to the accumulation of more soluble and more readily available compounds for the nutrition of the embryo.

Using microscopical methods on *Juniperus scopulorum* seeds, Afanasiev and Cress (1942) confirmed in the main Pack's conclusions insofar as qualitative methods are capable of doing. They found also that oxidase increased with germination and peroxidase during late stages of after-ripening and still more with germination. Duperon (1949) found the fats changed to sugars during the low-temperature vernalization of mustard seeds. He found no change in the non-saponifiable fat fraction and made no determination of the phospholipids.

Jones (1920) followed some of the chemical changes occurring in sugar maple (*Acer saccharum* Marsh) seeds during low-temperature after-ripening and early germination. These seeds after-ripen in about five weeks when kept at optimum conditions; 5° C., fully imbibed, and with full air supply. On the dry weight basis the dormant seed contains 11.5 per cent total carbohydrates, 44.8 per cent protein, 17 per cent fats, and about 5 per cent ash. The embryo contains about 50 per cent proteins.

Table XXII shows the changes that take place in the carbohydrates during after-ripening and early germination of the seeds. The reducing sugars, very low in the dormant seeds, rise ten-fold with after-ripening and continue to rise during very early stages of germination but later fall back to the seed content in a relatively early seedling stage. Sucrose falls during after-ripening and continues to fall with early germination after which it fluctuates at less than half the seed content. The acid-hydrolyzable polysaccharides (hemicelluloses?) fall somewhat with after-ripening and fall still further in very early germination, then rise to values higher than those of the seed in the early seedling stages. The total nitrogen did not change with after-ripening or germination but the proteins became more soluble as germination progressed. The ether extract fell from 17 per cent in the seed to 14 per cent in the young seedling. No oxidase effective on the chromogens, guaiaconic acid or benzedine, was present in either the dormant or after-ripened seeds. There was a slight increase in peroxidase with after-ripening. Catalase rose measurably during after-ripening and rose rapidly as the hypocotyl lengthened from 1 cm. to 7 cm.

Flemion studied some chemical changes occurring during low-temperature after-ripening in two rosaceous seeds, *Sorbus aucuparia* and *Rhodotypos kerrioides* (1933) and in *Symphoricarpos racemosus* (1934b) of the honeysuckle family. In the first two, the stored foods are mainly fats and proteins and are practically all in the fully developed embryos and in the latter, the stored foods are mainly in the endosperm and the embryos are small and only partially differentiated.

Sorbus seeds (Flemion 1931) after-ripened fastest, requiring two to four months, in a germinator at 1° C., while the optimum after-ripening temperature for *Rhodotypos* was 5° C. Several low daily or weekly alternating temperatures were highly effective after-ripening temperatures for both seeds. Catalase activity rose several-fold in both seeds as low-temperature after-ripening progressed. It was shown, however, for *Sorbus* that 5° C. and a variable temperature gave a much greater rise in catalase activity than the optimum after-ripening temperature, 1° C., hence increase in catalase activity was not an exact measure of progress in after-ripening. In germinators at 10°, 15°, and 20° C. the rise in catalase activity with a period in the germinator was less and less as the temperature rose. At 20° C. the rise was early and slight and the catalase activity after 15 weeks in the germinator was lower than in the dry seeds. Peroxidase activity, measured by the purpurogallin formed from pyrogallol at pH 6.5, rose four-fold in *Sorbus* and three-fold in *Rhodotypos* during after-ripening. There was no change in amylase or emulsin during after-ripening of *Sorbus* seeds. These enzymes were not determined in *Rhodotypos*. In *Rhodotypos* the nitrogen-fraction soluble in 80 per cent alcohol, the titratable acids, and sucrose rose with progress in after-ripening while the ether soluble fraction decreased due of course to transformation of fats to carbohydrates or their use in respiration. These fractions were not determined for *Sorbus* seeds. In *Symphoricarpos* the after-ripening of the seeds (embryos) progressed most rapidly in a germinator at 5° C. and required six months for completion. These seeds required a pretreatment to disintegrate the seed coats and remove coat hindrance to after-ripening. This was done by keeping the seeds in soil for four or five months at temperatures that favored the destruction of the coats by microorganisms or by partial destruction of the coats with concentrated H_2SO_4 followed by a shorter period in soil. During low-temperature after-ripening the embryos enlarged somewhat and the seeds rose several-fold in catalase and peroxidase activity.

Flemion has found the non-after-ripened rosaceous embryo sluggish in ability to absorb water and in water movement within the embryo. In most seeds low-temperature after-ripening involves extensive transformations of insoluble or large molecule compounds to soluble smaller molecule compounds. This means a great increase in osmotic pressure and the driving force for growth. Also the chemical changes brought about by low-temperature after-ripening put the organic reserves in the seeds into readily available form for nutrition of the embryo.

The respiratory quotient and its change in oak fruits during after-ripening in soil at low temperature (Brown 1939) is discussed under germination of fatty seeds.

The changes we have discussed that take place in seeds during low-temperature vernalization or after-ripening of the embryos arousing them to activity or to later modified growth as to sexual reproduction or dwarfishness have largely had to do with modification of the three main groups of nutrients, carbohydrates, fats, or proteins or with the enzymes that bring about the hydrolysis, synthesis, or oxidation of these substances. The possible exception is the enzyme, catalase, and even it is considered by some workers as being involved in catalyzing the oxidation of certain compounds in the organism.

Much attention ought also to be given to changes taking place in accessory nutritive and growth factors during low-temperature vernalization and after-ripening and the part they may play in exciting the dormant embryos to active growth or in modifying the later growth as to reproduction or dwarfishness. Amongst these accessory nutrients the following and perhaps others should be included: vitamins, hormones, possible essential amino acids, and intermediate products of respiration. We will discuss a few later researches that are suggestive in these connections.

Ruge (1947) used the basal half (to facilitate ready entrance of substance into the embryo) of partially age-degenerated oat grains to demonstrate the existence of substances stimulatory to germination. In sunflower seedlings, 3 to 7 mm. total length, he found substances that hasten the germination of the old oat embryos. In dry sunflower achenes and cereal grains he (Ruge 1939) had already found non-specific substances that inhibited germination which as germination progressed were displaced in all the seed organs even the fruit coats by substances that accelerate germination. By the half-oat-grain method he demonstrated that not only did germinated seeds give off substances that stimulated or released germination but that vitamins B_1, B_2, and C as well as glutathione are such substances. He also found that ethylene, ethylene chlorohydrin, ethylene glycol, and lactic acid act similarly. He speaks of ethylene and lactic acid as intermediate products of respiration and emphasizes that both stimulate respiration and thereby release or stimulate germination.

Ruge distinguishes sharply between the special germination accelerators or releasers and the hundreds of chemicals that are known to increase germination; the former act in very low concentrations, approximating that required for vitamins, and they accelerate germination markedly, while the latter are effective only in high concentration and increase germination slightly. Ruge thinks that age degeneration of seeds is due to these special accelerators falling in amount in seeds with lengthening periods of storage and a general run-down of the readily oxidizable materials as shown by a fall in the redox potential of the old seeds. Addition of the accelerators to old seeds amounts to restoring the special materials they have lost during aging. The failure of the addition of certain vitamins to accelerate the germination of old seeds is interpreted as meaning that these vitamins still exist in optimum concentration in such seeds. He also assumes that these special accelerators, in sufficiently high concentration, inhibit germination; this is no doubt true of ethylene. These substances are assumed to exist in optimum concentration in seeds with good germination. Ruge mentions as in accord with his concept the work of Brunner (1932) which proves the presence of a water-soluble ether-insoluble substance in the endosperm of pine seeds which during germination enters the embryo through the seed leaves and promotes normal growth of the seedling; the work of Schander (1934) which shows that the aleurone layer of cereals produces a substance that accelerates the growth of embryo during germination; the work of Burgeff (1934) and Schaffstein (1938, 1941) showing that a vitamin was necessary for the growth of embryos of some kinds of *Orchidaceae* seeds up to the chlorophyll-containing or autotrophic stage; and the work of many other authors showing the existence of special germination stimulative substances in connection with saprophytes and parasites.

The *Orchidaceae* vitamin needs further consideration. Schaffstein named this vitamin "Vandophytin" because its need was first discovered for the growth of *Vanda* seedlings. It seems to be required for the *Dendrobiums* and *Phalaenopsis* species studied but not for *Cattleya, Laelia, Epidendrum,* and *Paphiopedium* species. Very few of the seeds of the species needing the vitamin will grow to the autotrophic stage on nutrient solution with sugar and an inorganic nitrogen source in absence of the vitamin but the seedlings supply their own vitamin after they become green.

Most organs of plants contain the vitamin but many organs of higher plants are much richer in it than the symbiotic *Rhizoctonia* that supplies it in nature. Vandophytin is adsorbed readily by charcoal from juices of crushed plant organs while inhibiting substances in such juices are left in solution. The adsorbed vitamin is released from the charcoal by dilute alcohol. A method was worked out for concentrating the vitamin from *Vicia faba* seeds that increased its effectiveness 4000-fold on a weight basis. Biotin and B_1 were not effective while nicotinic acid or nicotinic acid amide were highly effective. The best preparation of Vandophytin showed optimum growth in 0.1 p.p.m. Nicotinic acid was equally effective in one-half this concentration. Schaffstein thinks Vandophytin is neither nicotinic acid nor nicotinic acid amide. He did not determine whether it is a derivative of these. He suggests that the vitamin acts as a cohydrase in carbohydrate metabolism. This would seem to aid in settling the long-standing dispute between Knudson who maintained that the fungus was not necessary for germination of orchid seeds and Bernard and Burgeff (earlier work) who thought it was. Yet Knudson (1941) in a very brief article denies the claim of Burgeff (1934) that a vitamin is necessary for the germination of *Vanda* seeds. He also finds some inhibitor to photosynthesis in orchid seedlings after they have become green.

Let us turn to the consideration of some of Ruge's conclusions. One is surprised to hear him speak of ethylene and ethylene chlorohydrin as similar compounds physiologically. The high physiological activity of ethylene is due to its unsaturation (Crocker et al. 1935). Ethylene chlorohydrin is a saturated compound that produces none of the hormone-like effects of ethylene and must be used in relatively high concentrations compared with ethylene to produce any effects (Denny 1926; Denny and Stanton 1928). One also hardly sees the justification in speaking of ethylene chlorohydrin as a special chemical for stimulating dormant plant organs, since Denny found many chemicals almost as effective as this compound in forcing dormant fruit or vegetative buds of shrubs and dormant buds of the potato tuber. Amongst these for buds of shrubs were propylene chlorohydrin, ethylene dichloride, vinyl chloride, furfural, carbon tetrachloride, and others and for dormant potato buds in addition thiocyanates, thiourea, and others. Miller (1933) found many sulfur compounds that forced the growth of dormant potato buds. These chemicals, at least in great part, displace the need for low temperatures for after-ripening the buds of temperate zone woody plants. Flemion (unpublished work in this laboratory) was unable to force the epicotyls of rosaceous seeds out of their dwarfishness with the highly effective bud forcer, ethylene chlorohydrin, but ethylene chlorohydrin is extremely toxic to the delicate rosaceous epicotyl. Sanders and Burkholder (1948) found that isolated rudimentary embryos of *Datura inoxia* and *D. stramonium* grew much better if to a basal nutrient medium casein hydrolysate with cysteine and tryptophane were added. A mixture of 20 amino acids in about the same proportion as found in the hydrolysate was about as good for growth. The species differed in their responses both to mixtures and to single amino acids. The authors state that balance of amino acids is a controlling influence on both growth and differentiation of plant embryos. In summarizing the literature on the need of amino acids for plant tissue or embryo cultures the authors conclude that some tissues and embryos need certain amino acids faster than they can make them while others can synthesize the amino acids from nitrates as fast as they need them for maximum growth.

There are probably many organic substances unknown as yet that may not be synthesized fast enough by the axis organs of various embryos to take care of maximum growth rate. Galston and Hand (1949) find that adenine, an amino purine, stimulates the growth of epicotyl sections, leaf buds, and roots of etiolated peas. It also prevents the thermal inactivation of these organs.

Commoner and Thimann (1941), Commoner and Mazia (1942, 1944), and Commoner et al. (1943) give indole-3-acetic acid in combination with 4-carbon atom acids (fumaric, malic, succinic) a special role in increasing the growth and respiration of *Avena* coleoptile and potato tuber tissue. Under this treatment the tissues absorb more salts and more water apparently due to the hormone and the acids act as respiratory agents. As we have learned, Ruge gives ethylene, some of its saturated derivatives, and lactic acid as special substances that increase respiration and initiate growth. Perhaps too many compounds can be elevated to the position of special substances so the 4-carbon atom acids may be subject to the same criticism we have offered against some of Ruge's special substances. There can be no doubt, however, that hormone-like substances need special consideration in the regulation of growth. Guttenberg and Lehle-Joerges (1947) find both acid-stable (auxin) and alkali-stable (heteroauxin) phytohormones in *Zea* grains and have followed the changes in amount and the distribution of them in the several seed organs during germination. In winter buds of *Syringa vulgaris* heteroauxin began to appear in December and auxin in February. These changes seem to fit into the low-temperature after-ripening of the buds.

This section has presented a number of new biochemical attacks that ought to be made to aid in the explanation of significant changes occurring in seeds during low-temperature after-ripening and vernalization.

References:—

Afanasiev, M., & M. Cress, 1942: Changes within the seeds of *Juniperus scopulorum* during the processes of after-ripening and germination (Jour. Forestry 40:798-801).

Brown, J. W., 1939: Respiration of acorns as related to temperature and after-ripening (Plant Physiol. 14:621-645).

Brunner, G., 1932: Beiträge zur Entwicklungsphysiologie der Kiefernkeimlinge (Jahrb. Wiss. Bot. 76:407-440).

Burgeff, H., 1934: Pflanzliche Avitaminose und ihre Behebung durch Vitaminzufuhr (Ber. Deutsch. Bot. Gesell. 52:384-390).

Commoner, B., S. Fogel & W. H. Muller, 1943: The mechanism of auxin action. The effect of auxin on water absorption by potato tuber tissue (Amer. Jour. Bot. 30:23-28).

Commoner, B., & D. Mazia, 1942: The mechanism of auxin action (Plant Physiol. 17:682-685).

———, ———, 1944: The mechanism of auxin action: the effect of auxin and the C₄ acids on salt and water absorption in *Avena* coleoptile and potato tuber tissue (Amer. Jour. Bot. 31:8s-9s).

Commoner, B., & K. V. Thimann, 1941: On the relation of growth and respiration in the *Avena* coleoptile (Jour. Gen. Physiol. 24:279-296).

Crocker, W., A. E. Hitchcock & P. W. Zimmerman, 1935: Similarities in the effects of ethylene and plant auxins (Contrib. Boyce Thompson Inst. 7:231-248).

David, R., 1944: Sur les phénomènes biologiques provoqués chez les céréales par la printanisation des semences (Compt. Rend. Soc. Biol. 138:849-851).

———, 1945: L'aleurone et l'amidon transitoire de l'embryon de Blé printanisé (Compt. Rend. Soc. Biol. 139:560-562).

———, 1947: L'évolution des inclusions lipidiques du germe de Blé pendant le traitement de printanisation (Compt. Rend. Acad. Sci. [Paris] 224:146-147).

———, 1949: L'influence de la printanisation sur les glucides de l'albumen du grain de Blé (Compt. Rend. Acad. Sci. [Paris] 228:1242-1243).

Denny, F. E., 1926: Hastening the sprouting of dormant potato tubers (Amer. Jour. Bot. 13:118-125; *also in* Contrib. Boyce Thompson Inst. 1:59-66, 1926).

Denny, F. E., & E. N. Stanton, 1928: Chemical treatments for shortening the rest period of pot-grown woody plants (Amer. Jour. Bot. 15:327-336; *also in* Contrib. Boyce Thompson Inst. 1:355-364, 1928).

Duperon, R., 1949: Influence de la printanisation sur l'évolution des lipides et des glucides chez le *Sinapis alba* (Compt. Rend. Acad. Sci. [Paris] 228:192-194).

Eckerson, S. H., 1917: Microchemical studies in the progressive development of the wheat plant (Washington Agric. Exp. Sta. Bull. 139, 20 pp.).

———, 1931: Seasonal distribution of reducase in the various organs of an apple tree (Contrib. Boyce Thompson Inst. 3:405-412).

———, 1932: Conditions affecting nitrate reduction by plants (Contrib. Boyce Thompson Inst. 4:119-130).

Evans, J. W., 1941: Changes in the biochemical composition of the corn kernel during development (Cereal Chem. 18:468-473).

Eyre, J. V., 1931: Notes on oil development in the seed of a growing plant (Biochem. Jour. 25:1902-1908).

Finch, A. H., & C. W. Van Horn, 1940: Notes on the relation of warm winter temperatures to blossoming and nut setting of the pecan (Proc. Amer. Soc. Hort. Sci. 37(1939):493-497).

Flemion, F., 1931: After-ripening, germination, and vitality of seeds of *Sorbus aucuparia* L. (Contrib. Boyce Thompson Inst. 3:413-439).

———, 1933: Physiological and chemical studies of after-ripening of *Rhodotypos kerrioides* seeds (Contrib. Boyce Thompson Inst. 5:143-159).

———, 1934a: Dwarf seedlings from non-after-ripened embryos of peach, apple, and hawthorn (Contrib. Boyce Thompson Inst. 6:205-209).

————, 1934b: Physiological and chemical changes preceding and during after-ripening of *Symphoricarpos racemosus* seeds (Contrib. Boyce Thompson Inst. 6:91-102).

Galston, A. W., & M. E. Hand, 1949: Adenine as a growth factor for etiolated peas and its relation to the thermal inactivation of growth (Arch. Biochem. 22:434-443).

Gortner, R. A., 1929: Outlines of biochemistry (793 pp., John Wiley & Sons, Inc., New York).

Gross, R. A., & C. H. Bailey, 1937: Chemical constitution of the oils from superior and inferior flaxseeds (Oil & Soap 14:260-263; *abstr. in* Exp. Sta. Rec. 81:470-471, 1939).

Guttenberg, H. v., & E. Lehle-Joerges, 1947: Ueber das Vorkommen von Auxin und Heteroauxin in ruhenden und keimenden Samen (Planta 35:281-296).

Haas, P., & T. G. Hill, 1929: An introduction to the chemistry of plant products. Vol. II. Metabolic processes (2nd ed., 220 pp., Longmans, Green & Co., London).

Jones, H. A., 1920: Physiological study of maple seeds (Bot. Gaz. 69:127-152).

Jones, W. W., 1938: The physiology of oil production in the *Macadamia* (*Macadamia integrifolia*, Maiden et Betche) (Proc. Amer. Soc. Hort. Sci. 35(1937):239-245).

Jones, W. W., & L. Shaw, 1943: The process of oil formation and accumulation in the *Macadamia* (Plant Physiol. 18:1-7).

Karon, M. L., & A. M. Altschul, 1944: Effect of moisture and of treatments with acid and alkali on rate of formation of free fatty acids in stored cottonseed (Plant Physiol. 19:310-325).

Knudson, L., 1941: Investigations on delayed photosynthesis in chlorophyll-bearing embryos of orchids, and other studies on orchid seed (New York [Cornell] Agric. Exp. Sta. Ann. Rept. 54:117-118).

Koblet, R., 1940: Untersuchungen über die stofflichen Veränderungen im wachsenden und reifenden Weizenkorn (Ber. Schweiz. Bot. Gesell. 50:99-232; *abstr. in* Biol. Abstr. 15:19851, 1941).

Konovalov, I. N., & I. E. Rogalev, 1937: The behavior of nitrogenous substances during the yarovization of plants (Compt. Rend. Acad. Sci. U.R.S.S. 16:65-68).

Kretowitch, W. L., A. I. Sokolowa, & E. N. Uschakowa, 1940: Ueber die stabile Feuchtigkeit des Kornes und ihren Einfluss auf die Arbeit der Lipase (Compt. Rend. Acad. Sci. U.R.S.S. 27:701-704).

Lillevik, H. A., & W. F. Geddes, 1943: Investigation of a death by asphyxiation in a grain elevator bin containing flaxseed (Cereal Chem. 20:318-328).

Lutz, H., & M. B. Hardy, 1940: The effect of foliar conditions on the photosynthetic activity of pecan leaves (Proc. Amer. Soc. Hort. Sci. 37(1939):484-488).

Miller, C. D., & L. Louis, 1941: Chemical analyses and vitamin assays of *Macadamia* nuts (Food Res. 6:547-552).

Miller, E. C., 1938: Plant physiology (2nd ed., 1201 pp., McGraw-Hill Book Co., Inc., New York).

Miller, L. P., 1933: Effect of sulphur compounds in breaking the dormancy of potato tubers and in inducing changes in the enzyme activities of the treated tubers (Contrib. Boyce Thompson Inst. 5:29-81).

Murneek, A. E., & R. O. Whyte, 1948: Vernalization and photoperiodism. A symposium (196 pp., Chronica Botanica, Waltham, Mass.).

Pack, D. A., 1921a: After-ripening and germination of *Juniperus* seeds (Bot. Gaz. 71:32-60).

————, 1921b: Chemistry of after-ripening, germination and seedling development of juniper seeds (Bot. Gaz. 72:139-150).

————, 1925: Dispersion of lipoids (Bot. Gaz. 79:334-338).

Painter, E. P., 1943: The composition of linseed oil (North Dakota Agric. Exp. Sta. Bimo. Bull. 5(6):32-36).

Painter, E. P., & L. L. Nesbitt, 1943: The stability of linseed oil during storage of flaxseed (North Dakota Agric. Exp. Sta. Bimo. Bull. 5(6):36-40).

Painter, E. P., L. L. Nesbitt & T. E. Stoa, 1944: The influence of seasonal conditions on oil formation and changes in the iodine number during growth of flaxseed (Amer. Soc. Agron. Jour. 36:204-213).

Rittenberg, D., & K. Block, 1944: The utilization of acetic acid for fatty acid synthesis (Jour. Biol. Chem. 154:311-312).

Ruge, U., 1939: Zur Physiologie der germinen keimungshemmenden und keimungs-beschleunigenden Stoffe von *Helianthus annuus* (Zeitschr. Bot. 33:529-571).

————, 1947: Untersuchungen über keimungsfördernde Wirkstoffe (Planta 35:297-318).

Sahasrabuddhe, D. L., 1933: A biochemical study of the formation of the oil in niger seed (*Guizotia abyssinica*) (Indian Jour. Agric. Sci. 3:57-88; *abstr. in* Chem. Abstr. 27:4558, 1933).

Sanders, M. E., & P. R. Burkholder, 1948: Influence of amino acids on growth of *Datura* embryos in culture (Proc. Nat. Acad. Sci. 34:516-526).

Schaffstein, G., 1938: Untersuchungen über die Avitaminose der Orchideenkeimlinge (Jahrb. Wiss. Bot. 86:720-752).

————, 1941: Die Avitaminose der Orchideenkeimlinge (Jahrb. Wiss. Bot. 90:141-198).

Schander, H., 1934: Keimungsphysiologie Studien über die Bedeutung der Aleurone-schicht bei *Oryza* und anderen Gramineen (Zeitschr. Bot. 27:433-515).

Schreiber, E., 1942: Effect of glycerol concentration on the enzymic synthesis of fats by seed lipases (Zeitschr. Physiol. Chem. 276:56-62; *abstr. in* Chem. Abstr. 37:6706, 1943).

Sechet, J., 1949: Influence de la printanisation sur la teneur en glucides des semences de céréales (Compt. Rend. Acad. Sci. [Paris] 228:334-336).

Sell, H. M., F. A. Johnston, Jr. & F. S. Lagasse, 1946: Changes in the chemical composition of the tung fruit and its component parts (Jour. Agric. Res. 73:319-334).

Thor, C. J. B., & C. L. Smith, 1935: A physiological study of seasonal changes in the composition of the pecan during fruit development (Jour. Agric. Res. 50:97-121).

————, ————, 1939: A physiological study of the prefilling period of fruit development in the pecan (Jour. Agric. Res. 58:905-910).

Chapter XIII

METABOLIC AND ENERGY CHANGES
IN SEED DEVELOPMENT AND GERMINATION, II

Metabolic Changes Occurring During Germination:—Miller (1938) reviews the literature on the chemical changes occurring in carbohydrates, fats, and proteins of seeds during germination. In this brief statement it is best to consider first starchy and later oily seeds dealing with changes in proteins in both groups as they are discussed.

Starchy seeds.—Of the starchy seeds the cereals are by far the most important to man. Many beans are also rich in starch along with proteins. Figure 6 taken from Toole's article (1924) shows the structure of the corn grain. The grain aside from the thin coat (6 per cent of grain) consists of an embryo and endosperm. According to Hopkins *et al.* (1903) the embryo constitutes about 11 per cent of the total dry weight of the grain. In wheat and barley the embryo makes up a much smaller per cent of the grain; in wheat (Bailey 1938) generally less than 3 per cent. The embryo consists of root and stem organs, their parts and coverings, and the scutellum. The latter bears stored foods, especially proteins and fats, and acts as a digestive and absorptive organ for the growing embryo during germination. The outer layer of palisade cells of the scutellum adjoining the endosperm are of especial interest. With the inception of germination these elongate and begin secreting cytase and amylase which digest the cell walls and starch of the endosperm as a source of carbohydrate for the growing embryo. This digestion begins next to the scutellum and proceeds outward as germination progresses.

The endosperm of the corn kernel consists of horny endosperm and of starchy endosperm and of an outer layer of aleurone cells rich in proteins. The endosperm aside from the aleurone layer consists according to most investigators of inert parenchyma cells while the aleurone layer is apparently alive and secretes enzymes. We have already mentioned it as the source of hormones or some other substance that aids germination.

For the history of the development of our knowledge on the chemical changes during the germination of cereals, the reader is referred to Toole cited above. A series of researches carried out by Malhotra (1931*a* and *b*, 1932*a*, *b*, and *c*, 1933*a* and *b*, 1934) gives a picture of the main chemical changes occurring in starchy seeds during germination. He gives in addition the calorific value of the seed organs at various stages of germination.

Table XXIII shows the chemical composition and calories of heat per gram of dry weight in ungerminated corn and after two, four, six, and eight days of germination. There is no change in the percentage of ash or total nitrogen during the eight days of germination. The fat falls measurably and the dry weight about 12 per cent. The latter change is due to the use of stored foods in respiration before the photo-

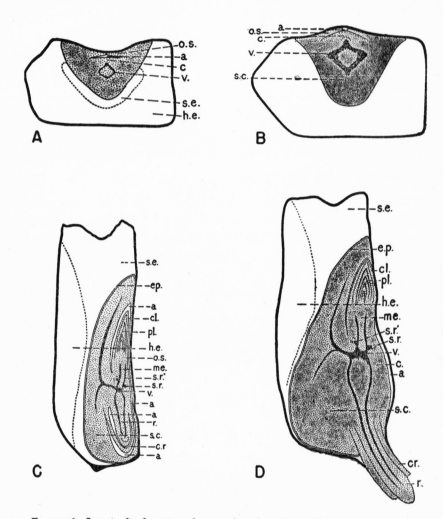

FIGURE 6.—Longitudinal section of grain after about forty-eight hours' germination.
h. e., horny endosperm; *s. e.*, starchy endosperm; *sc.*, scutellum; *ep.*, epithelium; *cr.*,
coleorhiza; *r.*, radicle; *s. r.* and *s. r'.*, initials of secondary radicles; *v.*, vascular tissue;
cl., coleoptile; *pl.*, plumule; *me.*, mesocotyl; *c.*, cortical tissue which greatly enlarges in
germination; *a.*, air spaces between tissues in the grain; *o. s.*, scutellum overlapping
face of embryo. (× 5.) (Courtesy of E. H. Toole.)

synthetic apparatus is developed. Soluble sugars rise markedly while both starch and hemicelluloses, especially the latter, fall markedly. The fall in the last two reserves accounts almost entirely for the loss in respiration and the increase in soluble sugars, while the fall in fats supplies some of these needs. The slight fall in calorific energy is accounted for by the respiration of the high energy fats or by their transformation

TABLE XXIII: *Distribution of Reserve Materials* and Heat Energy in Corn Seeds during Germination* (Malhotra 1934):—

TREATMENT	FATS %	LOSS IN DRY WT. %	ASH %	SUGARS %	STARCH %	HEMI- CELLULOSES %	TOTAL NITRO- GEN %	CALORIES OF HEAT PER GRAM
Ungerminated	4.88	0.0	1.30	2.5	27.5	30.7	1.7	3,480
Germinated 2 days	4.71	10.8	1.42	5.2	23.2	19.9	1.5	3,458
Germinated 4 days	4.60	11.6	1.42	10.2	21.1	16.1	1.4	3,428
Germinated 6 days	4.40	11.3	1.45	8.6	20.0	11.6	1.2	3,414
Germinated 8 days	4.09	12.2	1.42	15.6	18.1	11.1	1.7	3,301

* Results as percentages of dry weight.

to the low energy carbohydrates. In the germination of corn seeds there is little fall in calorific energy during germination because the percentage of fats is low. In seeds rich in fats there is a great fall in calorific energy per gram of dry weight with germination.

TABLE XXIV: *Distribution of Reserve Materials* in attached Embryo and Endosperm during Germination* (Malhotra 1934):—

TREATMENT	ASH %	FATS %	SUGARS %	STARCH %	HEMI- CELLULOSES %	TOTAL NITROGEN %	CALORIES OF HEAT PER GRAM
Endosperm:—							
Ungerminated	0.56	0.93	7.3	38.0	19.6	1.3	3,392
Germinated 2 days	0.56	1.40	13.2	36.2	13.9	1.7	3,352
Germinated 4 days	0.47	1.38	4.2	34.4	10.0	1.1	3,314
Germinated 8 days	1.03	1.15	9.1	26.2	9.5	1.7	3,302
Germinated 10 days	0.80	1.56	6.0	20.8	9.0	1.5	3,280
Embryo:—							
Ungerminated	8.74	30.0	14.8	5.5	10.8	3.7	4,415
Germinated 2 days	11.99	28.82	13.4	4.7	10.5	3.5	4,350
Germinated 4 days	9.13	27.23	8.9	4.7	10.7	3.5	4,034
Germinated 8 days	9.92	19.0	13.0	4.8	10.4	2.8	4,005
Germinated 10 days	8.37	17.1	12.8	4.4	9.3	2.4	3,968

* Results as percentages of dry weight.

In Table XXIV it will be seen that the endosperms and embryos were separated at the different stages of germination before they were analyzed. In the endosperms the percentage of ash, fats, and sugars vary considerably while total nitrogen remains constant during ten days of germination. The starch and hemicellulose fall markedly. Much of the sugars formed from these two main carbohydrate reserves have moved into the developing embryos as building and reserve materials. There is a slight fall in the calories of energy per gram dry weight. In the embryo the ash is much higher than in the endosperm and the starch much lower with neither showing much change as germination progresses. The fat is much higher in the embryo than in the endosperm and shows a marked fall during germination. With it the calories of energy per gram show considerable fall. The sugar percentage fluctuates as germination progresses.

Table XXV gives the analyses of the endosperms and embryos when they were separated before they were placed in germinators. The endosperm showed low percentages of fats, ash, and total nitrogen and relatively high hemicellulose with little change in any of them during 12 days' germination. The soluble sugars rose and starch fell in about like percentages and there was little change in calories of heat per gram. There is no way of knowing how much of the starch digestion was due to seed amylase and how much to microorganisms. There was no removal of substance from the endosperms to the developing embryos as occurred in Table XXIV.

The isolated embryos during 12 days in the germinator showed little change in percentage ash or total nitrogen, a marked total but gradual fall in fat, and a marked fall in starch during the last one-third of the 12 days. The calories of heat per gram fell markedly because of the great fall in fats. The soluble sugars rose as germination progressed. The embryo-seedlings grew faster than the intact-seed seedlings during the early germination but fell far behind them in the later stages. Supplying a 10-day-old embryo-seedling with dextrose for a month did not enable it to equal the growth of the seed-seedling. The embryo-seedlings showed fewer cells in cross section than seed-seedlings and the cells were smaller. The poor and abnormal growth of embryo-seedlings is due in part to shortage of stored foods and in part to lack of accessory foods.

TABLE XXV: *Distribution of Reserve Materials* and Energy in isolated Embryos and Endosperms during Germination* (Malhotra 1934):—

TREATMENT	FATS %	ASH %	NITROGEN %	SUGARS %	STARCH %	HEMI- CELLULOSES %	CALORIES OF HEAT PER GRAM
Embryo:—							
Ungerminated	28.5	8.7	2.4	15.6	21.0	16.7	4,350
Germinated 2 days	21.5	6.8	3.0	17.2	32.7	16.4	3,920
Germinated 4 days	15.7	8.0	5.1	18.3	28.2	14.0	3,920
Germinated 8 days	10.4	7.5	5.6	18.9	24.6	13.1	3,682
Germinated 12 days	8.0	9.1	2.1	26.4	3.8	11.3	3,207
Endosperm:—							
Ungerminated	1.1	0.60	1.3	7.0	38.8	19.2	3,327
Germinated 2 days	1.0	0.61	1.3	13.2	31.6	19.1	3,311
Germinated 4 days	0.98	0.60	1.3	15.4	29.1	19.2	3,300
Germinated 8 days	0.95	0.60	1.3	15.9	28.4	19.0	3,279
Germinated 12 days	0.92	0.59	1.1	18.8	24.7	19.0	3,262

* Results as percentages of dry weight.

Malhotra's results with the isolated embryos are what should be expected from simultaneous or later work done by Schander, DeRopp, Brunner, Pohn, Cholodny, and others on growth regulating substances from the endosperm that modify the growth of the seedling. Some of this work has been mentioned in the previous chapter and it has all been critically reviewed recently by Brown (1943) who implies that many factors are involved in the influence of the endosperm on the embryo during germination.

In comparison with previous analyses Malhotra's values for the hemicelluloses of seeds and seedlings are very high. To determine the hemicellulose Malhotra (1931a) first removed from the ground material the soluble sugar and the starch following saliva digestion. The residue was then heated with 2.5 per cent HCl for four hours under standard conditions and the resulting sugars were used as the basis for calculating the hemicellulose. Malhotra thinks hemicelluloses are important storage carbohydrates in many seeds aside from those in which hemicelluloses entirely displace starch as a storage carbohydrate. He mentions Murneek (1928) and others as giving hemicelluloses like importance as storage materials in vegetative organs.

Malhotra (1931b) also determined for a number of seeds (castor bean, peanut, cotton, sunflower, flax, hemp, Windsor bean, pea, maize, and wheat) the percentage loss in dry weight and fat and the percentage of the original calorific value still left in the seedlings and seed residues after eight days of germination. While these data are of interest the main principles involved are covered later in greater detail under Energetics of Germination. The respiratory quotient was also determined for all these seeds during the fourth day of germination. For the first six, which are fatty seeds, and the next two, which are rich in proteins, the respiratory quotient was about 0.8 and for maize and wheat, starchy seeds, the quotient was about 1.0. The respiratory quotient of seeds during germination and factors that modify it will be discussed more fully under fatty seeds and under Energetics of Germination. It should be mentioned that calorific values of seeds and seed residues found by Malhotra are low.

Brown (1946) followed the changes in the nitrogen compounds of the growing embryo (seedling) of barley during 96 hours of germination. In one set of cultures the embryos were removed from the grains after two hours of soaking and grown in contact with water. In the other cultures the intact grains were grown in contact with water and the embryos removed just before analysis. The following data are selected from Table IV of Brown's article. They show the total nitrogen, soluble nitrogen, and protein nitrogen, milligrams per seedling, in the isolated and attached embryos after various periods of germination.

Age of seedling (hours)	Isolated			Attached		
	Total—N	Sol.—N	Prot.—N	Total—N	Sol.—N	Prot.—N
2	0.08	0.016	0.064	0.08	0.016	0.064
36	0.077	0.013	0.064	0.085	0.02	0.065
54	———	———	———	0.096	0.022	0.074
60	0.073	0.024	0.049	0.126	0.045	0.082
84	0.077	0.028	0.049	0.192	0.054	0.138
96	0.073	0.026	0.047	0.272	0.078	0.194

With the isolated embryos there are relatively slight changes in the nitrogen fractions during 96 hours of germination, a slight fall in total nitrogen probably due to leaching, a moderate gain in soluble nitrogen, and a moderate fall in protein nitrogen. In the attached embryos there is a continuous slow increase in the nitrogen fractions during the first 54 hours of germination but from the 54th to the 96th hours there is a very rapid increase in total nitrogen as well as in the soluble and protein fractions. During this later period all three go up nearly three-fold; the seedling is drawing heavily on the endosperm for its nitrogen needs. The author mentions that during this period there is an exponential form of increase in all fractions.

Oily seeds.—In studying the chemical changes occurring in fatty seeds during germination it is well to keep the problem as simple as possible by preventing photosynthesis by the seedling. This, of course, does not enter in for the very early stages before chlorophyll develops in the seedling. The photosynthetic complication is avoided in the later stages by growing in light but in a CO_2-free atmosphere (Miller 1910) or by growing in darkness. Miller (1910, 1912) prefers the former method because the seedling gets all the tonic effects of sunlight while photosynthesis is avoided. Before the middle of last century de Saussure found that during the early stages of germination fatty seeds fall in fat content and increase in sugar and that in respiration the volume of oxygen consumed is greater than the volume of CO_2 produced. Since that time many investigators have confirmed these conclusions and added many details on the changes. The previous work is reviewed by Miller (1910, 1912) and Murlin (1933).

The fatty seeds that have been studied as to chemical changes during germination show three types of storage organs. In castor bean, cotton, and pine seeds the fats are stored in the endosperm which encloses the cotyledons that later become seedling leaves. In many nuts, acorns, and other seeds the fats are stored in the cotyledons that remain underground and serve merely as storage organs. In sunflower and cucurbit seeds the fats are stored in the cotyledons that are leaf-like in the seed and later become seedling leaves. In the last type it is hard to decide when the cotyledon ceases to be a storage organ and become a leaf.

Miller (1938, p. 752-761) summarizes his earlier studies of the chemical changes occurring in sunflower seeds at various periods during 14 days of germination. There is a rapid fall in the amount of fat per cotyledon as germination progresses; more than two-thirds has disappeared in seven days and nearly 95 per cent in 14 days of germination. There is relatively little increase in the following fat values of the ether extract of the cotyledons during the first seven days of germination and considerably more increase from the 7th to the 14th day of germination: acid value, percentage free fatty acid, soluble fatty acid, and saponification number. There is little fall in the following acid values of ether extract of the same organ during the first seven days of germination but considerably more from the 7th to the 14th day: percentage insoluble acids and I number. The acetyl value of the ether extract of the cotyledons falls gradually by about 4 per cent during 14 days of germination. In considering these facts one should remember how rapidly the fats have been disappearing during the 14 days of germination.

The total amount of ether extract per root and hypocotyl was reduced by nearly one-third during 14 days of germination. These organs were enlarging continuously so the percentage dry weight of ether extract fell to one-fifth or one-sixth the original value. During the first seven days of germination the fat values of ether extract from these organs were similar to the fat values of extracts of the cotyledons. During the next seven days of germination the following fat values of similar extracts of the same organs increased much more than those of the cotyledons: acid value, percentages of free and soluble fatty acids, and saponification value. The percentage insoluble fatty acids and I number decreased much faster in the ether extracts of the root and hypocotyl than in that of the cotyledons and the acetyl value was much higher at all times in extracts of the former than in that of the latter. Miller concludes from the facts just mentioned that the fatty changes in the root and hypocotyl during germination consist of a breakdown of the higher glycerides and fatty acids into those of lower molecular weight, a saturation of the fatty acids, and the accumulation of hydroxyl groups. There is also a great decrease in the percentage of fats as germination progresses.

Van Ohlen (1931) followed the chemical changes occurring in the soybean during germination by microscopical chemical methods. While these methods are no substitute for quantitative analysis they do show the location of the main transformations and materials within the organs of the seeds or seedlings. In the depletion of fats from the cotyledons the digestion starts at the base and proceeds apically. The removal from the palisade cells is slower than that from the parenchyma cells. The fat and the non-reducing sugar largely disappear from the cotyledons during the first four days of germination. There is little starch in the cotyledon in the seed but the starch increases early and rather rapidly with germination in both the cotyledons and proximal portion of the hypocotyl reaching a maximum about the 5th day and falling in the cotyledon to zero on the 19th day. The first changes observed were the appearance of reducing sugar and the appearance or increase of starch in the various organs. Asparagine appeared in the hypocotyl on the third day and increased in various organs thereafter. Asparagine has long been known (Schulze 1906) as an intermediate in protein decomposition and synthesis and is especially abundant in leguminous seedlings. Organically bound phosphorus and magnesium are released and move from the cotyledons to the roots and hypocotyl. Phytin (Miller 1938) is a common form of phosphorus storage in seeds.

MacLachlan (1936a and b) found that soybeans use up stored fats of the cotyledons faster when germinated during three weeks in light than in dark but that leaves, stems, and roots synthesize fats with equal facility in light and dark. The I number of the fats of the cotyledons did not change during germination but the fats in leaves, stems, and roots had a much lower I number than those of the cotyledons. He connects the sterol increase with the utilization of fats. Pack (1921) found a great accumulation of phospholipids in the fatty seeds of *Juniperus* during low-temperature after-ripening and germination. The phospholipids formed were of course in part at the expense of fats that disappeared.

Murlin (1933), an animal physiologist, and associates published in three short articles excellent researches on the transformation of fats during the germination of the castor bean. These authors used some new techniques that give important new evidence. Murlin directed researches previously in his laboratory on the hotly debated question, whether mammals can convert fats to carbohydrates. This investigation led to the conclusion that in the mammalian organism this conversion is extremely difficult and under the conditions studied not demonstrable. This caused him to wonder whether the botanists might be partly mistaken in the conclusion that plants readily convert fats to carbohydrates. The botanists had claimed that conversion of fats to carbohydrates not only occurs in the germination of oily seeds but that it is common in the mature plant. We have already seen that conversion of carbohydrates to oils occurs in developing oily seeds. It is likewise common in mature plants as well as mammals.

Murlin and associates used the castor bean in these investigations because the bean and the seedling were of the right size to run a single bean in the Brodie-Warburg respirometer for determining $CO_2:O_2$ ratio in respiration. They had also used the bean previously in the laboratory as a source of lipase. The flax seed was also used for determining the respiratory quotient of a germinating fatty seed.

The R. Q. of flax seed was determined at early stages of germination, hypocotyl tip just visible up to hypocotyl length of 5 to 8 mm. The period of exposure in the respirometer was 6.5 to 23 hours. The R. Q. varied from 0.487 to 0.750 with an average of 0.633. The quotient did not show strict correlation with hypocotyl length or duration of experiment. Respiration studies were made on single castor beans at various times after start of germination, also on groups of beans in enclosed vessels in which the respired air was analyzed by the Haldane method. The R. Q. varied from 0.30 to 0.58. The quotient varied with the stage of growth. The lowest quotient for the whole seedling including the hypocotyl and endosperm appeared when the hypocotyl was 20 to 35 mm. long. The author concludes that the low quotient indicates the conversion of oils to carbohydrates. The R. Q. of the young plant hypocotyl and cotyledons without the endosperm was 0.78 to 1.00 indicating considerable combustion of sugar. The R. Q. of the endosperm alone was low but somewhat higher than that of the entire germinating structure. The young plant alone per unit weight produced 2.6 times as much CO_2 as the endosperm and absorbed only 1.3 times as much O_2.

In a second paper Daggs and Halcro-Wardlaw (1933) determine $CO_2:O_2$ ratio of the entire seed structure and various parts of it at several stages of germination by complete combustion in an oxycalorimeter. The ratios obtained with the oxycalorimeter check with those obtained by organic combustion. The oxycalorimeter gave $CO_2:O_2$ ratio of about 1.00 for sucrose which attested to its accuracy. The ungerminated seed gave a $CO_2:O_2$ ratio of 0.756 and as the hypocotyl increased in length up to 112 mm. the ratio gradually increased to 0.919, indicating a change in the whole structure from oxygen-poor to oxygen-richer substance, probably mainly fat to sugar. The endosperm alone with the hypocotyl 35 mm. long gave a ratio of 0.813. This ratio gradually increased until with a hypocotyl length of 134 mm. the ratio was 0.868. The embryo, hypocotyl and cotyledons without endosperm, gave an average ratio of 0.947 varying little with the stage of development from a hypocotyl of 35 to 134 mm. This indicates that the seedling without the endosperm is oxygen-rich. This paper also leads to the conclusion that the seat of the formation of oxygen-rich compounds, carbohydrates, is the endosperm.

The third paper (Pierce et al. 1933) gives the chemical analyses of the entire castor bean structure at different stages of seedling development from the ungerminated seed to a seedling length of 175 to 250 mm. During this period the following changes occur: on the dry weight basis the ether extract falls from 67.85 to 11.97 per cent; the total reducing matter after acid hydrolysis rises from 1.18 to about 40 per cent when the seedling is 80 to 140 mm. after which it falls to 14.28 per cent with a seedling length of 175 to 250 mm.; there is little glucose present in the early stages but the glucose rises from about 4.5 per cent with seedling length of 60 to 80 mm. to 18.45 per cent with a seedling length of 100 to 150 mm., then finally falls to 10.75 per cent at seedling length of 175 to 250 mm.; the crude fiber of course rises as the seedling develops, 1.87 per cent to 12.89 per cent; the percentage protein ($N \times 6.25$) fluctuates somewhat and is 25.72 per cent at the beginning and 34.68 per cent at the latest stage; the ash shows a similar change running from 2.61 to 4.42 per cent and the total of all of these falls from about 99 per cent at the early stages to about 78 per cent.

Certain observations ought to be made on the methods and results reported in these three excellent papers. In the development of seeds we have already emphasized the desirability of having results reported on the basis of change per seed or per 1000 seeds. This might have called for the choice of some other fatty seed that gives better germination and perhaps a smaller seed in which a few failing to germinate would not introduce as large an error because of the great number necessary for the experiment. Denny (1946) has emphasized the great amount of CO_2 absorbed by the tissue and its interference in calculating the $CO_2:O_2$ ratio. He worked with massive tissues such as potato tuber, fruit of squash, and the turnip where the accumulation is much greater than in the castor bean. The authors seemed to find this error of minor significance in the castor bean. Absorption of CO_2 by the tissue would of course give too low a respiratory quotient. The quotient found for castor bean is low.

Brown (1939) found a R. Q. as low as 0.06 for the fat-richer and dormant acorn of the northern red oak when it had reached gas exchange equilibrium in moist

storage at 2.5° C. The white oak fat-poorer, non-dormant acorn also showed a low
R. Q. at this temperature. The R. Q. of both rose as the storage period continued.
By mid-winter in soil at 2.5° C. the R. Q. of the red oak acorn was higher than that
of the white oak. As the temperature of the soil rose, the R. Q. of the acorn of the
red oak also rose, but even at 10° to 12.5° C., good after-ripening temperatures, the
quotient was still lower than 0.3.

If the only conversion in the fatty seeds were oils to carbohydrates the quotients
would of course be 0.00. The complete oxidation of fatty acids to CO_2 and H_2O
gives the following quotients: palmitic 0.695, stearic 0.692, oleic 0.706, linoleic 0.720,
linolenic 0.735; trioleate gives 0.701. The triglycerides give a slightly lower quotient than the constituting fatty acids because they are oxygen-poorer. The respiratory
quotient in certain stages of germination of fatty acids is much lower than would
result from the complete oxidation of fatty acids or glycerides. The complete oxidation of sugar would give, of course, only a quotient of 1.00. The lowest quotient
found by Brown, namely 0.06, indicates that the main conversion under these conditions is the oxidation of oils to sugar or some other oxygen-rich substances. Karon
and Altschul (1946) find the R. Q. of a fatty seed (cotton) in storage (10 to 17 per
cent moisture) is unity. This indicates that in fatty seeds in dry storage there is no
or little conversion of oils to carbohydrates. The low respiration is probably carried
on at the expense of the soluble sugars present. The low respiratory intensity of
seeds in dry storage is attributed to the inactive condition of hydrolytic and respiratory
enzymes.

Energetics of Germination:—During seed germination heat is produced
and set free, also there is as we have seen an extensive transformation and
movement of foods from storage organs to the growing seedling. The latter
like the former involves extensive energy as well as material changes. In
measuring these two sets of changes the seeds are germinated in darkness
to avoid the complication introduced by photopsynthesis.

Peirce (1908) demonstrated qualitatively heat production during germination by
placing sterilized imbibed seeds in Dewar flasks and noting the later rise in temperature. Peirce, in one of his experiments, showed that five flasks bearing 80 g. each
(dry weight) of soaked pea seeds showed an average rise of temperature of about 17°
C. in three days, while a similar flask bearing dead soaked peas showed a fall of 1° C.
due to fall in atmospheric temperature. Later Peirce (1912) conducted his experiments in such a way that he could determine the calories of heat produced per kilogram of peas per minute by the respiring seeds. He got the very low maximum
value of 8.55 cal. per kilogram minute.

Bonnier (1893) used both the Berthelot calorimeter and the Renault
thermocalorimeter for measuring the heat given off by germinating seeds
and other plant organs of several kinds of plants. He concluded that there
are two periods of maximum heat production in the life of flowering plants;
one is during the early stages of germination and the other is during flowering. The heat released during the growth at either maximum could not
be calculated exactly from the CO_2 released or O_2 absorbed or both in
combination. The maximum heat given off during germination agreed
reasonably well with the maximum O_2 absorption or with the minimum of
the respiratory quotient. In all cases amount of heat released coincided
more nearly with that calculated from the total oxidation than that calculated from the CO_2 released. At a given stage of development a rise in
temperature caused a marked rise in the rate of heat production.

Some of the higher values obtained by Bonnier are as follows:

KIND OF SEED	TEMP., ° C.	STAGE OF DEVELOPMENT	SMALL CAL. PER KG. PER MIN.
Peas	10.15	Radicle 5 mm. av.	125
Wheat	10.6	Radicle just appearing	52
Maize	15	7 days germ.	138
Maize	15	15 days germ.	90
Bean	15.3	5 days germ.	72
Rice	13.7	12 days germ.	125

It will be noted that Bonnier used low temperatures ranging from 10° to 15° C. The later investigators to be cited used, in the main, temperatures of 20° or 25° C. If Bonnier had used such temperatures his results would have been increased in some cases as much as three-fold. In the case of the cereals, Bonnier was dealing with tissue the greater part of which is endosperm, tissue of low activity. Even in peas the storage organs, cotyledons, are hypogenous and probably of low activity. While the beans are epigenous the cotyledons never become as effective as leaves as do those of the sunflower studied later by Krasinska.

Rodewald's (1883) early work on the energy and material changes of red clover seeds during five and nine days of germination seemed to have involved some error that led to unaccounted-for energy loss. Wilsing (1884) a year later repeated this work and found that the heat of combustion of the seeds was 5052 cal. per g.; 3-day seedlings, 5080; 5-day, 4948; 7-day, 4826; and 9-day, 4768; and the ether extract of the seeds, 9264. The values indicate the transformation of some of the fats in the reserves to carbohydrates in the seedlings. The elementary and other chemical analyses indicated the same. The following changes took place in the embryos as germination progressed: a fall in C and H percentages, a marked fall in fat percentage, a rise in O_2 percentage as well as asparagine. There was no unaccounted-for loss of energy as Rodewald had found. This disposes of any concept of vital energy aside from that involved in measurable physical and chemical changes.

Doyer (1914) determined by use of a new method the amount of heat released by germinating wheat during various periods of germination. She also determined the heat of combustion of the dry seeds, and that of the seedlings and the seed residues at various stages of germination. The heat production increased with a rise in temperature up to 35° C. At the lower range of temperature a 10° C. rise more than doubled the heat liberated. At 40° C. the heat production fell off again. The heat production figures by Peirce were found too low and those by Bonnier too high and the results seemed to agree more nearly with those of Rodewald than with those of Wilsing. Results of later investigators showing much higher values indicate an error in Doyer's elaborate method of measuring heat production.

Krasinska (1929) made the following determinations on sunflower embryo and seedlings at various stages of germination: heats of combustion, analysis of the seed fats, carbon dioxide production, and oxygen absorption. She got a complete balance of the chemical energy of germination and, unlike Rodewald and Doyer, found no unaccounted-for energy. The experiments were run at 25° C. and the maximum heat production occurred on the 4th day. During the first six days the seeds lost 0.362 gram of fat per gram dry weight or per 0.582 gram of fat. During this period the heat of combustion of the embryo fell from 7330 to 5275 calories per gram corresponding to 60 per cent of the caloric value of the fats used. The respiratory quotient during the first six days averaged 0.523. The quotient fell from 0.928 for the first day to 0.488 on the 4th day of germination after which it rose to 0.664 on the 7th day. Assuming that the fats used but not completely oxidized were converted to carbohydrates the author concludes from her data that 93 per cent of the energy used in germination is covered by the fats and the rest by other materials, probably some by hydrolysis of proteins. About 44 per cent of the fats used underwent complete combustion, 56 per cent being converted to carbohydrates. Hence about 23 per cent of the energy supplied by the fats was furnished by the latter reaction and 77 per cent by the complete combustion.

Krasinska gave the heat losses during various periods of germination as follows:

> 1 to 48 hours, 214 cal. per gram dry weight of seeds
> 48 to 96 hours, 873 cal. per gram dry weight of seeds
> 96 to 144 hours, 968 cal. per gram dry weight of seeds
> 1 to 144 hours, 2055 cal. per gram dry weight of seeds

Calculating the six days' heat loss of 2055 cal. per gram dry weight as loss per kg. dry weight per minute gives about 238 cal. The similar value for the 5th and 6th day is 336 cal. If one were to calculate the highest value which appeared on the 4th day, the figures would be much higher. These values are much higher than those found even by Bonnier. This is to be expected because the temperature used was more than 10° C. higher than those used by Bonnier which would more than double the values. Also the sunflower embryo including the storage organs, the cotyledons, are relatively active tissue. About 28 per cent of the energy stored in the sunflower seed is given off as heat of respiration during six days of germination in dark at 25° C. During this time, Krasinska's figures show there was a slight gain in the dry weight of the seedling because much of the high energy fats was converted to low energy carbohydrates.

By use of an adiabatic microcalorimeter Solodkowska and Rudowska (1932) determined the heat of swelling and the heat of germination of seeds of pea, sunflower, and clover. The heat production curves were plotted over long periods, in many cases for individual seeds. The heat of swelling was greatest when the first drops of water were absorbed. The heat of swelling is very evident in the curves for sunflower and clover, hence for these the total heat of production curves show high values at first, but the values fall rapidly as swelling progresses and rise again considerably later as respiration increases due at first to increased water content and later to germination of the seeds. The curves for the heat of germination showed a single maximum between the 4th and 6th day at the constant temperatures used, 17° to 21° C.

Solodkowska (1938) by use of a similar instrument found that the greatest heat was produced between the 4th and 5th day of germination. She concludes (1939) that the heat of germination of the sunflower seeds comes partly from the complete combustion of fats and partly from the transformation of fats to carbohydrates.

The heat of respiration or the energy loss during germination, so far as known, does no useful work for the plant. In mammals heat production is necessary for maintaining a constant temperature. There are many changes in organic materials and energy relations during germination that are of significance to the seedling: materials are digested in the storage organs, moved to the seedling and there transformed into living or structural tissues that may differ markedly from the storage substances. Terroine et al. (1924) studied the counterpart of the material and heat losses during germination. They determined the efficiency with which the materials and energy in the storage organs were moved to the growing seedling.

The material efficiency was expressed by the following formula $\frac{P}{P_1 - P_2}$, in which P = the dry weight of the seedling; P_1 = the dry weight of seeds at the start; and P_2 = the dry weight of the seed residue at a given stage of germination. The energy efficiency formula was $\frac{E}{E_1-E_2}$, in which E was the heat of combustion of the seedling, E_1 that of the seed, and E_2 that of the seed residue at a given stage of germination. The authors concluded that the energy efficiency for germination of seeds rich in starch (rice and sorghum) was very high, about 73 per cent; lower for those rich in proteins (peas and lentils), about 63 per cent; and much lower for those rich in fats (peanuts and flax), 53 per cent. In material efficiency peanuts and flax exceeded rice and sorghum for as the authors state during germination much of the stored fats in peanut and flax seeds were oxidized to carbohydrates which were installed into the seedlings. The authors concluded that the energy efficiency during germination was determined by the chemical composition of the seed. Higher temperatures hastened the germination speed but did not modify the energy efficiency at a given stage of germination. The same energy efficiency for a given seed was shown at every stage of germination provided the seedling had reached considerable size and there was still an abundance of reserves in the storage organs.

References:—

Bailey, C. H., 1938: Germ content of American wheats (Cereal Chem. 15:102-106).

Bonnier, G., 1893: Recherches sur la chaleur végétale (Ann. Sci. Naturelles 18:1-34).

Brown, J. W., 1939: Respiration of acorns as related to temperature and after-ripening (Plant Physiol. 14:621-645).

Brown, R., 1943: Studies on germination and seedling growth. II. The effect of the environment during germination on the subsequent growth of the seedling of barley (Ann. Bot. n. s. 7:275-296).

————, 1946: Studies on germination and seedling growth. III. Early growth in relation to certain aspects of nitrogen metabolism in seedling of barley (Ann. Bot. n. s. 10:73-96).

Daggs, R. G., & H. S. Halcro-Wardlaw, 1933: The conversion of fat to carbohydrate in the germinating castor bean. II. The combustion respiratory quotient as determined by a modified oxycalorimeter (Jour. Gen. Physiol. 17:303-309).

Denny, F. E., 1946: Gas content of plant tissue and respiration measurements (Contrib. Boyce Thompson Inst. 14:257-276).

Doyer, L. C., 1914: Energieomzettingen tijdens de kieming van tarwekorrels (Energieumsatz zur Zeit der Keimung der Weizenkörner) (Diss. Utrecht, 90 pp., P. den Boer; abstr. in Bot. Centralbl. 126:585, 1914).

Hopkins, C. G., L. H. Smith & E. M. Cast, 1903: The structure of the corn kernel and the composition of its different parts (Illinois Agric. Exp. Sta. Bull. 87: 77-112).

Karon, M. L., & A. M. Altschul, 1946: Respiration of cottonseed (Plant Physiol. 21: 506-521).

Kraskinska, Z., 1929: Przyczynek do energetyki kielkowania slonecznika (Contribution a l'étude du métabolisme énergétique de la germination [*Helianthus annuus*]) (Acta Biologiae Experimentalis 3(1928):101-141 [French summ. p. 101-103]).

MacLachlan, P. L., 1936a: Fat metabolism in plants, with special reference to sterols (Jour. Biol. Chem. 113:197-204).

————, 1936b: Fat metabolism in plants, with special reference to sterols. II. Differential changes in the cotyledons and in the roots, stems, and leaves (Jour. Biol. Chem. 114:185-191).

Malhotra, R. C., 1931a: Notes on the determination of hemicelluloses (Indus. & Eng. Chem. Anal. Ed. 3:161-163).

————, 1931b: A physio-chemical study of some economic seeds during germination with particular reference to weight and energy loss (Protoplasma 12:167-189).

————, 1932a: Biochemical study of seeds during germination. I. Periodic changes of reserve materials in normal germinating seeds (Bot. Centralbl. Beih. Abt. I, 50:1-7).

————, 1932b: Biochemical study of seeds during germination. II. Periodic changes of reserve materials in embryo and endosperm of germinating corn (Bot. Centralbl. Beih. Abt. I, 50:8-14).

————, 1932c: Biochemical study of seeds during germination. III. The distribution of some chemicals and energy in the previously isolated embryos during germination (Bot. Centralbl. Beih. Abt. I, 50:15-19).

————, 1933a: Biochemical study of seeds during germination. IV. The distribution of some chemical reserves and calorific energy in the previously isolated endosperm during the germinative conditions (Bot. Centralbl. Beih. Abt. I, 51:524-530).

————, 1933b: Biochemical study of seeds during germination. V. Successive elongation of shoots and roots in Zea mays seeds and embryo-seedlings with known chemical reserves and calorific energy (Bot. Centralbl. Beih. Abt. I, 51:531-540).

————, 1934: Chemistry of corn seed germination (Cereal Chem. 11:105-109).

Miller, E. C., 1910: A physiological study of the germination of Helianthus annuus (Ann. Bot. 24:693-726).

————, 1912: A physiological study of the germination of Helianthus annuus. II. The oily reserve (Ann. Bot. 26:889-901).

————, 1938: Plant physiology (2nd ed., 1201 pp., McGraw-Hill Book Co., Inc., New York).

Murlin, J. R., 1933: The conversion of fat to carbohydrate in the germinating castor bean. I. The respiratory metabolism (Jour. Gen. Physiol. 17:283-302).

Murneek, A. E., 1928: Nitrogen and carbohydrates distribution in organs of bearing apple spurs (Missouri Agric. Exp. Sta. Res. Bull. 119, 50 pp.).

Pack, D. A., 1921: Chemistry of after-ripening, germination and seedling development of juniper seeds (Bot. Gaz. 72:139-150).

Peirce, G. J., 1908: A new respiration calorimeter (Bot. Gaz. 46:193-202).

————, 1912: The liberation of heat in respiration (Bot. Gaz. 53:89-112).

Pierce, H. B., D. E. Sheldon & J. R. Murlin, 1933: The conversion of fat to carbohydrate in the germinating castor bean. III. The chemical analysis and correlation with respiratory exchange (Jour. Gen. Physiol. 17:311-325).

Rodewald, H., 1883: Ueber die Wechselbeziehungen zwischen Stoffumsatz und Kraftumsatz in keimenden Samen (Jour. Landw. 8, 35 pp.; abstr. in Bot. Centralbl. 17:297-299, 1884).

Schulze, E., 1906: Über den Abbau und den Aufbau organischer Stickstoffverbindungen in den Pflanzen (Landw. Jahrb. 35:621-666).

Solodkowska, W., 1938: Application of the adiabatic calorimeter to the investigation of the energetics of bursting seeds (Roczniki Chem. 18:771-783; abstr. in Chem. Abstr. 33:6392, 1939).

————, 1939: Energetics of germinating seeds. II (Roczniki Chem. 19:277-288; abstr. in Chem. Abstr. 34:2880, 1940).

Solodkowska, W., & K. Rudowska, 1932: O pomiarach ciepła kielkowania naison zapomoca mikrokalorymetru adjabatycznego (1) [Ueber Messungen der Keimungsswärme der Samen mit Hilfe des adiabatischen Mikrokalorimeters (1)] (Bull. Internat. Acad. Polonaise Sci. et Lett. Cl. Sci. Math. & Nat. Ser. A, 1932(1-7): 95-108 [German summ.]).

Terroine, E. F., R. Bonnet & P. H. Joessel, 1924: L'énergie de croissance. II. La germination (Soc. Chim. Biol. Bull. 6:357-393).

Toole, E. H., 1924: The transformations and course of development of germinating maize (Amer. Jour. Bot. 11:325-350).

Von Ohlen, F. W., 1931: A microchemical study of soybeans during germination (Amer. Jour. Bot. 18:30-49).

Wilsing, H., 1884: Stoffumsatz und Kraftumsatz in keimenden Samen (Jour. Landw. 32:523-538).

Chapter XIV

METABOLIC AND ENERGY CHANGES
IN SEED DEVELOPMENT AND GERMINATION, III

Digestive Enzymes of Seeds*:—The hydrolysis and synthesis of carbohydrates, proteins, and lipids in seeds are carried out through the action of enzymes. Every living cell has numerous enzymes that induce oxidations, reductions, deaminations, etc., as well as hydrolyses and syntheses. Enzymes are organic catalytic agents. Kirchoff before 1815 (Bayliss 1925, p. 11) found that strong acids convert starch to sugar. Berzelius, 1838, introduced the term catalysis [Greek, meaning loosener]. Many inorganic catalysts are now known and they are ever increasing in industrial importance. Catalysts hasten chemical change without being used up in the action. Amongst inorganic catalysts are: acids inverting cane sugar; spongy platinum hastening the union of hydrogen and oxygen to form water; and nickel promoting the absorption of hydrogen by liquid fats to form solid fats. According to Bayliss, Dubrunfaut in 1830 made an extract from malt which converted starch to sugar and Payen and Perzog in 1833 precipitated a substance from malt extract that could be dried and stored for some time and still show powerful hydrolytic action on starch. The latter workers called this substance diastase [Greek, meaning to separate]. The work just mentioned was the beginning of the isolation and purification of seed enzymes. In 1878 Kuhne proposed the term enzyme [Greek, meaning in yeast] to distinguish organic catalysts that could be separated from organisms and act independently of them from the so-called organized ferments that were assumed to owe their action to the living organism. This distinction was rendered meaningless when Buchner (1897) showed that an enzyme complex, zymase, in yeast rather than the living organism carries on alcohol fermentation.

Sumner and Somers (1947) mention the following characteristics of catalytic agents: (1) they increase the velocity of the reaction; (2) the agent is not used up to any extent in the reaction; (3) small quantities of the agent are very effective; (4) catalysts, especially enzymes, are very specific in their action; and (5) small amounts of certain foreign substances poison catalysts. All of these characteristics will be repeatedly mentioned later as the individual digestive seed enzymes are discussed.

In the early history of enzyme study the enzymes were named without system as pepsin, diastase, and papain. It is now customary to name them on the basis of the individual substance they attack (amylase, lipase, etc.) or on the basis of the class of

---

* In connection with this chapter on enzymes the reader should refer to general texts on enzymes such as Sumner and Somers (1947) and to texts on physical chemistry such as Glasstone (1940) for definition of terms used. The chemical dictionaries cited under Chemical Composition of Seeds will also be useful.

substances they attack (carbohydrases, lecithinases, etc.). Enzymes may be secreted by cells and act on substances outside of the cells in which they are synthesized. The palisade cells of the grass scutellum secrete amylase that digests the starch of the endosperm. Leaves of insectivorous plants secrete proteases that digest insects. Such enzymes are termed extracellular. The amylase of the green leaf is intracellular; it acts on the starch within the cell where the enzyme is produced. Zymase is strictly intracellular in normal alcoholic fermentation, hence it was early thought to be an organized ferment.

So far as they have been crystallized enzymes are high molecular weight simple proteins, but some proteins and enzymes bear prosthetic or non-amino groups. Sumner and Somers state that molecular weight of crystalline pepsin is 36,000 to 37,000. The molecular weight of catalase is 248,000 and urease 483,000. Enzymes are ampholytes moving to the cathode when positively charged and to the anode when negatively charged. Enzymes are also very sensitive to changes in pH as we shall see later in discussing seed enzymes.

Genes and enzyme specificity.—Beadle and Tatum (1941) by use of X-ray produced mutants of *Neurospora sitophila* and *N. crassa*, a genus of fungi belonging to the class Ascomycetes. The wild forms of these species have the following minimal nutrient requirements for normal growth on agar: mineral nutrients, a nitrogen-free carbon compound such as sucrose or fat, and biotin. These species can synthesize all needed amino acids and vitamins except biotin. Single ascospore strains were individually derived from perithecia X-rayed prior to meiosis. Out of nearly 2000 such isolated strains three mutants were found that grew normally on complete nutrient medium (containing as many normally synthesized constituents as possible), but scarcely at all on the minimal medium mentioned above. One mutant of *N. sitophila* was able to grow on the minimal medium with the single addition of vitamin B_6 (pyridoxine). A second strain of the same species needed vitamin B_1 added to the minimal medium to give normal growth. In this case the mutant could synthesize B_1 if the thiazole portion of the molecule only was added to the minimal medium but not if only the pyrimidine half was added. A third mutant of *N. crassa* was able to grow on the minimal medium only when *p*-aminobenzoic acid was added, so *p*-aminobenzoic acid is an essential nutrient for this strain.

Beadle and Tatum (1945) isolated 68,198 single spore strains of these two species of *Neurospora* from material treated with X-rays, ultraviolet, or neutrons and found more than 380 strains with altered nutritional requirements. Most of these differed from the wild types only by single genes. The altered requirements involved B-vitamins, amino acids, and purine or pyrimidine bases. The authors suggest that genes act by determining the specificities of enzyme proteins and as a consequence control specific chemical reactions. It is hard to overestimate the biochemical and biological significance of this new discovery and approach: the effect of genes can be measured by metabolic alterations as well as morphological changes as in the past; it furnishes a method by which the intermediates in synthesis of essential biological compounds can be determined; and it is likely to lead to the discovery of numerous very specific enzymes involved in metabolism. Already many able biochemists are turning their attention to this field, and *Neurospora* genetics and metabolism is becoming almost a science in itself (Srb and Horowitz 1944; Bonner 1946a and b; Doermann 1945). Perhaps sometime by use of this approach we may learn all the steps various organisms take in synthesizing the essential amino acids from nitrates and simple carbohydrates and like progress may be made for synthesis of vitamins, purine bodies, and others.

Kinetics of enzyme action.—In later discussions of seed enzymes frequent reference will be made to the kinetics of enzyme action. At this point the reader should become familiar with a number of terms used in connection with the kinetics of chemical reactions (Sumner and Somers 1947). For instance, the speed of enzyme reaction under one condition or another may follow the zero order of reaction (rate constant over a period of time); the first, or monomolecular order of reaction (where the rate is determined at any moment by the concentration of the substrate being hydrolyzed) or the second, or bimolecular order of reaction (where the rate at any moment is determined by the concentrations of two substances). Under certain conditions the speed may follow the Schütz-Borrisow rule, where the enzyme activity is proportional to the square root of the amount of enzyme. The rate of enzyme activity increases as the temperature rises. The temperature coefficient $= \frac{\text{Velocity at } T° + 10°}{\text{Velocity at } T°}$. The temperature coefficient for enzyme action generally lies in the region of 1.5 and 2.0. The effect of temperature on enzyme action is the result of two effects: the enzyme action increases with the temperature and as the temperature rises the rate of denaturing of the enzyme increases. The denaturing rises rapidly at higher temperatures because of the high temperature coefficient for coagulation of proteins. The temperature optimum is the temperature at which the accelerating effect of the temperature balances the destructive effect. The energy of activation is another term commonly used in connection with enzyme action. Sumner and Somers mention that over the temperature interval 20° to 30° C. a temperature coefficient of 1.25 corresponds to energy of activation of about 3900 cal.; 1.50 to 7000; and 2.0 to 12,000. The temperature coefficient and the energy of activation is much higher for heat coagulation of proteins. We shall also see later that the same is true for the speed of action of enzymes below the congealing temperature, which is of significance in deep freeze operations.

Carbohydrases:—Carbohydrases are a large group of enzymes that hydrolyze various carbohydrates of plants such as starches, inulin, reserve cellulose, di- and trisaccharides.

Amylases.—Starch, the very abundant and widely distributed carbohydrate storage substance of seeds, must of course be rendered soluble and digested before it can be used by the growing seedling. This digestion is carried out by amylases. The amylases longest used industrially are those of the cereals, especially barley. Kneen (Kerr 1944, Chap. XV) states that there are records of malt preparation as early as 7000 B.C. and that brewing was an established craft in 5000 B.C. This is the first seed enzyme reported and has received more study than any other because of its importance in the brewing industry.

Amylases are apparently specific proteins. They are irreversibly inactivated by high concentrations of acids and alkalies or boiling temperatures and do not dialyze through cellophane membranes. They are soluble in water and dilute salt and ethanol solutions and are precipitated by strong solutions of ammonium sulfate and ethanol. The precipitate can be dissolved in water as an active enzyme.

Industrial uses of amylases.—Amylases from many sources have been extracted and studied—seeds and other organs of higher plants, fungi, bacteria, yeasts (Wickerham et al. 1944), and animals. Besides the physiological importance of these to the various organisms, several amylases from different sources are on the market in more or less purified form and some of these have important industrial applications as in sizing and desizing, preparation of special dextrins and sugars and clarifying sugars, and other solutions containing undesirable starch and dextrin.

Two seed amylases.*—It is well established that there are two types of seed amylases that have been variously named but have finally come to be termed α and β amylases. The first has been called the amylase of activity because it appears after germination starts, and the second is the amylase of dormancy for much of it is already present in the ungerminated barley grain. The first is also called dextrinogenic and the second saccharogenic amylase because of the main products of their actions on starch.

There are three steps in the digestion of gelatinized starch or starch grains by

---

* The amylases of leaves do not corrode starch grains as do the amylases of seeds. The amylases of leaves are endoenzymes but the same is true of the amylases of many seeds where the starch is stored in the cotyledon rather than endosperm.

amylases: liquefaction, dextrinization, and saccharification. The first process may involve mainly the transformation of the paste or starch grain into molecular distribution in water much as can be done by beating gelatinized starch. The second involves the hydrolysis of the starch molecules into smaller and smaller dextrin molecules. In the earlier stages of dextrinization the dextrin molecules stain blue with iodine but as the molecules become smaller they stain purple, then brown, and finally fail to stain at all. Apparently α-amylase is especially effective in liquefying and dextrinizing starch but these processes are also partially dependent upon β-amylases. The third phase of starch digestion is saccharification. In this process the starch molecules are hydrolyzed to a large extent to reducing and fermentable sugars. The sugar resulting from the action of amylases on starch is largely maltose. Glucose is also found in the digested products. This may result from the action of maltase on maltose or from the action of other hydrolytic enzymes on glucose complexes.

When both α- and β-amylase are present, as in the case of barley malt, there is a rapid liquefaction and dextrinization followed by a rapid production of maltose. In the later stages the reaction slows down but sugar production proceeds until the conversion approaches the complete degradation of starch to sugar. If the amylase of ungerminated barley, β-amylase, free from α-amylase, acts upon starch, saccharification is rapid at first but sugar production slows down and ceases when about 60 per cent of the starch is converted to maltose. Apparently β-amylase breaks maltose from the end of the chain until residues are left that are not hydrolyzed by this enzyme and 40 per cent of the starch remains as limit or residual dextrin. α-Amylase alone brings about rapid liquefying and dextrinization of starch. Small amounts of reducing sugars are produced in addition to reducing dextrin during dextrinization and following dextrinization a steady production of sugar occurs. Most amylases are of this type. α-Amylases vary greatly in their post-dextrinization, or sugar forming activity, and a high concentration of the α-amylase is sometimes necessary to give good sugar production.

Part of the amylases of seeds is bound to compounds (probably proteins) within the seeds and their release is brought about by various agents, proteolytic enzymes (papain) (Davidson 1945), H_2S (Chrzaszcz and Janicki 1936), and dilute salt solutions. α-Amylase of barley, as do the amylases of pancrease and *Aspergillus oryzae* (Balls and Schwimmer 1944), acts on raw native starch. The former is stabilized by calcium salts, is relatively stable at 70° C., and most stable at the neutral point, while β-amylase of barley does not attack most native starches, is rendered unstable by calcium, is rather rapidly denatured at 70° C., and is most stable at pH 5. α-Amylase is precipitated by 25 to 35 per cent $(NH_4)_2SO_4$ or 60 per cent ethanol, while β-amylase requires higher concentrations of both of these for precipitation.

Amylase inhibitors.—Soluble and insoluble inhibitors are found in various seeds and the inhibiting action is sometimes specific for certain amylases. A protein inhibitor for saliva amylase extracted from wheat flour seems to bear tryptophane as the active group. Treatment of β-amylase from barley or barley malt (Weill and Caldwell 1945*a* and *b*) with reagents generally held to react specifically with sulfhydryl groups causes a marked inhibition of enzyme action. Kneen and Sandstedt (1946) have found water-soluble protein inhibitors digested by pancreatic proteases in rye and two varieties of sorghum, and Bowman (1944) in the navy bean. Van Slyke (1942) mentions that amylase in concentrated starch solution digests the starch in proportion to the enzyme concentration while in a very low concentration of substrate the monomolecular law is simulated, that is, the rate of digestion is proportional to the starch concentration remaining at any moment.

The inversion of sucrose or the hydrolysis of maltose with dilute acid follows the monomolecular type of reaction. Myrbäck and Magnusson (1945) find the hydrolysis of starch to glucose with dilute acid does not follow this law but that the rate of hydrolysis slows down as it draws to completion. The marked decrease in rate in the advanced stages of hydrolysis is assumed to be due to the higher percentage of isomaltose linkages which form the branching points of the saccharide chain and which are much more resistant to acid hydrolysis than the ordinary maltose linkages.

Malts of wheat and rye are similar to that of barley except perhaps α-amylase of wheat is less thermostable than that of barley and the reverse is true of the β-amylases. Malts of oats, sorghum, maize, and rice contain large quantities of α-amylase similar to that of barley malt but little β-amylase.

There are other good plant sources of amylases. Soybeans and sweet potatoes are rich in β-amylase, although the soybeans (Davidson 1945) contain little if any starch. Amylase of *Aspergillus oryzae* is α-amylase. It has a pH optimum of about 5. The fungal amylases have lower thermal stability than malt α-amylase. Fungal amylases were much used in Japan while malt amylases were used in the Occident. Kneen (Kerr 1944) states that bacteria α-amylases with great saccharifying power are available. They are stabilized by calcium, have a pH optimum of about 7, and are stable at a higher temperature than malt amylases.

Sandstedt and Beckord (1946) state that α-amylase is found in the pericarp of immature wheat grains. It increases during the first week of development when the pericarp is growing fastest, then decreases. Only traces of α-amylase appear in the endosperm at any time. β-Amylase increases all during the development of the kernel, most of the increase being due to the growth of the endosperm. An inhibitor that did not affect wheat or malt amylases but did inhibit salivary amylases appears in the endosperm but not in the pericarp of wheat when the kernel reaches full length. Elion (1945) states that β-amylase is found only in the endosperm and α-amylase in the aleurone layer and epithelium of the scutellum. The resting grain contains β-amylase chiefly.

Other amylases have been named and described. Amylophosphatase was supposed to be a starch liquefying amylase which released phosphorus from the starch molecule and amylocytase was supposed to attack the resistant outer layer of the starch grain. Both of these are probably α-amylases. Phosphorylase is certainly not identical with either α- or β-amylase; it has been found in both plant and animal tissues and its synthetic as well as its hydrolytic action has been established.

Other carbohydrases.—There are a number of other carbohydrate hydrolyzing enzymes. Amongst these are inulase which hydrolyzes the polysaccharide, inulin, directly to fructose. Inulases need not concern us in connection with seed studies for inulin is found mainly if not exclusively in underground storage organs, especially of the *Compositae,* and probably not at all in seeds. Seeds have sucrose as a storage material and of course bear invertase as the enzyme that inverts this sugar into dextrose and levulose. Maltase, an α-glucase, is present in seeds, seedlings, and malts. Miller (1938) states that it is often overlooked in these because of its heat lability and destruction by drying. There are also several carbohydrases that hydrolyze various other disaccharides as well as trisaccharides. Amongst these are melibiase, gentionase, and raffinase. Pectinase hydrolyzes pectose to arabinose.

There are also various carbohydrases that split glycosides liberating a simple sugar and other substances. Emulsin, β-glycosidase, hydrolyzes amygdalin to benzaldehyde, hydrocyanic acid, and glucose. Emulsin hydrolyzes phlorizin, salicin, arbutin, or any other β-glucoside. Hydrocyanic acid, liberated from glycosides of seeds and more especially seedlings, often proves poisonous to animals. Such glycosides are present in flax, lupine, zamia, and vetch seed, also in rosaceous and bitter almond seeds and others.

Maltase acts as an α-glucosidase. Phytase, rhamnase, and myrosin are other glucosidases. The latter hydrolyzes sinigrin of mustard seeds to allyl isothiocyanate, glucose, and potassium hydrogen sulfate. It seems to hydrolyze all sulfur-containing glucosides.

Cytases.—Cytases (Newcombe 1899) are of great interest in seed physiology for they digest the reserve hemicelluloses in the cell walls of endosperms and cotyledons of seeds rendering these soluble and available for the use of the growing seedlings. In growing grass seeds they also digest the endosperm cell walls under the epithelium of the scutellum preparatory to digestion of starch in these cells. Cytases were first discovered in fungal mycelia. Fungal cytases digest cell walls of higher plants enabling the mycelia to penetrate the host.

Newcombe worked with cytase extracts from *Aspergillus oryzae*, seedlings of *Lupinus albus* and *Phoenix dactylifera*, endosperm of *Phoenix*, and barley malt. There was no relation between the power of these extracts to attack starch on one hand and reserve cellulose on the other, consequently the cytases are not amylases. *Lupinus* and *Phoenix* extracts acted energetically on reserve cellulose and very weakly on starch. The several cytases showed no specific action on reserve celluloses from different plants, but they all first rendered the walls hyaline without reducing their thickness. Later the walls appeared more and more transparent and finally melted away. Newcombe implies that these cytases dissolve true cellulose if given sufficient time. Pond (1906) claims that the endosperm of ungerminated *Phoenix* seeds bears no cytase and that the later source of cytase is the growing embryo. He also considers the starchy endosperms of cereals as lifeless and believes that the main source of enzymes for digesting the endosperm is the scutellum and aleurone layer.

Carbohydrase secreting cells.—More generally the storage carbohydrates of seeds are digested by enzymes secreted within the storage cells, or at least there are no special enzyme cells. There are two types of seeds, however, that have special enzyme secreting cells: the cereals and certain seeds in which the storage carbohydrate is hemicellulose stored in the walls of the endosperm. In the cereals the enzyme cells are all laid down as the grain is formed as an epithelium layer of the scutellum adjoining the endosperm. In seeds like *Phoenix* the enzyme secreting cells must be formed in part as the embryo foot enlarges to digest regions of the endosperm more and more distant from the embryo. Not only do the enzyme layers secrete the enzyme for digesting the endosperm, but the hydrolytic products must be absorbed by these cells and later pass to the growing seedling so the cells are both enzyme glands and parts of the seedling absorbing organs.

Torrey (1902) followed the changes mainly in the enzyme secreting cells of maize during germination referring also incidentally to barley, and Reed (1904) followed changes in enzyme secreting cells of both maize and *Phoenix* during germination. Both workers agree that the gland cells enlarge considerably during growth of the seedling; Torrey says three to four times their original volume. Both agree that the cytoplasm becomes less granular as enzyme secretion advances. Enlargement of gland cells and fall in the granularity of the cytoplasm took place in *Phoenix* as in maize but the gland cells of maize are much larger than those of *Phoenix*. The gland cells of the grains apparently secrete cytase as well as diastase for the cell walls of the endosperm of the cereal clear up and finally dissolve under the action of the secreted enzyme. It is assumed that the gland cells of *Phoenix* secrete mainly cytase.

Proteases:—Protein metabolism, of course, occurs in every living cell of every organism so proteases are universally present in living cells catalyzing protein and peptide hydrolysis and synthesis. While the early knowledge about plant proteases was gained by a study of insectivorous plants and seeds, later more exact knowledge has come from the study of proteases from fruits, vegetative organs, or latices of flowering plants, and proteases from microorganisms.

Historical and practical applications.—While the utilization of proteolytic enzymes has no such a venerable history as amylase, Vines (1909) says that the latex of papaw

(*Carica papaya*) was long known to act proteolytically. He states that the milk of the unripe fruit was used in Barbados and Jamaica, about 1750, to tenderize very tough meats and that it was claimed that hogs eating the raw fruits of this plant continuously had the mucous membrane of the stomach and intestines digested and finally destroyed. Sumner and Somers (1947) state that in Central and South America fig (*Ficus glabrata* and *F. laurifolia*) sap has been taken internally for centuries as a cure for intestinal worms. These authors also report that Caldwell and Caldwell found that the sap destroys the round worm, *Trichuris trichura,* and that Robbins showed that the sap digests and destroys the intestinal worm, *Ascaris.*

Schwann (Anderson 1946, p. 242) is credited with the discovery of pepsin in 1836. Vines (1909) gives Hooker, 1874, and Darwin, 1875, credit as starting scientific investigation of plant proteases. Hooker reported his work on proteases of insectivorous plants in his presidential address before the British Association. Darwin, 1875, describes his researches in his book on insectivorous plants. Darwin's experiments with *Drosera* were very extensive and determined the various substances dissolving or failing of dissolution when attacked by the glandular hairs. The digestible materials grasped by the hairs stimulate both the enzyme and acid secretion, both of which are necessary for digestion. The digestion could be stopped by alkalies and started again with acids. Pepsin had been much studied and was known to act in acid medium so it was natural that Darwin should consider the *Drosera* enzyme as similar to if not identical with pepsin. Vines (1909) gives the history of our early knowledge on plant proteases. Von Borup-Besanez, 1874-75, found leucine and asparagine in seedlings of vetch and assumed that they resulted from digestion of reserve proteins, but the enzyme he extracted from seeds with glycerol produced peptone but no leucine from fibrin. In the earlier period this was considered a pepsin.

Asenjo and de Fernandez (1942) found the juice of *Bromelia pinguin* 17 times as active as pineapple juice, both proteolytically and in its milk-clotting action. They called the enzyme pinguinain. They believe the enzyme has commercial possibilities both as a protease and as rennin in cheese-making. Castaneda *et al.* (1942) believe that mexicain from the latex of *Pileus mexicanus* compares favorably with papain. Iyengar (1943) worked out pharmaceutical standards for packaged papain. Crude preparations kept better than more highly purified products. Balls and Kies (Anderson 1946) speak of papain and ficin as the only plant proteases with considerable industrial use; the first chiefly as a clarifier for beer and the latter as a pharmaceutical. Mergentime and Wiegand (1946) find that proteases of frozen peas remain active at many degrees below freezing even in the presence of ice. This raises for consideration proteolytic degeneration of vegetables in quick freeze and the importance of preblanching.

Classification of proteases.—When a protein is completely hydrolyzed with acid all amino acids are liberated. No single protease will accomplish this end but it takes the combined action of a proteinase followed by peptidases to accomplish complete hydrolysis. Formerly the incompletely hydrolyzed products of tryptic digestion, such as peptones, proteoses, and polypeptides, were supposed to be hydrolyzed to amino acids by a single enzyme, "erepsin." It was later found that "erepsin" is not a single enzyme but that it consists of several peptidases. The "erepsin" of plants as discussed by Miller is now explained on the same basis. Calvery (1933) determined the percentage of the amino and carboxyl groups liberated when various plant and animal enzymes acted alone or in combination upon crystalline egg albumin. The degree of hydrolysis was the same whether measured by the free amino or carboxyl groups of the amino acids. Pure proteinase of pancreas split one-third of the peptide linkages. Proteinase and pepsin acting in combination gave the same value but this proteinase and papain-HCN acting together split two-thirds of the peptide linkages or gave 67 per cent hydrolysis. Pepsin and "erepsin" working in combination gave complete hydrolysis. Pepsin, protaminase, and aminopolypeptidase; pepsin and protaminase + carboxypolypeptidase; or pepsin and aminopolypeptidase each gave two-thirds hydrolysis. Proteases that hydrolyze the large protein molecule are known as *proteinases* and those that attack only split products of the protein molecule (peptones, proteoses, or peptides) as *peptidases.**

It is doubtful whether the size of the molecule attacked is the real basis of difference between proteinases and peptidases for it is well established that the crystalline proteinases hydrolyze synthetic peptides. They also apparently give some free amino acids, if tardily, in protein hydrolysis. Bergmann and Fruton (1941) mention that crystalline pepsin hydrolyzes the peptides that contain tyrosine or phenylalanine in the complex and attacks the peptide linkage in these amino acids that involve the amino group. Crystalline chymotrypsin also hydrolyzes peptides with these two amino acids, but splits them at the peptide linkage that involves the carboxyl group. Crystalline trysin acts at the carboxyl linkage of lysine and arginine. The authors also mention that a free amino or carboxyl group in the chain near to the linkage attacked by the enzyme may render the peptide less sensitive to attack, also a variation in the non-essential amino acids in the peptide chain may modify the sensitiveness of the peptide to hydrolysis by the particular enzyme. It appears then that the nature of the linkages involved rather than the size of the protein or peptide molecule determines whether the molecule is hydrolyzed by a given protease. The authors suggest that the term *exopeptidases* be used for those that can hydrolyze only terminal peptide linkages and *endopeptidases* for those that can hydrolyze terminal as well as more centrally located peptide bonds in the molecule. Laine (1944) also shows that trypsin and pepsin attack the zein molecule at different linkages.

Various classifications have been offered for proteases, both proteinases and peptidases. Some proteases act within the cells in which they are formed or are endoproteases; some bacterial proteases and the proteases of organs like the bean cotyledons are endoproteases. Other proteases are secreted by glandular organs and act upon proteins outside the cells that produce them; proteases of insectivorous plants and latex proteinases are exoproteases. Proteinases that are inactivated by oxidizing agents (H_2O_2, iodoacetic acid, etc.) but activated by reducing agents (H_2S, glutathione, cysteine, HCN, etc.) like papain from the latex of *Carica papaya* are called papainases. The latex of this plant contains a natural activator. In the latex of *Carica* papain is associated with a rennin-like enzyme, chymopapain, which coagulates milk. Both papain and chymopapain have been crystallized. Several of the more studied plant proteinases are papainases; ficin from the genus *Ficus*; asclepain m from *Asclepias mexi-*

---

* In the early studies crude extracts of proteases were used. Later the proteases were partially purified by extracting with water or glycerol and precipitating with alcohol, ammonium sulfate, or other salts. The real advance in exact knowledge of the action of enzymes awaited the important accomplishment of Sumner (1926) in crystallizing urease, the amidase that hydrolyzes urea to carbon dioxide and ammonia. Since that time several proteinases have been crystallized and their action studied. There has been less success in crystallizing peptidases. Peptidases are partially purified by adsorption of the peptidases or their impurities on inorganic materials. The crystallization of proteinases often requires repeated use of one or more of the following steps before they are pure enough to crystallize: (1) acidulation; (2) heat denaturing; (3) salting out fractionation; (4) electrophoretic separation; (5) adsorption on inorganic material; or (6) precipitation with protamines for removing either an impurity or the proteinase itself from the mixture. Finally, the nearly pure protein is precipitated with alcohol, dioxane, acetone, or salt. The purity of the crystals is confirmed by electrophoretic and ultracentrifuge tests. If all the molecules are alike in their electrophoretic and ultracentrifuge behavior they may be alike chemically. There are also other methods of testing for purity.

cana; asclepain s from *A. speciosa;* mexicain from *Pileus mexicanus;* pinguinain from *Bromelia pinguin.* Some proteinases from plants are not activated by reducing agents and are therefore not papainases: solanain from *Solanum elaeagnifolium,* a squash proteinase, and hurain from *Hura crepitans* are examples. The plant proteinases mentioned above have a pH optimum ranging from 5 to 8; grain proteinases and ficin have an optimum of pH 5, and the others have an optimum of 6.5 or above.

Much has been learned about peptidases by studying their action on synthetic peptides of known composition. Amongst such synthetic di- and tripeptides are leucylglycine, leucyldiglycine, alanylglycine, alanyldiglycine, leucylglycyltyrosine, and many others. Balls and Kies, however, emphasize the fact that our knowledge of peptidases must remain defective until more of them can be obtained as pure proteins.

Effect of condition on the action of proteases in seeds and seedlings.—Balls and Kies discuss the earlier work on peptidases of germinated grains and bacteria. Bamann and Schimke (1941) studied the peptidases of germinated seeds of wheat, rye, oats, barley, peas, lentils, etc. The undialyzed enzyme preparations split both D- and L-leucylglycine while the dialyzed preparations did not act on the D-component. The rate of splitting of L-leucylglycine was accelerated by Mn^{++} and Mg^{++}. Even the D-component was split to some extent in the presence of Mn. Mn plus cysteine was more effective than Mn alone. Products of hydrolysis, L-leucine, inhibited enzyme activity. The different sources of enzyme varied in the rate at which they split the D-component. All the studies were made at pH 7.8. Mounfield (1936) states that proteinase of sprouted wheat is relatively stable in buffer solutions at 4 and 6 pH and is destroyed at 8 pH. The dipeptidase loses its activity slowly at 6 and 8 pH but is quickly destroyed at 4 pH. Glycerol stabilizes the dipeptidase in wheat extracts by maintaining the pH at about 6; aqueous extracts develop acidity readily. Both the proteinase and dipeptidase of sprouted wheat are activated by cyanide, the former more than the latter. The optimum pH for the proteinase is shifted from pH 4.1 to 4.8 by the cyanide, that of the dipeptidase for leucylglycine from 7.3 to 7.8 pH, and for glycylglycine from 7.9 to 8.1 pH.

Bottelier *et al.* (1943) find little peptidase in the root cap, much just back of the root cap, and a diminishing amount as the older part of the root is approached. Avery and Linderstrøm-Lang (1940) find that for any coleoptile 4 mm. or more in length peptidase activity per unit of weight of tissue or per cell was consistently greater at the tip. There was a correlation between the morphological structure and auxin and peptidase gradients. Asenjo *et al.* (1943) studied the protease content of the papaya plant at various stages of development. All parts except the seed showed varying degrees of proteolytic activity. Milk-clotting activity appeared first in the leaf and later in the stem and root. The green rind of the fruits showed greatest activity with decreasing quantities in leaf, fruit pulp, stem, and root. In the leaf the maximum activity was reached between the 4*th* and 9*th* months and fell at the 13*th* month. A similar but less marked curve was shown for the stem and root.

Engel and Heins (1947) find that in the resting grains of wheat, rye, and barley proteinases and peptidases are located mainly in the aleurone cells while the bulk of the endosperm is almost free of the two enzymes. Doty *et al.* (1946/47) find that the proteolytic amyloclastic and lipolytic activities in oats and tomato seeds increase greatly with 24 hours' germination while the cytochrome oxidase activity had not appeared after 48 hours. They suggest that lack of seed viability may be due, at least in part, to some defect in the enzyme system. Mounfield (1936) found that the proteases, both proteinases and dipeptidases, of wheat increased greatly with germination; with two days' germination there was little increase but by seven days the proteases had risen ten-fold. Grains stored in stoppered bottles in dark at 18° C. gradually fell in their power to produce proteinases later during germination; they lost 67 per cent of this power in two years of storage. Either the storage condition must have been very poor (high moisture) or the power to develop proteinase during germination throws little light on germination power, for Whymper and Bradley (1947) found that English wheats stored with 4 to 5 per cent moisture dropped only 17 per cent in germination power in 19 years and 31 per cent in 32 years. Nakamura (1940) found that at like stages of germination the amount of amylases and proteases in different varieties of barley varied greatly. Proskuryakov *et al.* (1941) state that wheat grains show a fall in proteinase content, also an increased resistance of the grain proteins to proteinase attack as the grains mature. The reserve changes occur with germination.

It is well established (Koblet 1937) that white pine seeds and freshly harvested wheat grains are favored in germination by a prechilling period in germination condition. Seeds showed a slight increase in protease content during prechilling but as great or greater increase occurred in a warm germinator. It is concluded that the favorable effect of low-temperature pretreatment on germination of white pine and wheat is not due to increased catalytic activity.

HCN and cysteine (Prokoshev and Babichev 1936) (reducing agents) activate proteolysis (autolysis) in the materials from dormant grains of wheat and barley and inhibit proteolysis in materials from the sprouts. Iodoacetic acid (oxidizing agent) inhibits strongly proteolysis in dormant grain material but shows little inhibition in proteolysis in the material from sprouts. In soybean sprout material HCN and cysteine activate proteolysis. The nature of the proteases varies in the different organs of the same plant and in like organs of different plants. Prokoshev *et al.* (1936) found that dry wheat grains that had been gassed with various concentrations of H_2S for three days showed an increase in the autolytic capacity of the sprouts that grew later.

A trypsin inhibitor is found in raw soybeans that interferes with protein digestion in the chick (Ham and Sandstedt 1944; Ham *et al.* 1945) and the rat (Klose *et al.* 1946). The inhibitor seems to be a globulin (Kunitz 1945) and the injurious effect is overcome by autoclaving the beans. Several raw legume seeds contain the inhibitor (Borchers *et al.* 1946) (peanut, chick pea, soybean, mung, scarlet runner, lima, garden and velvet beans, and black eye pea). Some legume seeds (jack bean, guar, lentil, and garden pea and horse beans) and all non-leguminous seeds studied do not contain the inhibitor. Apparently not all nutrient disturbance caused by raw legume seeds is caused by interference with tryptic digestion (Desikachar and De 1947; Klose *et al.* 1948).

Methods of determining the action of proteases.—In the early researches the appearance of leucine or tyrosine or the dissolution of coagulated egg white, fibrin, or cooked meat were used as indicators of protein hydrolysis. Miller (1938) mentioned the following as quantitative methods used for determining protein digestion: (1) weight of coagulated protein that remains in the digestive mixture; (2) determination of total nitrogen of the digested material; (3) the measurement of the increased amino nitrogen by the Van Slyke method; (4) determination of the increase in electrical conductivity; (5) determination of the changes in optical activity; (6) determination of the free carboxyl groups formed (Sorensen's method); and (7) use of the tryptophan and biuret color reactions in a quantitative way.

For proteinase activity Balls and Kies (Anderson 1946) point out that the methods used are chosen to fit the needs of the particular problem. If very little proteinase is present reduction in the viscosity of gelatin solution is the desirable method. If more proteinase is present the hemoglobin method of Anson is recommended. This is run under standard conditions. The digestion is allowed to go on for a given time, the undigested protein is precipitated with trichloroacetic acid, and the filtrate is analyzed for reducing substance by Folin-Crocalteau phenol reagent. The principal reactants are tyrosine and trytophan peptides. The formol titration method of Northrup consists in titrating the digested product under standard conditions with N/50 alkali using phenolphthalein as an indicator. The new partition chromatograph method (Gordon *et al.* 1943*a* and *b*; Consden *et al.* 1944) of separating and identifying amino acids in protein hydrolysates or other mixtures of amino acids has promise. The authors claim that all amino acids in a mixture can be separated and identified by this method. It is valuable as a qualitative method and the authors find it of assistance in quantitative determinations. Ninhydrin is used to stain and locate the several amino acids. Concentration and nature of solvents as well as other factors determine the position of the several amino acids.

Synthetic action of proteases.—Gale (1948) very recently discussed the synthesis of proteins stating that it occurs in three main steps: (1) synthesis of amino acids; (2) synthesis of polypeptides; and (3) synthesis of proteins. He mentions that we have little detailed knowledge concerning any of the steps but that more knowledge has accumulated and is accumulating faster on the synthesis of amino acids than on either of the other two steps. The synthesis is evidently brought about by enzymes that are reversible in their action. While Gale's discussion deals with synthesis by enzymes from microorganisms, it gives a good picture of the whole field of protein synthesis.

Gale discusses tryptophan synthesizing system of certain bacteria. They are unable to synthesize this essential amino acid unless furnished indole. They can condense indole and the amino acid, l-serine, into tryptophan. An enzyme system consisting of a protein and prosthetic group from *Neurospora* catalyzes this synthesis. Gale also describes the glutamine synthesizing system by bacterial enzymes.

Gale believes that a great advance in the knowledge of intermediates in amino acid synthesis will come from the study of mutants of *Neurospora* and other fungi. He illustrates the method as follows: a wild strain synthesizes an essential amino acid D from A through the steps A→B→C→D. One mutant lacks the enzyme that transforms A to B. It requires B, C, or D. A second strain lacks the enzyme that transforms B to C. It requires C or D. And a third mutant lacks the enzyme that transforms C to D. It must have D. Gale gives specific cases for various *Neurospora* mutants in connection with the synthesis of tryptophan and iso-leucine and valine. This does not mean that every organism uses the same intermediates in synthesis of a given amino acid but quite the opposite as is evident from what has just been said.

Gale mentions that our knowledge of the synthesis of peptides in organisms is much more limited than the knowledge of the synthesis of amino acids. He states that we do not know the properties of an enzyme system that synthesizes peptides *in vivo* although we do know cell-free proteinases and peptidases that synthesize peptides *in vitro* (Bergmann and Fraenkel-Conrat 1937) under somewhat artificial conditions. If we knew essential peptides for various organisms as we know essential amino acids, advances in knowledge of peptide synthesis might come more readily. Gale speaks of the few natural peptides found in organisms: glutathione, germicidin S, and the various pteroylglutamic acids. In the latter, glutamic acid seems to hold a key position in synthesis. Glutamic acid is also an amino donator in transaminase synthesis and an amino acid in the biologically important tripeptide glutathione. Gale says our knowledge of the enzymes and processes concerned in the final stage in which peptides are condensed and organized into functional proteins is nil.

Seed Esterases:—The greater part of the stored lipoids in seeds exists as glycerides of the higher fatty acids. These are hydrolyzed as well as synthesized by lipases. This gives lipases a special interest in seed metabolism. We have also seen that phospholipids (lecithins and cephalins) make up a small fraction of extracted seed fats. Lecithinases that hydrolyze these bodies are of course of interest and will be discussed later. Phytosterols are also present generally as a still smaller fraction of seed fats.

These often combine with fatty acids to form phytosterol esters. In the animal cholesterol esterases hydrolyze the cholesterol esters. It is likely that in plants phytosterol esterases are present. The lecithinases and cholesterol esterases, as is the case with most enzymes, have received more attention in animals than in plants.

The following general citations will be found of great value in a study of esterases: Miller (1938), section on esterases or lipases of plants; Anderson (1946), chapter on esterases by Longenecker; Sumner and Somers (1947), chapter on esterases. Besides those just mentioned there are a number of other well known plant esterases that should be briefly defined before we discuss lipases and lecithinases. Jansen et al. (1947) have characterized an esterase from citrus fruit as acetyl esterase because it hydrolyzes esters of acetic acid best. It hydrolyzes monoacetin about 100 times as fast as monobutyrin. The pH optimum for acetins is 5.5 to 6.5 and the esterase is destroyed readily at pH 4. Chlorophyllase, tannase, and pectase are other well known plant esterases.

There are many plant phosphatases. Under lecithinases we will discuss *glycerophosphatase* and *choline phosphatase*. *Phytase* is a phosphatase that splits phytin into inositol and phosphoric acid. Phytin is a common storage form of phosphorus in seeds. Various other phosphatases are found in cereal grains. Certain organic compounds of plants and animals are esters of sulfuric acid or sulfates. *Sulfatases* hydrolyze these compounds releasing sulfuric acid or sulfate. It was earlier thought that sinigrin of the mustard seed is hydrolyzed into its three constituents (glucose, allyl isothiocyanate, and $KHSO_4$) by a single enzyme, sinigrinase. Neuberg and Schoenebeck (1933) offer good evidence that sinigrinase is a mixture of two enzymes, a myrosulfatase that releases the sulfate and a myro-glucosidase. A number of sulfatases have been found in malt and cereal grains. The fatty substance of jojoba (*Simmondsia californica*) nuts, as previously stated, consists of wax esters. It is of interest to know whether any of the various esterases known to date including lipases will hydrolyze these esters, or whether the nuts contain a special esterase.

Lipases:—Green (1890) was the first to establish the existence of lipase in germinating seeds. He used the castor bean for his study and no other source of equally active plant lipase has been found to date. *Ricinus* lipase does have the disadvantage of containing toxic substances, ricin, ricinin, and an allergen. We have already discussed these under toxalbumins and alkaloids. Sumner and Somers caution workers with *Ricinus* lipase about dangers of poisoning. Longenecker (Anderson 1946) mentions that Kaneth has attempted to rid *Ricinus* lipase of these substances.

Historical.—Green reviews some of the earlier work on the changes that occur in the oils of fatty seeds during germination. Sachs, 1859, assumed that the fats were transformed directly to starch in the seed after which the starch was changed to sugar for mobilization to the seedling. Fleury, also Helriegel working on various fatty seeds, found sugar rather than starch as an intermediate. Muntz, in 1871, found that fatty acids increase as germination of fatty seeds progressed, but did not find glycerol. Schutzenberger, in 1876, found that if oily seeds are emulsified in water, fatty acids and glycerol soon appear. He postulates an enzyme that hydrolyzes fats but gives no experimental proof of its existence. Miller (1938) states that Pelouse, 1855, suggested the presence of a fat-splitting enzyme in flax, mustard, and rape, and Longenecker (Anderson 1946) offers evidence that Boussingault found that decomposing fatty seeds produce fatty acids.

Green showed that lipase exists as a non-active proenzyme in the resting *Ricinus* seed. The proenzyme is changed quickly to active lipase in the powder of the resting seed by treating with weak acetic acid or slowly by suspending the powder in water with an antiseptic. The changes occurring in the seed during germination also activate the lipase. The endosperm rather than the embryo is the source of *Ricinus* lipase.

There have been many investigations of seed lipases since the classical experiments by Green. A number of points of disagreement have developed in the later researches, perhaps partly because the lipases have resisted all attempts at purification by crystallization. Takamiya (1935) claims to have prepared a lipase from castor bean seeds that on the dry weight basis had 240 times the activity of the bean itself. He mentions that Willstätter's best preparation had only 100 times the activity of the bean. With such preparations variation in impurities modifies the speed of reaction or, perhaps, the effect of other conditions on the speed of reaction. Also lipases have been confused with other esterases because of the great range of substrates used for determining their hydrolytic and synthetic action. These substrates range all the way from simple esters, such as methyl acetate, to mixed glycerides with long fatty acid chains such as are found in seed oils. A third thing that may account for some of the disagreements concerning lipases and other esterase determinations is the fact that the act of hydrolysis liberates acids thus making it difficult to maintain a constant pH. Leonard (1941) shows that this may be overcome by using continuous titration or continuous titration in combination with buffers, instead of buffers alone, to maintain a constant pH.

Castor bean lipase.—Willstätter and Waldschmidt-Leitz (1924) made a rather elaborate study of *Ricinus* lipase. It did not yield to purification and lost its activity readily in moisture in absence of fats. It was most active at pH 5 in the acetate buffer and at 35° but was inactivated readily at 50° C. A powder could be prepared with little loss of activity but dry preparations were less stable than oil emulsions. The lipase content of the seeds increased with germination with the maximum after three days' germination at 30° C. after which it fell. The authors distinguish between seed (spermatolipase) and seedling (blastolipase) lipases. Blastolipase was more stable in dry form and showed more pronounced synthetic action than spermatolipase.

Guillemet (1931a and b) found the highest lipase activity in castor beans maturing in late summer and in *R. communis sanguineus* of four varieties tested. The lipase fell rapidly in stored seeds at first but 75 per cent of it still remained after ten years of storage. The optimum pH for activity varied from 3 to 4.3 in various buffers. Padoa (1932) and Padoa and Spada (1931, 1933) found that treating growing plants with various alkaloids increased the lipase and other enzymes in *Ricinus* seeds and amylase and other enzymes in barley. In germinating *Ricinus* seeds greatest lipase activity occurred on the *7th* day and the synthetic action was evident on the *9th* day. Ricin lipase hydrolyzes various plant and animal fats at different rates (Longenecker and Haley 1935; Ahmad and Bahl 1946; Ahmad and Sareen 1946). Takamiya (1935) and Ito (1936) found a substance in the castor bean that in the reduced state stimulates the hydrolytic activity of *Ricinus* lipase and in the oxidized state inhibits this action. In the intermediate state it is inactive. *Ricinus* seeds (Lischkewitsch and Prizemina 1929) grown at higher altitudes and latitudes have higher lipase content and acidity than seeds grown at lower altitudes and latitudes because the former are less mature. Altitude and latitude had similar effect on the catalase, amylase, and protease of cereal grains.

Soybean lipase.—Leonard (1941) reviewed the earlier literature on the esterases of soybeans. He found that soybeans contain both an esterase and a lipase. The esterase was present in the dormant seeds of the five varieties studied in about equal and in considerable amounts. It hydrolyzes triacetin readily but not ethyl butyrate or olive oil and does not increase with germination. Some lipase was present in dormant seeds of Black Wilson variety and absent in dormant seeds of Easycook variety. The lipolytic action increases rapidly, however, with germination. The dormant seeds have esterase as the dominant esterase and the germinating seeds lipase. Soybean lipase, unlike castor bean lipase, is not activated by acid. The author considers the two enzymes as very different.

Cotton seed lipase.—Olcott and Fontaine (1941a and b) found no lipase in resting cotton seeds when they were shaken with various buffers giving pHs from 3 to 11 and treated with $CaCl_2$ solution as an activator. The same treatment produced lipase from germinated seeds. As germination progressed lipase and fatty acids increased and total lipids decreased. The effective pH for activity was 6 to 9 with the optimum at 7. The authors contrast cotton seed lipase with castor bean lipase stating that the former resembles pancreatic lipase so far as the optimum pH is concerned, but that this may be due to the degree of purification since lipases change with purification. The best preparations from germinated cotton seeds showed lipolytic activity equal to commercial pancreas lipase and equal to one-fourth to one-tenth that of defatted castor bean preparation. This lipase hydrolyzes triacetin, tributyrin, benzyl butyrate, and oils. The authors had some success in concentrating cotton seed lipase by extracting it with 87 per cent glycerol. Karon and Altschul (1944) found that the acidity of stored cotton seed rose when the moisture content rose from 7.5 to 20 per cent. The most rapid rise was with moisture increasing from 15 to 18 per cent. Treating the seeds with NH_3 or HCl retarded greatly the acid increase. Ammonia treatment also improved the oil extracted from treated seeds.

Singer and Hofstee (1948) studied a partially purified wheat germ lipase. The enzyme hydrolyzed many water-soluble simple esters, mono- and triglycerides, and esters of hexalcohols tested. A single enzyme, a water-soluble protein, is supposed to produce all these hydrolyses. Wessel (1941) studied the esterase of defatted tung oil seed meal. The optimum was pH 6 for continuous titration and pH 7.5 with buffers. The optimum temperature was 37° C. and the temperature coefficient varied from 1.44 to 1.65. Dyer (1947) found that potassium salts protect the lipids in the peanut cotyledons against lipase hydrolysis during germination. Sodium salts were less effective. Bamann and Ullman (1942) determined the esterase content of seeds of 100 species and the esterase content of vegetative organs of 60 species using tributyrin and triacetin as substrates. It may be other esterases than lipase that caused much of the hydrolysis. The seeds showed 3 to 10 times as much esterase activity per dry weight as the vegetative organs.

Caesalpinia bonducella (Patwardhan 1929) seeds, dormant and germinated, are claimed to lack lipase. Similar claims have been made for *Cannabis indica* and *Cucurbita pepo*. Schreiber (1940) found lipase in both *Cannabis* and *Cucurbita* seeds and believes earlier claims to the contrary were based on faulty technique. We have seen that lipase appears in some seeds only after germination starts. The lipase in dry seeds seems to be very resistant to high temperatures. Iwamoto (1930) heated para rubber seeds to 105° C. for five hours without destroying the lipase. Theis *et al.* (1929) found lipase in both flax seed meal and the oil after heating to 90° C. during pressing. Guillemet finds that *Ricinus* seeds dried over H_2SO_4 retain two-thirds of their lipase activity when heated to 130° C. for one hour.

Sherwood *et al.* (1933) found the objectionable flavor in stored granular wheat germs correlated with increased acidity. The degeneration was largely prevented by storing in vacuum at —10° C. Sizer and Josephson (1942) found in quick freeze studies that the temperature coefficient and the energy of activation were low for lipase, trypsin, and invertase above the solidification point and much higher below this point; that is, after the temperature reaches the congealing point the rate of enzyme action falls rapidly with fall in temperature.

Synthetic action of lipase.—Reichel and Reinmuth (1938) have re-studied the ability of the yeast fungi, *Endomyces vernalis,* to synthesize fats and store them, when grown in sugar solutions. The authors mention that Lindner had earlier established this synthesis for certain yeasts by microscopical methods and that Haehn and Kintto had found these yeasts synthesizing from sugar solutions as much as 25 per cent of their own dry weight in fats. The authors cultured these organisms in 1.5 per cent cane sugar and fructose solutions and 1.5 and 3 per cent glucose for eight days. In cane sugar the organisms produced as high as 14 per cent of their dry weight in fat and in fructose nearly as much but glucose was very much less effective as a sugar source. Developing seeds synthesize fats from sugars drawn from the plant. The complete synthesis requires the synthesis of glycerol and the fatty acids followed by their esterification to fats. We know little about the synthesis of the fatty acids and glycerol. Lipase catalyzes only the last step, the condensation of fatty acids and glycerol into the triglycerides.

In 1900 Kastle and Loevenhart (1900) showed that in favorable conditions and in proper concentrations of ethyl alcohol and butyric acid pancreatic lipase synthesized ethyl butyrate. Since that time a number of researches have been published on the synthetic action of animal lipases and perhaps a somewhat smaller number on fat synthesis by plant lipases. Jalander (1911) found that when 40 g. of oleic acid, 100 g. of glycerol, and 0.5 g. of *Ricinus* lipase were allowed to stand 12 days, 8.4 g. of triolein were formed or there was 11 per cent esterification. Bournot (1914) found that the fat-free very finely-ground powder of *Chelidonium majus* seeds had great lipase activity, both hydrolytic and synthetic. Hydrolytic action was fastest with 50 per cent water and synthetic action fastest with 5 per cent water in the fatty acid-glycerol-powder mixture. The percentage synthesis varied considerably with the fatty acids and alcohols used in the mixtures. The enzyme was especially effective in synthesizing triolein. It has been stated already that *Ricinus* seedling lipase has greater synthetic action than the seed lipase and that there is a substance in *Ricinus* seeds which when reduced activates synthesis by the lipase. Schreiber (1942) studied the lipase activity of 29 different species and varieties of seeds belonging to ten different families of plants. Lipase of eight species and three varieties of *Ricinus communis* gave noteworthy synthetic action. The optimum concentration of glycerol for synthetic action varied from 55 to 90 per cent for the several lipases. The author questions whether glycerol ever reaches such high concentrations in living cells and how much light synthesis *in vitro* throws on synthesis *in vivo*.

Lecithinases:—Sumner and Somers (1947) assert that lipases do not hydrolyze lecithin as some textbooks claim, but that there are four enzymes involved in the complete hydrolysis of phospholipids into glycerol, two fatty acids, phosphoric acid and the nitrogen base (choline in the case of lecithins or amino ethyl alcohol in cephalins). *Lecithinase (a)* is a toxin found in the venom of snakes and bees. This releases an unsaturated fatty acid from the molecule forming hemolytic lysolecithin. *Lecithinase (b)* liberates the remaining fatty acid from lysolecithin and destroys its hemolytic action or, acting upon the whole molecule of phospholipid, it releases both fatty acids without disturbing the linkages between the phosphoric acid and glycerol or the phosphoric acid and the nitrogen base. The third enzyme is *glycerophosphatase* which hydrolyzes the bond between the glycerol and phosphoric acid, and the fourth enzyme is *choline phosphatase* which hydrolyzes the bond between the phosphoric acid and the nitrogen base.

Hanahan and Chaikoff (1947) mention that lecithinase (b) is found in rice hulls and *Aspergillus oryzae*, that glycerophosphatase is found in *Clostridium welchii*, but that he and his co-worker were the first to find *choline phosphatase* in plants. They obtained a specific enzyme from carrots that split the base from phospholipids without disturbing the other three linkages. It would not hydrolyze acetyl choline, but it did release more nitrogen from phospholipids than could be accounted for by the choline. The optimum pH was 5.2 to 5.9 in 0.05 M phosphate buffer and it acted faster at 26° than at 37° C. although it could be heated to 95° C. for 15 minutes without loss of activity. The hydrolysis is a monomolecular reaction. Hanahan and Chaikoff (1947) found a similar enzyme in fresh cabbage leaves.

Catalase:—Because the effect of after-ripening, germination, maturity of seeds, etc. on their catalase activity has been repeatedly mentioned, a word should be said about the function, nature, and methods of determining this enzyme. Sumner and Somers (1947) and others think the only function of this enzyme is to protect the living organism against the accumulation of H_2O_2 and that while catalase resembles oxidases, peroxidases, and cytochromes in having iron in the prosthetic (hematin) groups it does not take part in oxidation. Keilin and Hartree (1945) claim that it catalyzes the couple oxidation of alcohols. Since there is doubt of its having significance in connection with oxidation it is, for convenience, briefly described at this point.

In 1811 Thenard (Sumner and Somers 1947) pointed out that animal and plant tissues and finely-powdered metals decompose H_2O_2. Schoenbein considered this a property of all enzymes but it was later shown to be a property of a specific enzyme which Loew (1901) named catalase. Catalase is relatively stable and has been crystallized and studied in a highly purified form. It is very active; Sumner and Somers state that one molecule of catalase decomposes five million molecules of H_2O_2 in one minute at $0°$ C. This is the "turnover number." Emden (1947) finds that the catalase in pumpkin seeds is about one-thirtieth as active as liver catalase.

Plant physiologists have generally measured the catalase activity of seed material without purification and by measuring the volume of oxygen liberated. This method would not meet the requirements of students of enzymes where the catalase "Fähigkeit" or catalase purity is to be determined. Sumner (1941) states that it is satisfactory to measure the oxygen evolved provided one possesses the necessary apparatus. He describes (p. 166) a modification of the Jolles titration method for estimating catalase in grossly impure material such as would be encountered in ground seeds. Lineweaver and Morris (1947) have also modified the Jolles titration method for determining the catalase in frozen vegetables. The reader is referred to Balls and Hale (1932) for the pitfalls that should be avoided in determining the catalase content of seeds.

References:—

Ahmad, B., & A. N. Bahl, 1946: Relative digestibility of common edible fats. II. Hydrolysis by pancreatic lipase (Jour. Sci. and Indus. Res. [India] 5:1-3; *abstr. in* Biol. Abstr. 22:229, 1948).

Ahmad, B., & R. N. Sareen, 1946: Relative digestibility of common edible fats. I. By ricinus lipase (Jour. Sci. and Indus. Res. [India] 4:710-712; *abstr. in* Biol. Abstr. 22:228, 1948).

Anderson, J. A. (*editor*), 1946: Enzymes and their role in wheat technology (371 pp., Interscience Publishers, Inc., New York).

Asenjo, C. F., D. H. Cook, M. del C. de Fernandez & L. A. Alvarez, 1943: Chemical changes of the papaya plant during development, with special reference to its proteolytic activity (Jour. Agric. Univ. Puerto Rico 27:1-15; *abstr. in* Biol. Abstr. 18:17417, 1944).

Asenjo, C. F., & M. del C. de Fernandez, 1942: A new protease from *Bromella* [*sic.*] *pinguin* L. (Science 95:48-49).

Avery, G. S., Jr., & K. Linderstrøm-Lang, 1940: Peptidase activity in the *Avena* coleoptile, phytohormone test object (Bot. Gaz. 102:50-63).

Balls, A. K., & W. S. Hale, 1932: The estimation of catalase in agricultural products (Jour. Assoc. Off. Agric. Chem. 15:483-490).

Balls, A. K., & S. Schwimmer, 1944: Digestion of raw starch (Jour. Biol. Chem. 156:203-210).

Bamann, E., & O. Schimke, 1941: d-Peptid-Spaltung durch Enzympräparate aus wachsenden Keimpflanzen; Beeinflussung durch natürliche und zusätzliche Aktivatoren. Zur Kenntniss der Peptidasen. II (Biochem. Zeitschr. 310:119-130).

Bamann, E., & E. Ullman, 1942: Untersuchungen über die Lipase höherer Pflanzen (Biochem. Zeitschr. 312:9-40).

Bayliss, W. M., 1925: Monographs on biochemistry. The nature of enzyme action (200 pp., Longmans, Green & Co., London).

Beadle, G. W., & E. L. Tatum, 1941: Genetic control of biochemical reactions in Neurospora (Proc. Nat. Acad. Sci. 27:499-506).

————, ————, 1945: Neurospora. II. Methods of producing and detecting mutations concerned with nutritional requirements (Amer. Jour. Bot. 32:678-686).

Bergmann, M., & H. Fraenkel-Conrat, 1937: The rôle of specificity in the enzymatic synthesis of proteins. Syntheses with intracellular enzymes (Jour. Biol. Chem. 119:707-720).

Bergmann, M., & J. S. Fruton, 1941: The specificity of proteinases (Advances in Enzymology 1:63-98).

Bonner, D., 1946a: Production of biochemical mutations in Penicillium (Amer. Jour. Bot. 33:788-791).

————, 1946b: Biochemical mutations in Neurospora (Cold Spring Harbor Symposia, Quant. Biol. 11:14-24).

Borchers, R., C. W. Ackerson & L. Kimmett, 1947: Trypsin inhibitor. IV. Occurrence in seeds of the Leguminosae and other seeds (Arch. Biochem. 13:291-293).

Bottelier, H. P., H. Holter & K. Linderstrøm-Lang, 1943: Studies on enzymatic histochemistry. XXXVI. Determination of peptidase activity, nitrogen content and reduced weight in roots of the barley, Hordeum vulgare (Compt. Rend. Trav. Lab. Carlsberg, Ser. Chim. 24:289-313).

Bournot, K., 1914: Ueber das Enzym der Chelidoniumsamen. II (Biochem. Zeitschr. 65:140-157).

Bowman, D. E., 1944: Fractions derived from soy beans and navy beans which retard tryptic digestion of casein (Proc. Soc. Exp. Biol. & Med. 57:139-140).

Buchner, E., 1897: Alkoholische Gärung ohne Hefezellen (Ber. Deut. Chem. Ges. 30:1110-1113).

Calvery, H. O., 1933: Crystalline egg albumin. The hydrolysis of crystalline egg albumin by pepsin, papain-hydrocyanic acid, and pancreatic proteinase and the subsequent action of some other enzymes on the hydrolysis products produced by these enzymes (Jour. Biol. Chem. 102:73-89).

Castañeda, M., F. F. Gavarron & M. R. Balcazar, 1942: On a new protease from Pileus mexicanus (Science 96:365-366).

Chrzaszcz, T., & J. Janicki, 1936: Sulphuretted hydrogen as a factor in the determination of free and bound amylase in ungerminated cereals (Biochem. Jour. 30:342-344).

Consden, R., A. H. Gordon & A. J. P. Martin, 1944: Qualitative analysis of proteins; a partition chromatographic method using paper (Biochem. Jour. 38:224-232).

Davidson, J., 1945: Total and free amylase content of dormant cereals and related seeds (Jour. Agric. Res. 70:175-200).

Desikachar, H. S. R., & S. S. De, 1947: Role of inhibitors in soybean (Science 106:421-422).

Doermann, A. H., 1945: A bioassay for lysine by use of a mutant of Neurospora (Jour. Biol. Chem. 160:95-103).

Doty, D. M., S. Hicks & L. C. Shenberger, leaders, 1946/47: Enzymes in relation to seed germination (Indiana Agric. Exp. Sta. Ann. Rept. 60:36).

Dyer, H. J., 1947: Influence of potassium and sodium on metabolism of peanut cotyledons during germination (Bot. Gaz. 108:570-581).

Elion, E., 1945: The cereal amylases (Baker's Digest 19:95-96, 112; abstr. in Biol. Abstr. 19:22816, 1945).

Emden, L., 1947: Ueber Kürbis-Katalase (Helvetica Chim. Acta 30:15-19).

Engel, C., & J. Heins, 1947: Distribution of the enzymes in resting cereals. II. Distribution of the proteolytic enzymes in wheat, rye, and barley (Biochem. et Biophys. Acta 1:190-196; abstr. in Chem. Abstr. 42:646, 1948).

Gale, E. F., 1948: Synthesis of protein by micro-organisms (Chem. & Indus. 1948(9): 131-134).

Glasstone, S., 1940: Text-book of physical chemistry (1289 pp., D. Van Nostrand Co., Inc., New York).

Gordon, A. H., A. J. P. Martin & R. L. M. Synge, 1943a: Partition chromatography in the study of protein constituents (Biochem. Jour. 37:79-86).

——, ——, ——, 1943b: The amino-acid composition of gramicidin (Biochem. Jour. 37:86-92).

Green, J. R., 1890: On the germination of the seed of the castor-oil plant (*Ricinus communis*) (Proc. Roy. Soc. London 48:370-392).

Guillemet, R., 1931a: Sur le pouvoir lipolytique de différentes variétés de graines de ricin; facteurs susceptibles de le modifier (Compt. Rend. Soc. Biol. 108:779-781).

——, 1931b: Sur le pH optimum d'hydrolyse des huiles végétales par la lipase de la graine de Ricin (Compt. Rend. Soc. Biol. 108:781-783).

Ham, W. E., & R. M. Sandstedt, 1944: a proteolytic inhibiting substance in the extract from unheated soy bean meal (Jour. Biol. Chem. 154:505-506).

Ham, W. E., R. M. Sandstedt & F. E. Mussehl, 1945: The proteolytic inhibiting substance in the extract from unheated soy bean meal and its effect upon growth in chicks (Jour. Biol. Chem. 161:635-642).

Hanahan, D. J., & I. L. Chaikoff, 1947: A new phospholipide-splitting enzyme specific for the ester linkage between the nitrogenous base and the phosphoric acid grouping (Jour. Biol. Chem. 169:699-705).

Ito, R., 1936: The existence of a substance which controls the hydrolytic and synthetic actions of lipase. I (Biochem. Jour. [Japan] 23:299-304; *abstr. in* Chem. Abstr. 30:4882, 1936).

Iwamoto, Y., 1930: The oil and the lipase-like enzyme in Para rubber seed (Jour. Soc. Chem. Ind. Japan 33:409-411; *abstr. in* Chem. Abstr. 25:2019-2020, 1931).

Iyengar, N. K., 1943: Standards for papain and its preparations (Indian Jour. Med. Res. 31:211-214; *abstr. in* Chem. Abstr. 38:6499, 1944).

Jalander, Y. W., 1911: Zur Kenntnis der Ricinuslipase (Biochem. Zeitschr. 36:435-476).

Jansen, E. F., R. Jang & L. R. MacDonnell, 1947: Citrus acetylesterase (Arch. Biochem. 15:415-431).

Karon, M. L., & A. M. Altschul, 1944: Effect of moisture and of treatments with acid and alkali on rate of formation of free fatty acids in stored cotton seed (Plant Physiol. 19:310-325).

Kastle, J. H., & A. S. Loevenhart, 1900: Concerning lipase, the fat-splitting enzyme, and the reversibility of its action (Amer. Chem. Jour. 24:491-525).

Keilin, D., & E. F. Hartree, 1945: Properties of catalase. Catalysis of coupled oxidation of alcohols (Biochem. Jour. 39:293-301).

Kerr, R. W. (*editor*), 1944: Chemistry and industry of starch. Starch sugars and related compounds (472 pp., Academic Press, Inc., New York).

Klose, A. A., J. D. Greaves & H. L. Fevold, 1948: Inadequacy of proteolytic enzyme inhibition as explanation for growth depression by lima bean protein fractions (Science 108:88-89).

Klose, A. A., B. Hill & H. L. Fevold, 1946: Presence of a growth inhibiting substance in raw soybeans (Proc. Soc. Exp. Biol. & Med. 62:10-12).

Kneen, E., & R. M. Sandstedt, 1946: Distribution and general properties of an amylase inhibitor in cereals (Arch. Biochem. 9:235-249).

Koblet, R., 1937: Ueber die proteolytische Aktivität von Weymouthskiefern- und Weisensamen unter besonderer Berücksichtigung des Einflusses der Vorkühlung (Proc. Internat. Seed Test. Assoc. 9:228-253).

Kunitz, M., 1945: Crystallization of a trypsin inhibitor from soybean (Science 101:668-669).

Laine, T. N., 1944: Investigations of the structure and enzymic splitting of the seed protein zein (Ann. Acad. Sci. Fennicae, Ser. A. II. Chemica 11:7-97; *abstr. in* Chem. Abstr. 40:3781-3782, 1946).

Leonard, J. M., 1941: A study of soy bean esterase (Diss. Catholic Univ. of Amer. Biol. Ser. 39, 81 pp., Washington, D. C.).

Lineweaver, H., & H. J. Morris, 1947: Preliminary report on development of methods for catalase determination in frozen vegetables (Jour. Assoc. Off. Agric. Chem. 30:413-416).

Lischkewitsch, M. J., & S. P. Prizemina, 1929: Ueber den Fermentgehalt in Samen verschiedenen Ursprungs (Biochem. Zeitschr. 212:280-290).

Loew, O., 1901: Catalase, a new enzyme of general occurrence (U.S.D.A. Rept. 68, 47 pp.; *abstr. in* Exp. Sta. Rec. 13:115, 1901/02).

Longenecker, H. E., & D. E. Haley, 1935: *Ricinus* lipase, its nature and specificity (Jour. Amer. Chem. Soc. 57:2019-2021).

Mergentime, M., & E. H. Wiegand, 1946: Low temperature characteristics of a pea proteinase (Fruit Prod. Jour. 26:72-80, 89, 91; *abstr. in* Biol. Abstr. 21:18270, 1947).

Miller, E. C., 1938: Plant physiology (2nd ed., 1201 pp., McGraw-Hill Book Co., Inc., New York).

Mounfield, J. D., 1936: The proteolytic enzymes of sprouted wheat. II (Biochem. Jour. 30:1778-1786).

Myrbäck, K., & B. Magnusson, 1945: Ueber Säurehydrolyse der Stärke (Arkiv Kemi, Min. och Geol. 20A(14):1-22; *abstr. in* Biol. Abstr. 20:9759, 1946).

Nakamura, H., 1940: Germination and enzyme action of barley (Jour. Agric. Chem. Soc. Japan 16:277-280; *abstr. in* Chem. Abstr. 34:6326, 1940).

Neuberg, C. v., & O. v. Schoenebeck, 1933: Ueber Aufteilung der Myrosinase (Naturwiss. 21:404-405).

Newcombe, F. C., 1899: Cellulose-enzymes (Ann. Bot. 13:49-81).

Olcott, H. S., & T. D. Fontaine, 1941a: Composition of cottonseeds. IV. Lipase of germinated seed (Jour. Amer. Chem. Soc. 63:825-827).

——, ——, 1941b: The absence of lipase in cotton seed (Oil and Soap 18:123-124; *abstr. in* Biol. Abstr. 16:5498, 1942).

Padoa, M., 1932: Action of the alkaloids and carbon monoxide on the enzymatic activity of plants (Nature 129:686).

Padoa, M., & A. Spada, 1931: *Ricinus* lipase (Giorn. Biol. Appl. Ind. Chim. 1:81-94; *abstr. in* Chem. Abstr. 26:1961, 1932).

——, ——, 1933: Influence of some substances (especially unsaturated) on the enzyme activity of germinating seed of *Ricinus,* lipase and peroxidase [trans. title] (Giorn. Biol. Appl. Indus. Chim. 3:121-131; *abstr. in* Exp. Sta. Rec. 70:456, 1934).

Patwardhan, V. N., 1929: Enzymes from the seeds of *Caesalpinia bonducella* (Jour. Ind. Inst. Sci. A12:191-192; *abstr. in* Chem. Abstr. 24:1131, 1930).

Pond, R. H., 1906: The incapacity of the date endosperm for self-digestion (Ann. Bot. 20:61-78).

Prokoshev, S. M., & I. A. Babichev, 1936: The specificity of protease in seeds and sprouts of various cultures (Bull. Appl. Bot., Genetics & Plant Breed. Ser. III, 14:79-96 [English summ.]).

Prokoshev, S. M., T. I. Margolina & I. A. Babichev, 1936: On the physiological action of hydrogen sulfide on wheat seeds (Bull. Appl. Bot., Genetics & Plant Breed. Ser. III, 14:3-23 [English summ.]).

Proskuryakov, N. I., A. A. Bundel & E. V. Bukharina, 1941: Alterations of the protease-protein complex in germinating and ripening wheat grain (Biokhimiya 6:347-354; *abstr. in* Chem. Abstr. 35:7469, 1941).

Reed, H. S., 1904: A study of the enzyme-secreting cells in the seedling of *Zea mais* and *Phoenix dactylifera* (Ann. Bot. 18:267-287).

Reichel, L., & W. Reinmuth, 1938: Ueber die Fettbildung aus Kohlenhydraten durch den Hefepilz *Endomyces vernalis* (Biochem. Zeitschr. 299:359-362).

Sandstedt, R. M., & O. C. Beckord, 1946: Photomicrographic studies of wheat starch. II. Amylolytic enzymes and the amylase inhibitor of the developing wheat kernel (Cereal Chem. 23:548-559).

Schreiber, E., 1940: Ueber Fälle angeblichen Fehlens von Lipase in ölhaltigen Samen (Ber. Deut. Bot. Ges. 58:250-255).

——, 1942: Ueber den Einfluss der Glycerinkonzentration auf die enzymatische

Fettsynthese vermittels Samenlipase (Hoppe-Seyler's Zeitschr. Physiol. Chem. 276:56-62).

Sherwood, R. C., J. S. Andrews, W. B. Wade & C. H. Bailey, 1933: The march of acidity in wheat germ during storage (Indus. & Eng. Chem. 25:437-440).

Singer, T. P., & B. H. J. Hofstee, 1948: Studies on wheat germ lipase. I. Methods of estimation, purification, and general properties of the enzyme (Arch. Biochem. 18:229-243).

Sizer, I. W., & E. S. Josephson, 1942: Kinetics as a function of temperature of lipase, trypsin, and invertase activity from —70 to 50° C. (—94 to 122° F.) (Food Res. 7:201-209).

Srb, A. M., & N. H. Horowitz, 1944: The ornithine cycle in *Neurospora* and its genetic control (Jour. Biol. Chem. 154:129-139).

Sumner, J. B., 1926: The isolation and crystallization of the enzyme urease (Jour. Biol. Chem. 69:435-441).

————, 1941: The chemical nature of catalase (Advances in Enzymology 1:163-176).

Sumner, J. B., & G. F. Somers, 1947: Chemistry and methods of enzymes (415 pp., Academic Press, Inc., New York).

Takamiya, E., 1935: Castor bean lipase. VIII. A new substance having the power of activation or retardation of lipase from the castor bean (Jour. Agric. Chem. Soc. Japan 11:216-221; *abstr. in* Chem. Abstr. 29:5466, 1935).

Theis, E. R., J. S. Long & C. E. Brown, 1929: Studies in the drying oils. XII. Changes in linseed oil, lipase, and other constituents of the flaxseed as it matures (Indus. & Eng. Chem. 21:1244-1248).

Torrey, J. C., 1902: Cytological changes accompanying the secretion of diastase (Bull. Torrey Bot. Club 29:421-435).

Van Slyke, D. D., 1942: The kinetics of hydrolytic enzymes and their bearing on methods for measuring enzyme activity (Advances in Enzymology 2:33-47).

Vines, S. H., 1909: The proteases of plants (VI) (Ann. Bot. 23:1-18).

Weill, C. E., & M. L. Caldwell, 1945a: A study of the essential groups of β-amylase. I (Jour. Amer. Chem. Soc. 67:212-214).

————, ————, 1945b: A study of the essential groups of β-amylase. II (Jour. Amer. Chem. Soc. 67:214-217).

Wessel, C. J., 1941: A study of the esterase activity of *Aleurites fordii* (Contrib. Biol. Lab. Cath. Univ. Amer. 38:1-72; *abstr. in* Biol. Abstr. 17:12256, 1943).

Whymper, R., & A. Bradley, 1947: A note on the viability of wheat seeds (Cereal Chem. 24:228-229).

Wickerham, L. J., L. P. Lockwood, O. G. Pettijohn & G. E. Ward, 1944: Starch hydrolysis and fermentation by the yeast *Endomycopsis fibuliger* (Jour. Bact. 48:413-427).

Willstätter, R., & E. Waldschmidt-Leitz, 1924: Ueber Ricinuslipase (Hoppe-Seyler's Zeitschr. Physiol. Chem. 134:161-223).

Chapter XV

VERNALIZATION

General:—The term "vernalization" is a Latinized form of the Russian word "Jarovization" which is derived from the word meaning of or belonging to the spring. It refers to the process by which winter annuals and biennials may be induced to flower and form fruit the same season from spring plantings. This change in habit is effected by suitable seed or bulb treatment before planting. The purpose is the acceleration of sexual production and hence the process is directly connected with seed production.

Several good review articles have appeared within the last twelve years setting forth the theories and practices of vernalization (Whyte and Hudson 1933; Maximov 1934; Newman and Kirk 1935; Caffrey and Carroll 1936; Bruman 1937; Whyte 1939; McKinney 1940; Murneek and Whyte 1948). The concept is based on the theory of the phasic development of plants as distinguished from growth of plants. Growth is increased in size and weight while development is characterized by qualitative changes in the plant. A Russian scientist, T. D. Lyssenko of the Ukrainian Institute of Plant Breeding at Odessa, was the first to formulate and publish a theory of vernalization. He regarded the development of a plant as a series of stages, each of which must be completed before the succeeding stage can be initiated. Every stage has certain environmental requirements for its completion. Lyssenko postulated that one of these stages, the "vernalization" stage, must be accomplished before sexual reproduction can proceed. This stage has been called the thermo-stage of development because of the importance of its temperature requirements. Low temperature (from 0° to 20° C.) is usually effective, but must be combined with proper moisture and aeration conditions. Light or darkness may or may not be significant. The initiation and the completion of this phase of growth does not depend upon the size or the age of the plant, but may take place under suitable environmental conditions, any time after active growth starts. Active growth starts in the seed soon after moisture has been absorbed. Thus even before the young seedling has pierced the seed coat and while there is still no visible evidence of plant growth, the embryo has really become a growing plant, and is capable of passing the "reproduction initiation" phase if suitable conditions are supplied. This is the basis of the vernalization process which can be applied before the seeds are planted.

The basic concepts of growth phases and even of vernalization itself did not originate with Lyssenko. They have been known for many years. It was reported before the middle of the nineteenth century (Anon. 1837/38) that a grower in Tennessee had subjected winter wheat seeds to low temperatures before sowing and had produced a crop of grain from a spring sowing of such wheat. Klippart, in 1858, stated that "To convert winter into spring wheat, nothing more is necessary than that the winter wheat should be allowed to germinate slightly in the fall or winter, but kept from vegetation by a low temperature or freezing, until it can be sown in the spring. This is usually done by soaking and sprouting the seed, and freezing it while in this state and keeping it frozen until the season for spring sowing has arrived. Only two things seem requisite, germination and freezing" (Klippart 1858, p. 757). Two years later, Allen also reported successful crops grown from winter wheat "sown early in the spring after having been saturated with water and frozen for some weeks" (Allen 1860). It was the group of Russian workers headed by Lyssenko, however, who developed and used the process extensively. The first work was with winter wheat and was stimulated by the need for early ripening in the semi-arid region of the Ukrainian steppes where the high summer temperatures damaged spring wheats just when the grains started to form. Later other seeds were used and the studies continued.

Temperature Factors Affecting Vernalization:—Two temperature ranges have been used. One is the low temperature originally used and perhaps most often associated with vernalization. This range is from just above freezing to about 10° C. The higher temperature range from 20° to 30° C. has been reported as effective for some forms. Regardless of the temperature to be used, the seeds are first soaked in water and allowed to absorb enough to initiate germination but not enough to allow actual breaking of the seed coats. Then they are subjected to the desired temperature for periods varying from 5 to 60 days, depending upon the seed. The amount of moisture taken up by the seed preliminary to temperature treatment is very important and should be carefully controlled.

Low temperature range.—Lojkin (1936) reported a rather extensive study on the moisture and temperature requirements for the vernalization of winter wheat, using two varieties. Both greenhouse and field tests were made. The moisture contents varied from 40 to 80 per cent and the temperatures used were 1°, 3°, and 5° C. and an alternating temperature of 3° to 5° C. Temperatures of 1° to 3° C. and continuously maintained moisture contents of 50 to 70 per cent were effective in producing vernalization. The length of the satisfactory vernalization treatment was dependent upon the subsequent sowing conditions. If the plants were kept continuously at a warm temperature after sowing, it was necessary to give them at least 68 days of cold pretreatment. If the seeds received as much as 30 days of cold weather after sowing, 27 days' pretreatment was sufficient. This total requirement of about 60 days cold moist treatment is, in effect, an after-ripening at low temperature. Kulchitzkaya (1945) also noted that chilling of winter wheat and rye seeds at −2° C. for 48 days after vernalization hastened their development and increased their productivity. Vernalization was in thawing snow for 2, 12, 22, 32, and 42 days. Vernalization must have proceeded for at least 22 days before the subsequent chilling at −2° C. became effective—again a rather long period (70 days). Vernalization effects on plant growth were noticeable soon after germination. Control plants showed more tillering, indicating a more vigorous vegetative growth. Vernalized seeds of the winter wheat varieties studied produced plants with shorter vegetative periods and accelerated grain production. This is not to say that seeds of these same varieties failed to head when grown continuously at temperatures of 16° to 22° C. but a very much longer time was required. Low temperature treatment of two spring cereals, Blue stem wheat and Clydesdale oats, on the other hand, failed to shorten the vegetative period. Many other investigators have been concerned with vernalization of winter cereals and for citations to these works the reader is referred to the general articles mentioned above.

It might be expected that seeds of other temperate-zone plants would behave in a similar manner. Some forage crop plants were brought into flower and fruit under unfavorable conditions by holding the moist seeds from which they were produced at 0° C. for 40 days (McKee 1935). Vegetable crop seed productions have also been hastened by seed treatment before sowing. Lettuce is one of those so affected though authorities differ in the description of requirements. Lachman (1938) soaked the seeds in water and stored them for 10 days at 0° or —5° C. Knott et al. (1938) vernalized sprouted lettuce seed by keeping them 10 days at approximately 5° C. but found no favorable effect of a temperature below freezing. Gray (1942) used 4° C. and periods of 28, 42, and 56 days. Twenty-eight days was long enough and the longer periods were apt to be injurious. More recently, Simpson (1943) kept moistened seeds of lettuce at 2° to 8° C. for 16 days. All of these workers reported flowering stalks on plants from vernalized seeds earlier than on plants from untreated seeds. Obviously this would be of value for seed production only and not in cases where the lettuce plants are to be sold.

Flowers were formed on one variety of onion grown from seeds treated at 2° C. for three weeks while plants from other treatments produced no flower buds during the growing season (Fry 1942). Chilling imbibed seeds of tomatoes made no significant difference in the date of first flowering or fruiting of the resulting plants but did result in increased yield of fruit at the beginning of the season (Goodall and Bolas 1942). The yield of both straw and seed of flax has been increased by seed treatment at low temperature (Mirolyubov 1940). Some vernalization effect has been obtained for seeds of Giant rape but very little for seeds of Broad-leaf Essex rape and none for seeds of marrow-stem kale (Thomson and Hyde 1939). Time of flowering of *Mathiola incana* was not affected by vernalization treatments (Howland 1944). James (1938) reported the use of seed vernalization to hasten the development of bulbs. The test material was *Leucocoryne ixioides odorata*.

High temperature range.—Winter wheat and other winter cereals are long-day plants; that is, they require a long day for maturation and seed production. Lyssenko was also interested in the effect of vernalization on short-day plants. He used maize, millet, Sudan grass, and soybeans for this study. He succeeded in vernalizing these seeds also but they differed from the winter cereals in that a higher temperature (20° C. or above) was required and darkness was essential. In the low temperature vernalization the presence or absence of light had no effect. The darkness required for maturation of some plants as evidenced by their response to short days could be supplied in one dose in a 5- to 15-day seed treatment and the resulting plants required no further periods of darkness to complete the reproduction process. As in the case of low-temperature vernalization, retarded germination during high-temperature treatment was brought about by means of a limited moisture supply. A more recent work (Sircar and Ghosh 1947) has claimed vernalization effects on summer varieties of rice from treatment at 35° C. for 10 or 20 days. The practical difficulty of vernalization at high temperatures, namely, emergence of the radicles and plumules from the seed during treatment thus making subsequent handling difficult, could be overcome by limiting the moisture content of the seeds during treatment to 30 per cent of the fresh weight. Here also light effects were important. Short days annulled the effect of vernalization at high temperature and delayed flowering.

There is less evidence for high-temperature vernalization than for low-temperature. Vernalized sorghum seed showed no advantage over untreated either in earlier heading or better growth, according to Martin (1934). Tree cotton seeds treated at 28° to 30° C. for 18 days produced no acceleration of growth (Konstantinov 1936). Similarly, plants from seeds of foxtail, millet, Sudan grass, soybean, and *Crotalaria* moistened and kept at high temperatures for five to nine days showed no advance in time of maturing over the untreated controls (McKee 1935). It seems, then, that although Lyssenko's results on winter cereals or the low-temperature vernalization process have been confirmed many times, such corroboration is lacking for high-temperature vernalization.

Light.—It has been noted that light is not considered important in low-temperature vernalization but that darkness is believed to be essential to high-temperature vernalization. Since length of day has an important bearing on flower induction and hence on the reproductive process and since the vernalization procedure is concerned with the same developmental phase of the plant, light might be expected to play an important role. A review of the literature on this phase as well as experimental results of the author is contained in an article by Cajlachjan (1934). Earing in winter plants was obtained without low-temperature pretreatment when the plantings were made early enough. Sowings made later so that low temperature could not be a factor revealed that winter rye and winter vetch could be converted into spring forms, *i.e.*, could be vernalized under continuous illumination. This light vernalization is most effective when the continuous light is applied from the time the sprouts appear. Cajlachjan maintained that the influence of light is so great both on winter and spring varieties that a spring plant may be converted into a winter one by artificially shortening the exposure to light, or a winter plant may be converted into a spring one by the action of continuous light. The rate of growth of spring and winter plants can then be equalized by corresponding adjustment of light action. Considering then the discovery of photoperiodism by Garner and Allard (1920) and Lyssenko's work on vernalization, it would seem that the decisive factor in the development of plants depends upon the combined action of temperature and light, working, of course, in conjunction with many other factors.

Other Factors Affecting Vernalization:—*Oxygen.*—In the literature on vernalization one finds repeated statements that the seeds must be well aerated during the process. It is also important that the vernalized seeds be supplied with oxygen in order to remain in the vernalized state (Filippenko 1940).

Chemicals.—It has been found that vernalization of wheat in nutrient solutions, especially those containing potassium, has had favorable effects on the plants (Abolina 1938). Also duration of vernalization or period of development of winter wheat plants could be shortened by treating the seeds with certain chemicals such as ethylene (Eremenko 1935).

Variety.—Different varieties respond in different degrees to the vernalization process. For example, varieties of winter rye require different lengths of time for vernalization (Kondratenko 1940). Also within any one variety one form may have a characteristic response which is different from another form. Indeed, within a single sample there may be individual seeds which are not vernalized at the same time as the majority of the lot. All of these variations may or may not be related to geographical locations.

Effect of subsequent growth conditions on the efficacy of the vernalization treatment.—The existence and importance of photoperiodic effects as well as many other factors which influence the growth of plants are not without influence on the vernalization results. The date of planting with the attendant cold or warm temperature is of importance (Bell 1936; Lojkin 1936). When winter wheat is sown early in the spring in regions where natural vernalization temperatures follow planting, the effective presowing treatments may be very short. On the other hand, if warm temperatures prevail at the time of planting and thereafter, the vernalization phase must have been completed in the presowing treatment and a longer period is required.

Very little work has been done on soil fertility effects but Lojkin (1936) reported that in poor soil and in weak plant development, head formation in wheat was stimulated by vernalization to the same degree as in normal plants.

Vernalization of Developing Seeds or Embryos:—Throughout the literature dealing with the subject, one finds references to the fact that a seed must have absorbed water and the germination process initiated before vernalization can proceed. In other words, the seed must be in an active and not a resting state. The question then arises as to whether vernalization can take place during the development on the parent plant and before full maturity and the resting stage is reached. A detailed study of this problem has been made by Kostjucenko and Zarubailo (1937). According to them, the physiological state of the embryo during ripening, as measured by a biochemical study of nutrient balance and enzyme activity, is nearer to germinated seeds than to fully ripe seeds. The seed is vernalized naturally while maturing on the plant. This fact has a direct bearing on the suitability of seeds produced in one region for sowing in another. Thus, when seeds of winter plants are reproduced in regions where the environment permits vernalization during ripening, the developmental behavior of the plants produced from them will be characteristic and different from those derived from seeds ripened under conditions not favorable for vernalization. A later report by Glinyany (1940) confirmed these findings.

Since the embryo is the part of the seed vitally changed by vernalization, it follows that it should be possible to vernalize excised embryos. It has been found (Gregory and Purvis 1936) that excised embryos of cereals grown on agar containing 2 per cent glucose can be vernalized in the same way as intact seeds. Embryos kept at 1° C. for six weeks were compared with those kept at 18° C. until they had reached the same developmental stage. Both lots were transplanted and normal seedlings resulted. Plants from vernalized embryos eared in ten weeks whereas untreated embryos showed no signs of sexual reproduction. The authors therefore concluded that the cause of vernalization was inherent in the embryo and was not dependent on the metabolism of the endosperm or aleurone layer. Similarly, excised mustard embryos were vernalized in the absence of the cotyledons (Sen and Chakravarti 1947). A note by Gregory and deRopp (1938), however, demonstrated that excised embryos were not vernalized in the absence of sugar during the low-temperature treatment. This led to the belief that some change in the absorbed carbohydrate occurred at low temperature and that this was a part of the vernalization process.

To find the exact tissues concerned in vernalization, Purvis (1940) used fragments of embryos, with the results of six weeks of exposure to 1° C. as shown in Table XXVI.

TABLE XXVI: *Embryos of Petkus Winter Rye.* *Results of six Weeks of Exposure to 1° C.:*—

TREATMENT	NUMBER OF REPLICATES	CONDITION OF PLANT 84 DAYS AFTER TREATMENT
Whole embryos	7	All past anthesis
Stem apex and 4th leaf retained	2	Both with ear emergence
Scutellum removed	2	One vegetative; one shooting
Scutellum and shoot apex removed	2	No plants obtained
Scutellum and roots removed	2	One with ear emerged; one shooting
Scutellum and coleoptile removed	2	One with ear emerged; one vegetative

Excised embryos may also be given low-temperature treatment for breaking dormancy. This will be discussed under "Embryo Culture."

Effect of Vernalization on the Plants Produced:—*Morphological.*— The plants produced from vernalized seeds have exhibited certain structural changes from the untreated control types (Bell 1936; Henkel and Kolotova 1938; Naugolnykh and Skorokhodova 1938). Control plants, as a rule, had more tillers while vernalized plants were more erect. Examination of the growing points revealed an early differentiation of ear primordia and greater rate of development in the treated plants. The structure of the leaves was also altered by vernalization. In one variety of wheat and one of oats the parenchyma cells and the guard cells were reduced in size and the number of veins and stomata was increased, thus producing xeromorphism.

Chemical.—Chemical studies in connection with vernalization have dealt with organic substances, enzymes, and hormones.

The increase of total organic matter in vernalized plants was more rapid and ultimately greater in bulk than in untreated plants. The total amount of nitrogenous substances was constant during vernalization, the amount of insoluble protein nitrogen diminishing with a corresponding increase in quantity of soluble protein nitrogen. Thus a resynthesis of nitrogenous compounds took place in vernalization at low temperature in contrast to decomposition of these substances into end products during seed germination at high temperature (Konovalov 1936; Konovalov and Rogalev 1937).

Diastase and catalase activity increased more during the vernalization of rice in light than in darkness. The diastase activity remained greater in vernalized seeds after full germination but the catalase activity at this time was lower than in the controls (Parthasarathy 1940).

Cholodhyj (1936) made a study of the meristem of the root during the vernalization process and found an increase in blastanin in the tissues. As a result, he advanced the hypothesis that the active embryo absorbs from the endosperm the large quantity of hormones there. The extra supply thus collected in the embryonic tissues hastens the passage of the meristematic cells through the first developmental phase thereby shortening the whole developmental cycle. Cholodhyj points out the theoretical character of this explanation and the small amount of experimental evidence. Drabkin (1936) compared the effects of the endosperms of vernalized and non-vernalized seeds on the induction of coleoptile curvature. The endosperm of vernalized seed caused no curvature, indicating the absence of hormones, while that of non-vernalized seed caused a curvature of 18° to 23°. This showed that the embryo absorbs the hormones of the endosperm in the initial developmental phase and provided additional evidence for Cholodhyj's hypothesis. Shibuya (1938) following a different line of investigation with the same purpose in view was able to get earlier and increased flowering in cotton and peanut by treating the seeds with β-indoleacetic acid. Since he obtained much better root systems from hormonized seeds, he was not sure of a direct vernalization-like effect of the hormone. Two years later, however, it was reported that plants of mustard, tomato, and rice from seeds treated with aqueous solutions of indole-3-acetic acid flowered from three to seven days earlier than the control plants (Tang and Loo 1940).

Direct determination of quantities of auxins in vernalized and non-vernalized seeds of fall wheat, semi-fall oats, and spring wheat led Chailakhian and Zdanova (1938) to conclude that growth hormones do not control the vernalization process. They found a decrease in hormones both in fall and spring grains, in entire seeds and in separate embryos, as a result of exposure to low temperature and limited moisture. More recently Hatcher (1945) traced auxin production during development and ripening of the anther and carpel of spring and winter rye and found no evidence connecting the auxin of the endosperm with the process of vernalization. He believed Cholodhyj's hormone hypothesis of vernalization invalid.

Physiological.—Vernalization increases the drought and frost resistance of plants by increasing their xeromorphic characteristics. This has been discussed under morphological effects. Increased osmotic pressure and water-holding capacity of the protoplasm was also characteristic of certain vernalized plants (Kliučnikova 1937). However, there seems to be no certainty that physiological responses of vernalized plants to their environment will always be advantageous. Vernalized *Taraxacum* seed became more sensitive to sowing conditions and were subject to reversion to secondary dormancy under unfavorable growth conditions. Also they tended to become infected with fungus growth (Munn 1943). Vernalized plants of seven barley strains were much more susceptible to stripe infection than untreated seeds. This difference was so marked that the possibility of developing a technique for testing varietal resistance to barley stripe on the basis of vernalization was suggested by Åberg (1945). On the other hand, kidney wax bush beans tolerated submergence in water ordinarily harmful after a "conditioning" which gave vernalization-like effects (Eyster 1938, 1941). Similarly vernalized lettuce plants were less subject to *Botrytis* rot by virtue of the shorter time in the hearted condition (Simpson 1943).

Devernalization:—On the basis of Lyssenko's concept of the phasic development of plants, each phase when completed is irreversible. Devernalization would be impossible according to this interpretation as would also partial vernalization. There is a considerable amount of evidence which refutes this theory in spite of definite morphological and physiological changes which apparently take place with vernalization.

Vernalized seeds of winter wheat when air dried and exposed to warm temperatures became devernalized (Lojkin 1936). The vernalization effect has also been nullified on winter wheat seeds by subsequent storage in non-aerated water at 3° C. for 5 to 10 days (Filippenko 1940). As recently as 1945, Purvis and Gregory (1945) reported the devernalization of winter rye which had been vernalized for 42 days at 1° C. by a temperature of 35° C., which temperature, of itself, had no effect on flowering behavior. Furthermore, these seeds could be revernalized after the heat treatment thus indicating the reversibility of the process. Also there were different "intensities" of vernalization depending upon the duration of the low-temperature treatment. Again using seeds of winter rye, Gregory and Purvis (1948) vernalized them for two, three, and four weeks and then exposed them for three days to a temperature of 35° C. The heat treatment increased the leaf number and retarded flowering on the plants produced which they consider conclusive evidence of a real reversal of the vernalization process and not just a reduced growth rate. There was a progressive reduction in the effect of the heat treatment as the vernalization treatment was prolonged. Lang and Melchers (1947) found that exposures to higher temperatures immediately after the cold treatment prevented the vernalization of *Hyoscyamus niger*. However, this "reversibility" was short-lived, not persisting for more than four days at normal temperature. It has been noted above (Sircar and Ghosh 1947) that short days caused the loss of vernalization effects on pretreated rice seeds. Devernalization of the seeds of mustard by drying can be prevented according to Sen and Chakravarti (1942) if the seeds are not allowed to split during the vernalization process. They state (p. 139), "Though the degree of vernalization induced by the same dose of chilling is greater in seeds which sprout during the period, only unsplit chilled seeds offer practical agricultural possibilities, since the latter can be dried without impairment of subsequent germinating capacity." A later report on these same seeds (Sen and Chakravarti 1946) indicated they can be stored at room temperature for over six years without significant devernalization.

Methods of Testing Vernalized Seeds:—With the demonstrated vernalization effects upon the development of plants it becomes of some interest to devise a test by which it can be determined whether vernalization is complete within the seed. The literature reveals at least three suggestions for such tests. One (Bell 1936) involves the examination of the growing points for differentiation of ear primordia. Another (Gavrilova 1935) makes use of isoelectric point displacement determined by pH values as an index of completion of vernalization. In one variety of cotton the change from pH 6.0 in the controls to pH 5.6 in the vernalized seeds was attained in ten days. In another variety, 15 days of vernalization were required.

With extension of the vernalization time in both varieties the isoelectric point returned to its initial position. This indicates the possibility of over-vernalization, which experiments of other workers fail to show. A third method of diagnosis of vernalized seed was used for sugar beet. Vernalized seeds submerged in a phenol red solution changed the color from yellow to red (Filatova 1939) while non-vernalized seeds produced no such effect.

Practical Significance of the Vernalization Process:—The most obvious practical application of this process and the one for which it has been studied extensively in Russia is in hastening the maturity of plants, especially winter cereals. With a shorter vegetative period it is possible to produce seed crops before unfavorable weather conditions such as drought, heat, etc. set in. There seems to be little doubt that low-temperature pretreatment has the desired effect. Even if the low-temperature treatment does not accelerate plant development as claimed, but merely transfers some of the required time to the period when the plant is still in the seed, there is still the advantage of shortening the period from sowing in the field to maturity and thus a shorter favorable growing season is required. The probability of a good crop is increased by vernalization. Vernalization of winter cereals in countries other than Russia is of doubtful or undetermined value. In fact, even in Russia, interest in the subject has lagged. Ashby (1946) in his discussion of Plant Physiology in the U.S.S.R. stated that there is very little research on vernalization in Russia and that it is now realized that the reports on the agricultural value of the process were exaggerated. In England (Purvis 1936), in America (Thomson 1936), and in India (Kar 1942/43), it seems to have little importance. According to Martin (1934), vernalization for farm practice has not proved feasible in any part of the United States. Vernalized winter wheat might give better production than non-vernalized winter wheat in certain cases, but it has never proved its superiority over spring varieties. Newman and Kirk (1935) in their excellent review article have discussed the vernalization experiments carried out in 26 different countries up to 1935. To this the reader is referred for further information.

The vernalization process as an aid in seed production of lettuce, especially of the slow bolting varieties, has been tested by Thompson and Kosar (1948) with negative results. A comparison of the effects of treatment of seeds of slow and fast bolting strains and of vernalized and control lots revealed no differences.

The success of treatment at high temperatures in darkness for vernalization of seeds such as sorghum and soybean which normally require short days for maturation seems to be somewhat questionable. If applicable this would permit the extension of the cultivation of short-day plants much farther north.

Theoretically, at least, the vernalization process is significant in plant breeding. The possibility of linking genetics and the biology of development and the opportunity of studying the influence of external conditions on factor expression is pointed out by Bruman (1937). Also since low-temperature treatment affects the growing points of the embryos of winter forms and has no such effect on spring forms, examination of these treated growing points could result in the isolation of desirable strains for plant breeding (Bell 1936).

References:—

Åberg, E., 1945: Effect of vernalization on the development of stripe in barley (Phytopath. 35:367-368).
Abolina, G., 1938: The significance of mineral elements in the process of yarovization (Compt. Rend. Acad. Sci. U.R.S.S. 18:199-202; *abstr. in* Chem. Abstr. 32:8471, 1938).
Allen, R. L., 1860: The American farm book or compend of American agriculture (325 pp., C. M. Saxton, Barker & Co., New York).
Ashby, E., 1946: Plant physiology in the U.S.S.R. (Nature 157:596-597).
Bell, G. D. H., 1936: Experiments on vernalisation (Jour. Agric. Sci. 26:155-171).
Bruman, A. J., 1937: The place of iarovization in plant breeding (Jour. Hered. 28:31-33).
Caffrey, M., & P. T. Carroll, 1936: Vernalization, its principles and practice (Ireland Dept. Agric. Jour. 34:53-62).
Cajlachjan, M. C., 1934: Investigations of the physiological nature of the differences between spring and winter plants. I. The influence of environmental factors on the development of spring and winter plants (Thesis (Ph.D.), Acad. Sci., Leningrad. 75 pp., with Engl. summ.).
Chailakhian, M. C., & L. P. Zdanova, 1938: Jarovizatsiia rastenii i izmeneniia gormonov rosta (Vernalization of plants and the alteration of growth hormones) (Acad. Sci. U.R.S.S. Cl. Sci. Math. et Nat. Ser. Biol. Bull. 1938(2):523-538).
Cholodhyj, H. G., 1936: On the theory of yarovization (Compt. Rend. Acad. Sci. U.R.S.S. 12:391-394).
Drabkin, B., 1936: (Sur la position de l'hormone de l'endosperme dans une semence "yarovisée") [with Fr. summ.] (Bull. Sci. Rec. Biol. Univ. Kiev 2:145-149; *abstr. in* Biol. Abstr. 14:9360, 1940).
Eremenko, V. T., 1935: Effect of chemical stimulants on duration of iarovization and on length of the vegetative period (Soviet Bot. 1935(6):36-45; *abstr. in* Biol. Abstr. 11:6744, 1937).
Eyster, H. C., 1938: Conditioning seeds to tolerate submergence in water (Amer. Jour. Bot. 25:33-36).
————, 1941: Practical value of seed conditioning process for beans (Proc. S. Dak. Acad. Sci. 21:40-43; *abstr. in* Biol. Abstr. 16:17012, 1942).
Filatova, T. A., 1939: The diagnosis of vernalized seeds of sugar beet (Osnov. Vyvod. Rabot V.N.I.S. 1937:342-343; *abstr. in* Chem. Abstr. 36:6584, 1942).
Filippenko, J. A., 1940: Inhibition of developmental processes in vernalized plants that have suffered partial anaerobiosis (Compt. Rend. Acad. Sci. U.R.S.S. 28:167-169).
Fry, J. M., 1942: Onions and vernalization (Nature 150:689).
Garner, W. W., & H. A. Allard, 1920: Effect of the relative length of day and night and other factors of the environment on growth and reproduction in plants (Jour. Agric. Res. 18:553-606).
Gavrilova, M., 1935: On the reversibility of the vernalization process (Compt. Rend. Acad. Sci. U.R.S.S. 6:562-563).
Glinyany, N. P., 1940: Vernalization of seeds in the period of embryo formation (Compt. Rend. Acad. Sci. U.R.S.S. 27:714-717).
Goodall, D. W., & B. D. Bolas, 1942: The vernalization of tomato seed (Ann. Appl. Biol. 29:1-10).
Gray, S. G., 1942: Increased earliness of flowering in lettuce through vernalization (Australia Counc. Sci. & Indus. Res. Jour. 15:211-212).

Gregory, F. G., & R. S. deRopp, 1938: Vernalization of excised embryos (Nature 142:481-482).

Gregory, F. G., & O. N. Purvis, 1936: Vernalization (Nature 138:249).

——, ——, 1948: Reversal of vernalization by high temperature (Nature 161:859-860).

Hatcher, E. S. J., 1945: Studies in the vernalization of cereals. IX. Auxin production during development and ripening of the anther and carpel of spring and winter rye (Ann. Bot. 9:235-266).

Henkel, P., & S. Kolotova, 1938: Hardening before sowing and frost-hardiness of the plants (Acad. Sci. d'Ukraine Inst. Botan. Symposium dedicated to the memory of V. N. Lubimenko, p. 206 [English summ.]).

Howland, J. E., 1944: Preliminary studies on low-temperature vernalization of column stocks, *Mathiola incana* (Proc. Amer. Soc. Hort. Sci. 44:518-520).

James, W. M., 1938: Vernalization and phasic development with special reference to Amaryllids (Herbertia 5:155-156).

Kar, B. K., 1942/43: Vernalization of Indian crops. I. Some observations on wheat (*Triticum vulgare*) (Bose Res. Inst. Calcutta Trans. 15:105-126).

Klippart, J. H., 1858: An essay on the origin, growth, diseases, varieties, etc., of the wheat plant (*In* Ohio State Bd. of Agric. Ann. Rept. 1857:562-816).

Kliučnikova, M. I., 1937: On the physiological characteristics of yarovized and non-yarovized perilla (Compt. Rend. Acad. Sci. U.R.S.S. 14:219-222).

Knott, J. E., O. W. Terry & E. M. Andersen, 1938: Vernalization of lettuce (Proc. Amer. Soc. Hort. Sci. 35(1937):644-648).

Kondratenko, F., 1940: (Analysis of populations of winter-rye according to length of vernalization stage) [with Engl. summ.] (Vestnik. Sotsial. Rast. [Soviet Plant Indus. Record] 1:27-34; *abstr. in* Biol. Abstr. 16:8019, 1942).

Konovalov, I. N., 1936: The effect of the yarovization of plants upon the accumulation of organic substance (Compt. Rend. Acad. Sci. U.R.S.S. 11:41-45).

Konovalov, I. N., & I. E. Rogalev, 1937: The behaviour of nitrogenous substances during the yarovization of plants (Compt. Rend. Acad. Sci. U.R.S.S. 16:65-68).

Konstantinov, N., 1936: The yarovization of tree-cotton (Compt. Rend. Acad. Sci. U.R.S.S. 11:299-301).

Kostjucenko, I. A., and T. J. Zarubailo, 1937: Vernalization of seed during ripening and its significance in practice (Herbage Rev. 3:146-157).

Kulchitzkaya, Z. A., 1945: Development of plants as affected by negative temperatures (Compt. Rend. Acad. Sci. U.R.S.S. 47:366-369).

Lachman, W. L., 1938: Vernalization of vegetable crops (Mass. Agric. Exp. Sta. Bull. 347:78).

Lang, A., & G. Melchers, 1947: Vernalisation und Devernalisation bei einer zwei-jährigen Pflanze (Zeitschr. f. Naturforsch. 2b:444-449).

Lojkin, M., 1936: Moisture and temperature requirements for yarovization of winter wheat (Contrib. Boyce Thompson Inst. 8:237-261).

McKee, R., 1935: Vernalization experiments with forage crops (U.S.D.A. Circ. 377:1-12).

McKinney, H. H., 1940: Vernalization and the growth-phase concept (Bot. Rev. 6:25-47).

Martin, J. H., 1934: Iarovization in field practice (U.S.D.A. Bur. Pl. Indus., mimeo., 13 pp.).

Maximov, N. A., 1934: The theoretical significance of vernalization (Imp. Bur. Plant Genet.: Herbage plants Bull. 16, 14 pp.).

Mirolyubov, K. S., 1940: Vernalization of flax (Leni Konoplya 1940(3):23-26; *abstr. in* Chem. Abstr. 36:6581, 1942).

Munn, M. T., 1943: Germination response of vernalized *Taraxacum* seed (Proc. Assoc. Off. Seed Anal. 34(1942):88-90).

Murneek, A. E., & R. O. Whyte, 1948: Vernalization and photoperiodism. A symposium (196 pp., Chronica Botanica Co., Waltham, Mass.).

Naugolnykh, V. N., & Z. F. Skorokhodova, 1938: The xeromorphism of plants hardened against drought before sowing [English summ.] (Perm. Inst. des Recherches Biol. Bull. 11:161).

Newman, L. H., & L. E. Kirk, 1935: Vernalization and phasic development of plants (Herbage plants and Occasional Publication of the Imp. Bur. Pl. Genet., for Crops other than Herbage, Bull. 17, 151 pp.).

Parthasarathy, S. V., 1940: Physiological studies during vernalization in rice (Madras Agric. Jour. 28:133-137; *abstr. in* Chem. Abstr. 36:6583, 1942).

Purvis, O. N., 1936: Vernalisation: a new method of hastening flowering (Sci. Hort. 4:155-164).

————, 1940: Vernalization of fragments of embryo tissue (Nature 145:462).

Purvis, O. N., & F. G. Gregory, 1945: Devernalization by high temperature (Nature 155:113-114).

Sen, B., & S. C. Chakravarti, 1942: Vernalization of mustard (Nature 149:139-140).

————, ————, 1946: Effect of high temperature on vernalized mustard seed (Nature 157:266).

————, ————, 1947: Vernalization of excised mustard embryo (Nature 159:783-784).

Shibuya, T., 1938: Preliminary studies on the responses of seeds to the hormone treatment giving vernalization-like effect (Soc. Trop. Agric. Jour. 10:269).

Simpson, A. C., 1943: Vernalization of lettuce (Nature 151:279-280).

Sircar, S. M., & B. N. Ghosh, 1947: Effects of high temperature and short days on vernalization response of summer varieties of rice (Nature 159:605-606).

Tang, P.-S., & S.-W. Loo, 1940: Tests on after-effects of auxin seed treatment (Amer. Jour. Bot. 27:385-386).

Thompson, R. C., & W. Kosar, 1948: Vernalization and seed stem development in lettuce (Proc. Amer. Soc. Hort. Sci. 52:441-442).

Thomson, J. R., 1936: Vernalisation (Sci. Prog. 30:644-651).

Thomson, R., & E. O. C. Hyde, 1939: Vernalization of rape and marrow-stem kale (New Zealand Jour. Sci. & Techn. Sec. A, 21:236A-239A).

Whyte, R. O., 1939: Phasic development of plants (Biol. Rev. 14:51-87).

Whyte, R. O., & P. S. Hudson, 1933: Vernalization or Lyssenko's method for the pre-treatment of seed (Imp. Bur. Plant Genet., Herb. plants and Occasional Publ. [Aberystwyth] Bull. 9, 27 pp.).

Anon., 1837/38: A suggestion for the coming year (The Cultivator 4:64).

Chapter XVI

EMBRYO CULTURE

General:—The idea of culturing embryos outside of the parent tissues is not a new one. Merry (1942) stated that Bonnet grew isolated embryos of mature seeds in 1754. He worked with *Phaseolus multiflorus* and studied germination of the embryos from which the cotyledons had been detached. Some idea of the increasing interest in embryo culture can be had from the report on a conference on plant embryo culture at Smith College in 1944. In this report Blakeslee (1944*b*) lists the topics discussed as follows:

1) What each is doing and why.
2) Applications in genetics engineering.
3) Instruments and methods of dissection.
4) Seed dormancy relieved by embryo culture.
5) Possible barriers to crossability.
6) Morphological changes in growth and differentiation of embryos *in vivo* and *in vitro*.
7) Abnormalities in hybrid embryos.
8) Micrografts.
9) Infection by bacteria and molds.
10) Why embryos fail to develop after starting.
11) Physical requirements of media.
12) Inorganic requirements.
13) Organic requirements.
14) Chemical nature of "Embryo Factor."
15) Effect of stage of development on nutrient requirements.
16) Speeding up growth at different stages.
17) Possibility of cultures in injected capsules.
18) Special problems.

This list of topics comprises an almost ideal outline for a chapter on "Embryo Culture," but unfortunately the published material to date does not permit of a discussion of all of them. In this chapter we shall include something of the growth patterns exhibited by excised embryos, studies on their nutrition, the relation of embryo culture to genetics and plant breeding and dormancy and vernalization effects on excised embryos.

One of the first people to excise embryos in various stages of development was Hannig (1904). He worked with *Raphanus* species and *Cochlearia danica* and was able to get growth of all embryos removed from the seeds. However, the growth of embryos of both genera was terminated after three or four weeks and did not continue to mature size as it does normally in the seeds. For example, embryos excised when they were 2.5, 14, 20, or 40 microns in length grew to 15, 50, 70, and 90 microns respectively instead of 130 microns which they reached when allowed to mature in the seed. He stated that the decreased growth was not caused by exhaustion of the food supply since that was renewed after ten days when the first evidence of diminished growth rate was noted. Thus he concluded that the cause was to be found in the embryos themselves. Later work which will be discussed in connection with nutrition of embryos indicates that Hannig's nutrient solution may have lacked some accessory substance necessary for normal development, which substance can be supplied artificially. As pioneer work in the field of embryo culture, however, the importance of Hannig's experiments must not be overlooked. Dieterich (1924) also grew immature embryos *in vitro* and succeeded in bringing them to maturity and germination. These embryos were from eight different families as follows: *Cruciferae, Leguminosae, Compositae, Cucurbitaceae, Linaceae, Solanaceae, Polygonaceae,* and *Gramineae.* Embryos of *Ipomoea* and *Altheae,* on the other hand, were found to grow only when they were almost mature at the time of removing from the seeds. When the embryos were taken out prematurely with undifferentiated organs, no further differentiation took place.

More recent work of which that of Newcomb and Cleland (1946) may serve as an example, has been concerned with aseptic cultivation of excised embryos. They give detailed methods for preventing contamination of the embryos of *Oenothera.*

Growth Patterns of Excised Embryos:—That the mature embryos of *Zea mays* could develop into normal plants when separated from the endosperm was demonstrated by Andronescu (1919). The seedling developed more slowly, however, than when attached to the endosperm. The author believed that the endosperm provided the young plant with carbohydrates which permitted more rapid growth. Almost all of the oil and a large percentage of the minerals are contained in the embryo itself and are available for use by the seedling. Excised embryos were supplied with 1 per cent sucrose and were not improved in growth rate by increasing this amount to 2, 3, 5, or 10 per cent.

Tukey (1938) cultured more than 20,000 immature embryos of 64 varieties of cherries, plums, peaches, apples, and pears during the five growing seasons from 1932 to 1936 inclusive, and compared their development with those allowed to remain on the mother plant. Embryos in culture did not pass through the embryonic stages characteristic of those on the mother plant. Also, there were different types of development in the individuals, the type being determined by the age of the embryo at the time of excision. Aseptic methods of culture were to be preferred over those with disinfecting agents since the latter delayed the response and injured the very young embryos.

A comparison of the development of the embryo of *Zizania aquatica* in the seed and in artificial culture was made by LaRue and Avery (1938). The normal growth was found to depend upon the tissues of the parent plant. Growth in culture was characterized by precocious development of the shoot and delayed growth of the primary root. These embryos were good subjects for such a study because of the marked elongation of the cotyledon and the epiblast during embryogeny within the parent plant. This provided a basis for measuring the departure from normal in artificial culture.

An extensive experiment involving the use of embryos of different sizes from several different kinds of plants showed that the older the embryo at the time of excision the easier the culture to maturity and the greater chance of seedling formation (LaRue 1936). Embryos were first cultured in liquid media and then later transferred to agar. Embryos of *Taraxacum officinale, Chrysanthemum leucanthemum, Lactuca canadensis, Coreopsis lanceolata, Lycopersicon esculentum, Nicotiana tabacum,* and *Bryophyllum crenatum* which were between 1.5 and 1.0 mm. in length when transferred to agar were grown to the seedling stage. Green seedlings were produced from embryos of *Avena sativa* which were less than 1.0 mm. long when excised and those which were under 0.5 mm. were grown successfully *in vitro* in the early stages. A number of other monocotyledonous forms were used as experimental material. All of them, whatever the stage of differentiation, ceased development of the normal embryonic stages when transferred from liquid to agar media, and grew into seedlings at once. Conifer embryos dissected out and grown on agar media developed into small but normal seedlings.

That the growth of excised embryos is different from normal embryonic development and resembles more closely that of seedlings has also been demonstrated by Merry (1942), who transferred *Hordeum sativum* embryos of various ages to an artificial medium. He removed the embryos at 5-day intervals for the period of a month and studied them histologically. Comparisons were made in size and differentiation of the tissues.

Hordeum vulgare var. *Chevron* was used by Kent and Brink (1947) to study the two main problems raised by other workers in the field: (1) the promotion of growth of the young embryos, and (2) bringing about the continuation of the embryonic type of growth after excision. Their main work was done on the second of these problems, which they accomplished by adding an "embryo factor" to the basic medium. More will be said about this in the discussion of nutrition of embryos. Continuation of the embryonic type of growth was favored in immature embryos of maize by growing in an atmosphere of nitrogen (LaRue and Merry 1939). Exposure to air, on the other hand, caused germination to form small seedlings.

Brown (1943) allowed barley seeds to absorb water and start to germinate, then excised the seedlings and placed them on artificial media. He then compared their water content, gaseous exchange, and dry weight with that of embryos still attached to the grain. Excised embryos tended to have more rapid water absorption, more rapid gaseous exchange, and to show a decrease in dry weight. The latter the author attributed to a leaching effect of the liquid medium and the former to the greater availability of water and the presence of nutrient in the solution. As a result, the embryos excised at any early stage advanced more rapidly in development than those excised later. It should be kept in mind, however, that these embryos had already matured and started to germinate while still in the grain, and thus would show a different growth pattern from immature, excised embryos.

Nutrition of Excised Embryos:—Artificial media used to culture plant embryos have included standard solutions of the inorganic nutrients. It was found as early as 1917 (Buckner and Kastle 1917) that no growth of the embryo axis of Lima bean took place unless glucose or a carbohydrate giving a hexose on hydrolysis was present. It was also shown that the dry bean does not contain the elements necessary to nourish its own embryo, but the green cotyledons of the germinated bean do contain these essentials. The change in chemical composition of a seed upon germination is well known and is discussed in another chapter. Also, wheat embryos as well as those of *Arum italicum* must have a source of carbohydrates for normal development (Dragone-Testi 1934*b*, 1937). Chakravarti (1948) confirmed the need for sucrose for growth of wheat embryos but found that mustard embryos (*i.e.*, axis organs minus cotyledons) were capable of germination and seedling establishment without any outside nutrients. The addition of borax and zinc sulfate to Knop's solution has stimulated the growth of the seedlings formed from germination of embryos outside of the grains (Dragone-Testi 1934*a*).

The importance of amino acids for the growth of very small *Datura* embryos has been demonstrated by Sanders and Burkholder (1948). Casein hydrolysate, mixtures of amino acids and single amino acids were added to a medium of inorganic salts, trace elements, vitamins, and sucrose. Casein hydrolysate with cysteine and tryptophane in the range of 100 to 800 p.p.m. markedly improved the growth, as did also a mixture of 20 amino acids. They concluded that amino acids were responsible for the growth stimulus of the hydrolyzed casein. Spoerl (1948) used 19 amino acids, with ammonium nitrate and no nitrogen as controls, in cultures of orchid embryos. Arginine was the only amino acid which supported good growth of very young embryos from immature seeds. Aspartic acid favored the growth of embryos from ripe seeds, and glutamic acid was without effect on these embryos. All the other acids used retarded growth under one or more conditions.

These and other reports have served to establish the fact that both inorganic and organic nutrients must be present in the culture medium if excised embryos are to grow and develop.

More recent work has dealt with certain accessory substances which are favorable for growth or which are required for the survival of certain very young embryos. Some of the early detailed work along this line was done with pea seeds (Bonner and Axtman 1937; Bonner and Bonner 1938). The embryos *in vitro* were found to grow better upon the addition of vitamin B_1, pantothenic acid, folliculin and vitamin C. The authors pointed out that all of these are known to be natural plant products. The length of time the seeds were allowed to soak before the embryos were removed was of importance in determining the need of the growing embryos for ascorbic acid, and perhaps for other accessory substances as well. With soaking periods of longer than six hours, increasing amounts of the growth substances are mobilized from the stored food in the cotyledons by the embryo. Different varieties of peas differed in their ability to synthesize vitamin C. This difference was correlated with a lack of response to the

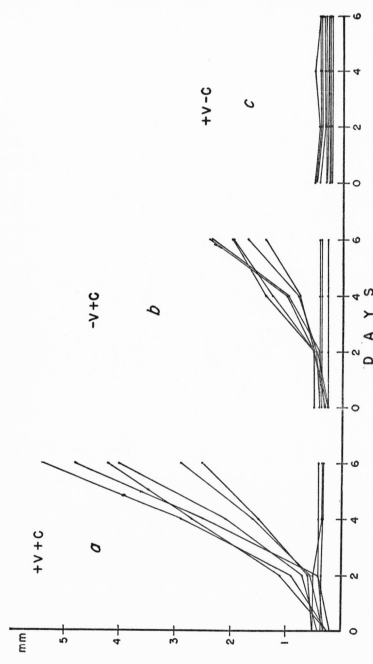

Figure 7.—Growth curves of individual embryos isolated when heart-shaped, twelve days after pollination. Ordinate: length in mm. Abscissa: days of cultivation at 25° C. (a) Agar medium containing sugar, mineral salts, vitamin mixture and non-autoclaved coconut milk; (b) similar to (a) with vitamin mixture omitted; (c) similar to (a) with coconut milk omitted. (Courtesy of J. van Overbeek.)

addition of the vitamin, and with a greater capacity for growth in the absence of added vitamin.

van Overbeek (1942) was successful in culturing very small *Datura* embryos by adding coconut milk to the medium. In a more detailed report of this work (van Overbeek *et al.* 1942), it was pointed out that *Datura* embryos as small as 0.15 to 0.2 mm. and as young as ten days after pollination could be grown *in vitro* under aseptic conditions in an agar medium containing dextrose, mineral salts, a mixture of physiologically-active substances and non-autoclaved coconut milk. The length of the embryos under these conditions sometimes increased from 0.2 to 5.0 mm. within six days. This corresponds to an increase in volume of 500 times. Not only did these embryos grow rapidly on the medium described, but they could be transferred after one week to a medium without coconut milk where they would continue to develop into viable seedlings. Transfer from the coconut milk medium was necessary for development of roots which was inhibited up to that time. The authors list three factors or complexes present in coconut milk which affect the growth of the embryos. These are: (1) a thermolabile factor causing both growth and differentiation; (2) a heat stable factor causing in some cases a callus-like growth, but no differentiation; and (3) a heat stable factor which inhibits root growth and which may be related to auxin.

Growth curves of individual very small embryos are shown in Figure 7. These have been taken from the publication of van Overbeek *et al.* (1942). Here the effect of the coconut milk is strikingly shown. It should be pointed out that mature embryos of *Datura* can be grown in a strictly inorganic medium, nearly mature embryos require sugar in addition to the inorganic salts, still younger embryos must have sugar plus the heat-stable factors found in yeast extract or fibrin digest, while the very small ones described above require the addition of coconut milk. The "embryo factor" in coconut milk necessary for growth is also present in extracts of *Datura* ovules, yeast extract, wheat germ and almond meal (van Overbeek *et al.* 1944).

Sugar-cane embryos also grew well on a standard medium plus coconut milk (Warmke *et al.* 1946). Blakeslee and Satina (1944) found that powdered malt extract could replace the "embryo factor" of coconut milk if it was sterilized by filtration instead of heat.

That the "embryo factor" present in coconut milk is not essential for the successful culture of all small embryos has been demonstrated by Haagen-Smit *et al.* (1945). Excised ten-day-old corn embryos above 0.3 mm. in length did not require coconut milk for continued growth *in vitro* and smaller embryos did not survive even when coconut milk was added to the medium. As a result of these tests, the authors conclude (p. 234): "It seems likely, therefore, that the growth factors derived from the corn kernel, which are necessary for the growth of the corn embryo, are different from those in coconut milk, which are required by *Datura* proembryos." Also, 12-, 13-, and 15-day-old embryos of *Solanum nigrum* were not favorably affected by sterilized raw coconut milk (Hall 1948).

Tomato juice has been shown to contain "embryo factors" promoting the embryonic growth of immature embryos of barley and thus preparing them for normal germination (Kent and Brink 1947). Comparable results have been secured with water extracts of dates and bananas, wheat gluten hydrolysate, lactalbumen hydrolysate, and milk. The importance of continued embryonic growth in very immature excised embryos has been discussed in the section on "Growth Patterns of Excised Embryos" above. It is obvious that the nature of the "embryo factors" is still undetermined. However, their importance in maintaining the embryonic type of growth and in making possible the production of seedlings from very young embryos *in vitro* is evident.

Embryos of *Pinus yunnanensis* and *Keteleeria davidiana* at the one- or several-cell stage were cultured *in vitro* in a modified Pfeffer's solution containing 2 per cent sucrose and 0.6 per cent agar. Various growth substances were added to this standard medium. Although none of these embryos were able to continue growth to produce plants, their size could be increased by the addition of indoleacetic acid or thiamin (Loo and Wang 1943). The authors concluded that the addition of still other growth factors might permit the maturation of the embryos.

In the final analysis, it may be necessary to develop a culture medium for each different kind of embryo studied. It has been demonstrated, for example, that the different species of *Datura* produce embryos with different abilities to utilize five carbohydrates (Doerpinghaus 1947). Excised embryos of ten species were tested in culture media in which sucrose, dextrose, levulose, mannose, and glycerol were used. While sucrose is the best source of carbon for most species, certain ones grew poorly with sucrose and certain others could not utilize mannose. A good medium for apple embryo culture has not yet been discovered, in spite of the use of inorganic salt solutions in agar with 20 and 40 p.p.m. of yeast extract or peptone, as well as 2 per cent sucrose, dextrose, and asparagine in various combinations (Murneek and Jackson 1937).

Another method of finding a suitable medium for the growth of small embryos was described by Blakeslee (1944a). It was found that small embryos could be grafted successfully on to normal stock of *Datura stramonium*. Grain embryos have also been transplanted on to foreign endosperms (Câmara 1943). A strong influence of the endosperm upon the embryos was noted and was apparent through such characters as earliness, texture, and external morphology of the plants produced from the embryos. These claimed endosperm effects would doubtless be questioned by many investigators in the field. Some progress has been made in the attempt to produce plants by culturing tissues of the endosperm itself (LaRue 1944). Adventitious buds developed on endosperm tissue of *Zamia floridana* which had been cultured for 10 to 12 months, and gave rise to shoots which had the appearance of normal sporophytes. Endosperms of *Pinus strobus* and *Tsuga canadensis* as well as those of pear and apple were also grown in culture but did not regenerate buds. Endosperms of castor bean regenerated roots in culture.

Ginkgo embryos are very poorly developed when the seed falls from the tree. It has commonly been supposed that this accounts for the slow germination. Li (1934) has reported experiments which showed that delayed germination was not due to immaturity of the embryo, but to the unripened condition of the endosperm. Embryos more than 3 mm. long developed normally when removed from the endosperm and supplied with oxygen and food. It was stated that the endosperm requires a certain length of time for internal adjustment before it can take up water. Also, it excluded oxygen from the embryo.

In *Ceratozamia*, a genus of cycads of the American tropics, also, the ovules are shed shortly after fertilization (Dorety 1908).

Relation of Embryo Culture to Genetics and Plant Breeding:—It is obvious that the practical application of embryo culture would relate to problems in incompatibilities in plants. Where failure to secure desired hybrids is due to the lack of development of the embryo after fertilization has taken place, there is a chance that the young developing embryo may be removed from the parent tissue before abortion sets in and may be successfully cultured and grown into a mature hybrid plant. Thus it becomes possible to cross species or varieties of plants which are incompatible, and get plant types which might never be possible without such techniques.

Interspecific crosses of this kind have been made with *Linum*, *Lycopersicon*, *Hordeum*, and *Datura*. When *Linum austriacum* is crossed with *L. perenne* no viable seeds are produced, but if the embryos are removed from the seed they can be grown in a suitable medium. One such hybrid was brought to maturity by Laibach (1929). This demonstration that the hybrid embryo, in itself, was capable of development, opens up an entire new field in the application of embryo culture to plant breeding.

The embryo culture technique was used to get hybrids between the normally cross-sterile species of *Lycopersicon peruvianum* and *L. esculentum* (Smith 1944). The latter was used as the seed parent in all cases. When *L. esculentum* was pollinated by *L. peruvianum* apparently normal fruits were produced, but the seeds failed to develop. The mature fruits contained small collapsed ovules with an occasional partially developed abnormal seedling. Embryo development began in practically all ovules, indicating that fertilization had taken place, but there was little sign of differentiation in any of the embryos. Twenty to 30 days after pollination the ovules contained embryos in all stages of development, from only a few cells to an occasional heart-shaped embryo. About 50 of these were cultured and 3 of them were grown to maturity in soil. The resulting plants were sterile.

New hybrids have been obtained from incompatible crosses in *Datura* by embryo excision and culture (Blakeslee and Satina 1944; McLean 1946). The production of these hybrids has made possible the analysis of chromosomal changes in the evolution of the ten herbaceous species of *Datura*, analysis which had been impossible before because such hybrids could not be obtained. Nine mature hybrid plants between *Datura ceratocaula*, a species endemic to Mexico, and other species of *Datura* resulted from embryo dissection. Arrested embryos were found in each of the nine possible interspecific crosses with *D. ceratocaula* as the pollen parent, and in only three of the possible crosses with *D. ceratocaula* as the seed parent. Eight of the former and one of the latter were grown to maturity from cultured embryos. Racial differences were found to affect embryo abortion, one race of *Datura leichhardtii* giving over eight times as much as another race when pollinated with *D. ceratocaula*.

Hybrid seeds between *Hordeum jubatum* and *Secale cereale* set easily, but collapse within 6 to 13 days (Brink *et al.* 1944). Eighty-one embryos were dissected from 9- to 12-day-old seeds and one of these was grown to maturity. The cytology of this plant which proved to be sterile was studied. In their discussion of the problem, Brink *et al.* state (p. 67): "There is now substantial evidence that the dominant tissue in the juvenile seed is the endosperm, a tissue that arises from the unique secondary fertilization occurring in the flowering plants. Furthermore, it is becoming increasingly apparent that when the crossing of distantly related species gives rise to a seed which collapses, the breakdown is an expression of hybridity in the endosperm rather than in the zygote. The facts suggest an important generalization relating to reproduction in this group of organisms: namely, that the capacity for development of the seed to a germinable condition and the inherent viability of the contained embryo vary independently of each other to a significant degree. A logical deduction from the above hypothesis is that, if suitable means of cultivating artificially the excised immature embryos are available, various hybrids whose development is terminated naturally in the seed may be grown to maturity."

Somewhat the same problem apparently exists in connection with the breeding of varieties of some of the deciduous fruits. It is characteristic of early-ripening varieties of peach, cherry, and plum to have a very low proportion of, or no viable seed. There are now several reports in the literature dealing with artificial culture of hybrid embryos resulting from crosses made with these early-ripening varieties, and with the new hybrid trees thus produced. Much of the credit for the success of the application of the embryo culture method to fruit tree breeding goes to Tukey (1933, 1935). During the seasons of 1932, 1933, and 1934, he cultured 12,000 embryos of peach, cherry, and plum. An examination of the seeds and embryos from crosses also revealed some anomalous embryos of cultivated varieties of *Prunus* (Tukey 1934). Anomalous development took the form of more than two cotyledons, suppression of one cotyledon, or anomalous shapes. It was found to occur more frequently among horticultural varieties than among the wild types. This emphasized the heterozygous condition in cultivated peaches and cherries, in contrast to the more homozygous condition among the wild species.

Davidson (1934) and Skirm (1942) are among those who have used embryo culturing as an aid in breeding *Prunus* and *Lilium*. Quite apart from its value for immature and anomalous embryos, Lammerts (1942) has found the method effective for shortening the breeding cycle of deciduous trees as well as for increasing the germination of the embryos of mature hybrid seeds. This last work will be discussed in more detail in the next section. Rose breeding, also, has been speeded up by culturing embryos (Lammerts 1946).

An external expression of embryo abortion has been found in the characteristic gumming on the fruit of the Phillips Cling Peach. Davis (1940) collected gummy and non-gummy fruits for each of the years 1929 to 1936 inclusive. He reported 72 to 95 per cent (with an average of 85 per cent) of the embryos of the gummy fruits aborted. Among the non-gummy fruits, on the other hand, the abortion varied from 0.3 to 37 per cent with an average of 19 per cent. A close association of gumming and embryo abortion was thus established.

Dormancy and Vernalization of Excised Embryos:—It is well known that normal seedlings of *Prunus* spp. result only after the seed has had a period of after-ripening in a moist medium at low temperature. It becomes of interest, then, to determine the dormancy of the excised embryos of these forms.

Tukey (1933) made some interesting observations on the behavior of sweet cherry embryos in this regard. The seed normally required four weeks of after-ripening in a moist medium at a temperature of 5° C. Aborting embryos, however, could be germinated from the time their development was checked, 38 to 43 days after full bloom, until 63 days later, or until their abortion had begun. This made a total of 101 to 106 days after full bloom. Embryos of a variety which normally develops viable seed, could be germinated readily 42 days after full bloom, but if they were allowed to stay on the plant for an additional 14 days, germination was much less rapid and no germination occurred from those left on the plant for a total of 67 days after full bloom. Tukey observed that the aborted embryos never reached the stage of development in which dormancy was imposed, and that viable seeds first passed through a period similar to that of the aborting seed, where no dormancy existed. More work should be done on this interesting phase of the dormancy problem. It should be kept in mind that the lack of requirement of the embryo for after-ripening does not exclude the need of the seedling for low temperature periods for normal development. This is discussed more fully in the section on "Dormancy" where the production of dwarf seedlings from non-after-ripened seeds is described.

By using embryo culture Lammerts (1942) secured a very high percentage germination of his mature hybrid peach seeds without low-temperature pretreatment. This is, of course, a very important consideration in plant breeding for each seed is potentially different from all the others and the plant it produces is necessary if genetically-random samples of the hybrid characters are to be had. Often very low germination percentages follow the regular after-ripening process. After germination, however, the young seedlings from non-after-ripened excised embryos soon ceased growth and entered a dormant period which had to be broken by chilling. Lammerts believed that this cold treatment may have been responsible for the early flowering of the peach trees from the cultured seeds. Ninety-one per cent of these flowered in two years as compared with 55 per cent of trees from after-ripened seeds. Thus almost twice as many trees in the embryo cultured group bore fruit after two years. Also, the number of flowers per tree was greater. Not only did this speeding up of the sexual maturity of the tree make possible an earlier evaluation of the hybrids produced, but it also conserved space needed in the nursery. A compact planting plan was possible because only one winter after setting in the field was necessary to determine the chilling requirements of the trees, and later the same season observations could be made on the fruit. Undesirable trees could then be removed leaving plenty of space for the ones to be kept for evaluation the third year. The hybrids described here were from early-ripening varieties which are known to produce less dormant seeds than those of the late-ripening varieties of peach. In a later paper Lammerts (1943) reported that in certain crosses of the latter varieties, hybrid seedlings from cultured embryos grew slowly and could not be brought into flower two years after pollination. Rosettes of leaves were formed in typical "dwarf" fashion soon after germination. However, rapid growth instead of rosettes took place when continuous light was supplied at temperatures of 70° to 75° F. minimum. This treatment did not entirely replace the need for cold and exposure to 40° F. which treatment was given for six weeks before the plants were placed in the field in the spring. Hybrid seedlings receiving the combination of continuous light and exposure to cold flowered abundantly the second spring after pollinations as did the less dormant embryos described above. It is seen, then, that the more dormant forms required the light in addition to the cold, whereas less dormant ones grew rapidly immediately after germination without the light requirement, but still needed the cold before placing in the field in the spring. In the experiments reported, the response of the embryo cultured peach seedlings to continuous light and relatively high minimum temperatures was inversely proportional to the after-ripening requirements of the parent varieties.

The dormancy of seeds of *Polygonum scandens* has been found to be centered in the embryo (Justice 1940). Less than 10 per cent of the excised embryos from mature untreated seeds germinated when placed on nutrient agar, while 76 per cent of those which had been isolated from stratified seeds germinated. Also the excised embryos could be given the low temperature necessary for after-ripening after they were placed on the nutrient agar. Five weeks at 2° to 4° C. resulted in 85 to 95 per cent germination when transferred to the germinator. Dormancy could also be overcome by submerging the embryos in a nutrient solution through which air was bubbled continuously, or by exposing them to oxygen concentrations of 50 to 80 per cent for six days at 21° C. Here again, as for the peach embryos, we see that other environmental conditions may be successfully substituted for low-temperature pretreatment for breaking the dormancy of isolated embryos. The failure of these substitutions to act on the intact seeds indicates the role of seed coats or endosperm in dormancy. Denny and Stanton (1928) were able to substitute chemical treatments for the low-temperature requirement for dormant buds of woody plants of the temperate zone. The most effective chemicals tried were ethylene dichloride and ethylene chlorohydrin, and the plants used were lilac (*Syringa vulgaris* L.), flowering almond (*Prunus triloba* Lindl.), *Deutzia gracilis* Sieb. and Zucc., crabapple (*Pyrus ioensis* Bailey), and *Azalea nudiflora* L. The dormancy of these buds is probably similar in nature to that of dormant embryos of seeds.

A germination-inhibiting substance in *Iris* seeds has been held at least partially responsible for the erratic behavior in seedling production (Randolph 1945; Monoyer 1947). Mature embryos removed from the seeds and placed on nutrient agar developed into strong seedlings within two or three weeks, at which time they could be transplanted to soil. The cycle from seed to flowering was reduced to less than a year instead of the two or three years normally required, appreciably speeding up the breeding program.

It will be recalled that Lammerts (1942) reported the hastening of flowering of the peach trees when the very young seedlings were exposed to a period of cold. The question naturally arises as to whether this cold treatment could be given to the embryos when first excised from the seed and thus hasten the sexual maturity of the plant. This process is called "vernalization" and is discussed in a separate section. Suffice it to say at this point that this operation has been carried out successfully for excised embryos of winter rye (Gregory and Purvis 1938; Gregory and deRopp 1938; deRopp 1939).

The field of "embryo culture" is comparatively new and offers great promise for solving certain problems in genetics, and in physiology, especially in regard to nutritional requirements of plants and the nature and causes of dormancy.

References:—

Andronescu, D. I., 1919: Germination and further development of the embryo of *Zea mays* separated from the endosperm (Amer. Jour. Bot. 6:443-452).

Blakeslee, A. F., 1944a: Micrografting, a method of securing seedlings from excised embryos which fail to develop roots (Amer. Jour. Bot. 31:1s).

————, 1944b: Smith College conference on plant embryo culture (Science 100: 497-498).

Blakeslee, A. F., & S. Satina, 1944: New hybrids from incompatible crosses in *Datura* through culture of excised embryos on malt media (Science 99:331-334).

Bonner, J., & G. Axtman, 1937: The growth of plant embryos in vitro. Preliminary experiments on the role of accessory substances (Proc. Nat. Acad. Sci. 23:453-457).

Bonner, J., & D. Bonner, 1938: Ascorbic acid and the growth of plant embryos (Proc. Nat. Acad. Sci. 24:70-75).

Brink, R. A., D. C. Cooper & L. E. Ausherman, 1944: A hybrid between *Hordeum jubatum* and *Secale cereale*. Reared from an artificially cultivated embryo (Jour. Hered. 35:67-75).

Brown, R., 1943: Studies in germination and seedling growth. I. The water content, gaseous exchange, and dry weight of attached and isolated embryos of barley (Ann. Bot. n. s. 7:93-113).

Buckner, G. D., & J. H. Kastle, 1917: The growth of isolated plant embryos (Jour. Biol. Chem. 29:209-213).

Câmara, A., 1943: Transplantação de embriões (Transplantation of embryos) (Agronomia Lusitana 5:375-386; *abstr. in* Biol. Abstr. 20:11735, 1946).

Chakravarti, S. C., 1948: A simple method of isolating mustard embryos and their cultivation (Current Sci. 17:299).

Davidson, O. W., 1934: The germination of "non-viable" peach seeds (Proc. Amer. Soc. Hort. Sci. 30(1933): 129-132).

Davis, L. D., 1940: Size of aborted embryos in the Phillips cling peach (Proc. Amer. Soc. Hort. Sci. 37(1939):198-202).

Denny, F. E., & E. N. Stanton, 1928: Chemical treatments for shortening the rest period of pot-grown woody plants (Amer. Jour. Bot. 15: 327-336; *also in* Contrib. Boyce Thompson Inst. 1:355-364, 1928).

deRopp, R. S., 1939: Studies in the vernalisation of cereals. IV. The effect of preliminary soaking of the grain on the growth and tropic responses of the excised embryo of winter rye (Ann. Bot. n. s. 3:243-252).

Dieterich, K., 1924: Ueber Kultur von Embryonen ausserhalb des Samens (Flora 117: 379-417).

Doerpinghaus, S. L., 1947: Differences between species of *Datura* in utilization of five carbohydrates (Amer. Jour. Bot. 34:583).

Dorety, H. A., 1908: The embryo of ceratozamia: A physiological study (Bot. Gaz. 45:412-416).

Dragone-Testi, G., 1934*a*: Action of certain salts on the germination of embryos of grain outside the seeds (Nature 134:983).

——, 1934*b*: Esperienze sulla germinazione di embrioni di frumento staccati dalla cariosside (Experiments on the germination of detached wheat embryos) (Ann. Bot. [Turin] 20:534-567; *abstr. in* Biol. Abstr. 10:18001, 1936).

——, 1937: Germination and development of embryos of *Arum italicum* depleted of the residual seed (Boll. Soc. Ital. Biol. Sper. 12:736-738; *abstr. in* Chem. Abstr. 32:7957-7958, 1938).

Gregory, F. G., & R. S. deRopp, 1938: Vernalization of excised embryos (Nature 142: 481-482).

Gregory, F. G., & O. N. Purvis, 1938: Studies in vernalisation of cereals. II. The vernalisation of excised mature embryos, and of developing ears (Ann. Bot. n. s. 2:237-251).

Haagen-Smit, A. J., R. Siu & G. Wilson, 1945: A method for the culturing of excised, immature corn embryos in vitro (Science 101:234).

Hall, C. B., 1948: Culture of *Solanum nigrum* embryos (Proc. Amer. Soc. Hort. Sci. 52:343-346).

Hannig, E., 1904: Zur Physiologie pflanzlicher Embryonen. I. Ueber die Cultur von Cruciferen-Embryonen ausserhalb des Embryosacks (Bot. Zeitg. 62:45-80).

Justice, O. L., 1940: Methods of breaking dormancy in isolated embryos of *Polygonum scandens* (Amer. Jour. Bot. 27:16s).

Kent, N., & R. A. Brink, 1947: Growth *in vitro* of immature *Hordeum* embryos (Science 106:547-548).

Laibach, F., 1929: Ectogenesis in plants. Methods and genetic possibilities of propagating embryos otherwise dying in the seed (Jour. Hered. 20:201-208).

Lammerts, W. E., 1942: Embryo culture an effective technique for shortening the breeding cycle of deciduous trees and increasing germination of hybrid seeds (Amer. Jour. Bot. 29:166-171).

——, 1943: Effect of photoperiod and temperature on growth of embryo-cultured peach seedlings (Amer. Jour. Bot. 30:707-711).

——, 1946: Use of embryo culture in rose breeding (Plants & Gardens 2:111).

LaRue, C. D., 1936: The growth of plant embryos in culture (Bull. Torr. Bot. Club 63:365-382).

——, 1944: Regeneration of endosperm of gymnosperms and angiosperms (Amer. Jour. Bot. 31:4s).

LaRue, C. D., & G. S. Avery, Jr., 1938: The development of the embryo of *Zizania aquatica* in the seed and in artificial culture (Bull. Torr. Bot. Club 65:11-21).

LaRue, C. D., & J. Merry, 1939: The development of excised maize embryos in an atmosphere of nitrogen (Amer. Jour. Bot. 26:18s).

Li, T.-T., 1934: The development of *Ginkgo* embryo in vitro (Peiping Nat. Tsing Hua Univ. Sci. Repts. Ser. B, 2:41-52).

Loo, S. W., & F. H. Wang, 1943: Culture of young conifer embryos in vitro (Science 98:544).

McLean, S. W., 1946: Interspecific crosses involving *Datura ceratocaula* obtained by embryo dissection (Amer. Jour. Bot. 33:630-638).

Merry, J., 1942: Studies on the embryo of *Hordeum sativum*. II. The growth of the embryo in culture (Bull. Torr. Bot. Club 69:360-372).

Monoyer, A., 1947: Technique de la culture aseptique des embryons d'Iris (Bull. Hort. n. s. 2:38-39).

Murneek, A. E., & J. R. Jackson, 1937: Artificial culture of apple embryos and ovules (Mo. Agric. Exp. Sta. Bull. 387:73-74).

Newcomb, M., & R. E. Cleland, 1946: Aseptic cultivation of excised plant embryos (Science 104:329-330).

Randolph, L. F., 1945: Embryo culture of iris seed (Plants & Gardens 1:241-246).

Sanders, M. E., & P. R. Burkholder, 1948: Influence of amino acids on growth of *Datura* embryos in culture (Proc. Nat. Acad. Sci. 34:516-526).

Skirm, G. W., 1942: Embryo culturing as an aid in plant breeding (Jour. Hered. 33:211-215).

Smith, P. G., 1944: Embryo culture of a tomato species hybrid (Proc. Amer. Soc. Hort. Sci. 44:413-416).

Spoerl, E., 1948: Amino acids as sources of nitrogen for orchid embryos (Amer. Jour. Bot. 35:88-95).

Tukey, H. B., 1933: Artificial culture of sweet cherry embryos (Jour. Hered. 24:7-12).

————, 1934: Anomalous embryos of cultivated varieties of *Prunus* with particular reference to fruit breeding (Bot. Gaz. 95:493-497).

————, 1935: Artificial culture methods for isolated embryos of deciduous fruits (Proc. Amer. Soc. Hort. Sci. 32(1934):313-322).

————, 1938: Growth patterns of plants developed from immature embryos in artificial culture (Bot. Gaz. 99:630-665).

van Overbeek, J., 1942: A coconut served as foster-mother to embryo plants (Sci. Suppl. 95(2459):10s).

van Overbeek, J., M. E. Conklin & A. F. Blakeslee, 1942: Cultivation in vitro of small *Datura* embryos (Amer. Jour. Bot. 29:472-477).

van Overbeek, J., R. Siu & A. J. Haagen-Smit, 1944: Factors affecting the growth of *Datura* embryos in vitro (Amer. Jour. Bot. 31:219-224).

Warmke, H. E., J. Rivera-Pérez & J. A. Ferrer-Monge, 1946: The culture of sugarcane embryos in vitro (Inst. Trop. Agric. Univ. Puerto Rico, 4th Ann. Rept. of the Director, pp. 22-23).

Chapter XVII

SEED TRANSMISSION OF DISEASE

Occurrence of Seed-Borne Organisms:—The association of plant disease organisms with seeds was reported over two hundred years ago and doubtless was recognized by farmers and other growers long before that time. Orton (1931) has given some of the historical background and a helpful bibliography of seed-borne parasites. Farmers near Bristol, England, noted that seed wheat which was recovered from sea water was not infected with bunt. This observation was recorded by Jethro Tull in 1733 and resulted in the development of a salt-water steep to free infected seeds of this fungus, which method of disinfection remained in favor for approximately 75 years. Proof of the transmission of the bunt disease of wheat by seed was furnished by Tillet in 1755. This was followed by other experiments which demonstrated that wheat seedlings developed bunt only when the planted grains harbored the spores of *Tilletia*. For many years knowledge of seed-borne diseases was confined entirely to the smuts of grains. In 1883 it was shown by Frank that the bean seed bore the fungus causing anthracnose. The mycelium was traced in its growth through the bean pod and into the seed coat. With proof that *Bacterium phaseoli* was seed-borne, Beach, in 1892, added bacterial plant pathogens to the list of diseases transmitted by seeds. Since that time many other diseases including those caused by virus as well as insect and nematode infestations have been studied in relation to seed transmission. Orton, in 1931, published an extensive list of seed-borne parasites according to host. Thirty-nine pages were required for this list, which enumerates the pathogens for each host plant. References are given to published reports on the diseases cited. New data are being added continuously to mounting numbers of diseases known to be seed-borne. Neergaard, in 1940, in a list of seed-borne fungous diseases of horticultural plants, enumerates 137 pathogens which affect 40 different genera. The number of diseases affecting each genus varies from one in the case of several to 14 in the case of *Pisum sativum*. Because of the numerous fungus associates of *Pisum sativum*, special studies of their prevalence and significance have been made (Crosier 1936). Six thousand five hundred samples examined between 1932 and 1936 revealed that only a few organisms were commonly present and the others should be regarded as probable associates. Doyer (1938) has published a manual for the determination of seed-borne diseases which contains a tabulation of infections and infestations arranged in parallel columns under headings according to the method of determination. Although this is not a complete manual it is very useful since it contains the pathogens most commonly encountered.

The status of the seed-treatment phase of disease control in 1926 has been reviewed (Leukel 1926). One hundred thirty-nine articles dealing with the subject are listed. The review is devoted mostly to a description of cereal diseases and their control and fungicidal materials. In a later review article (1948), Leukel discusses the recent developments in seed treatment. Fungicidal materials, cereal seed treatment, seed treatment for other field crops, seed treatment with hormones, synergism and antagonism, and the effect of storage on treated seed form the subject matter for this review of 173 papers.

Many seed-borne diseases have been encountered in commercial seed samples, especially those of grain and grasses and a few vegetable crops such as celery, Brassicas, beets, and peas (Brett 1939). Economic losses from these parasites have been enormous.

The manner in which the pathogen is carried by the seed varies. Orton (1931) gives a modification of Dorogin's outline as follows:

1) The pathogens are composed of sclerotia which become mixed with the seed but not attached to it (*Sclerotinia trifoliorum* and *Sclerotium rolfsii*).

2) The pathogen forms a mummified structure composed of seed or fruit and parasite in an intimate relation (pseudo-sclerotium of *Sclerotinia vaccinii, S. caruncu-loides, Claviceps purpurea,* and mummies of *Tylenchus tritici.*)

3) The pathogen forms a fructification on the surface of the seed (*Phoma lingam* on crucifers, *Botrytis cinerea* on corn).

4) Spores or other reproductive stages of the pathogen are carried mechanically on the surface of the seed (*Tilletia laevis, Urocystis occulta,* and many other smuts; *Fusarium lycopersici* and many other species of this genus; *Polyspora lini* on flax). Some bacterial pathogens are undoubtedly carried in this manner.

5) Bacterial organisms, certain viruses, and mycelium of pathogenic fungi are localized within the seed coat or in the reproductive organs of the seed (*Ustilago tritici* and some other smuts; *Gibberella saubinetii* in wheat and other cereals; *Diplodia zeae* and *Fusarium moniliforme* in corn seed; and a host of other parasites such as *Bacterium phaseoli, B. stewartii,* and numerous other bacterial pathogens, and mosaic of beans and other legumes).

Some Examples of Seed-Borne Pathogens:—From the voluminous literature which has been published to date showing the transmission of specific diseases by certain seeds, a few reports have been selected to give some idea of the type and significance of pathogens carried in this manner.

Transmission of *Macrophomina phaseoli* has been demonstrated in Henderson Bush Lima bean seed grown in Georgia (Andrus 1938). In non-sterilized seeds there was 85 per cent infection. This was reduced only to 57 per cent by surface steriliza-tion of the seeds. Thus in over half of the infected seeds, the fungus had penetrated the seed coat and had become established somewhere within the seed. Seed germina-tion was reduced by the pathogen and many seedlings developed from infected seed contracted the disease. Furthermore an inverse correlation was found between the amount of seedling injury and the percentage of germination. This indicated that the fungus was most active during the early stages of germination. The mere pres-ence of the organism on or in the seed is not sufficient proof that the disease is trans-mitted to the seedling in this way. Formal proof consisted of the following facts: (A) the fungus was observed on, developed on, and isolated from surface-sterilized seed planted in sterilized soil; (B) the fungus developed on plants from surface-sterilized seed planted in sterilized soil; and (C) no *Macrophomina* infections occurred on sev-eral thousand control bean plants grown both in the greenhouse and in the field during the same period.

Infection of the corn grain by *Helminthosporium* takes place while the embryo is developing, for ears harvested in the late milk stage have been found to be infected as heavily as mature ears (Valleau 1935). A study of serial sections of corn grains revealed that the fungus obtained entrance through the silks soon after pollination had occurred and penetrated between the pericarp layers. Sclerotium-like masses were sometimes formed before the pericarp walls had completed their development. The organism thus often became sealed in the pericarp and was incapable of further growth until the walls were broken down. In these instances the usual culture plate method for the determination of seed-borne organisms could not be relied upon to detect the presence of *Helminthosporium*. Practically all ears of corn examined by Valleau between 1920 and 1925 were infected with this fungus. Its presence was indicated by black markings on the coats of the grain.

Gibberella fujikuroi and *G. fujikuroi* var. *sublutinans* are also responsible for defective germination and pre-emergence and blight diseases of seedlings of corn. Laboratory and field inoculation experiments have been performed to determine at what stage of development the corn grain becomes infected (Edwards 1941). A high incidence of internal grain infection was obtained by inoculating the ears at all stages from pollination up to near maturity. Very little if any infection of mature grains was secured even under environmental conditions highly favorable for the growth of the fungi. The ears were most susceptible to the pathogens between pollination and the dent stage of development. A similarity in behavior of *Gibberella* and *Helminthosporium* as regards seed infection is evident. To eliminate seed transmission of these forms something more than surface sterilization of the seed is required.

Pathogenic fungi also occur within seeds of red and subterranean clover but in any one seed lot only 1 or 2 per cent of the seeds are affected (Chilton 1942). However, 28 out of 34 lots of red clover less than a year old contained infected seed. No fungi were found in 15 lots of seed which were two or more years old. This brings up the question of the longevity of the fungi which will be discussed in more detail later. Fungi were isolated from only one of six lots of subterranean clover seeds. Both red and subterranean clover seeds were surface-sterilized and then placed on potato-dextrose-agar plates. Data on fungi development were taken 10 to 21 days later. Here again as in the corn seed infection discussed above, the fungi had penetrated the seed coats and had become established inside the seed. *Ascochyta caulicola*, which causes a disease of sweet clover, has been isolated from seed but no details have been given (Jones 1938).

Several parasites and saprophytes are associated with grass seed and have been described (Crosier and Weimer 1940).

Cotton seed carry fungi of several different types, including *Diplodia gossypina*, *Fusarium* sp., and *Glomerella gossypii* (Crosier 1944a). However, a high incidence of the dissemination of disease organisms of cotton by seeds has been questioned by some workers. For example, it has been shown that it is highly improbable that seed produced on cotton plants affected by *Verticillium* wilt transmit the disease (Rudolph and Harrison 1944). Similarly the tomato seed is unimportant in the spreading of *Verticillium* wilt, as determined by an experiment conducted in California during five different seasons over a period of ten years (Rudolph 1944). More than 26,768 seeds were taken directly from 180 tomatoes with diseased receptacles and were cultured. The fungus was obtained from only two seeds. The majority of the seeds produced by diseased plants germinated readily and produced healthy seedlings in culture plates. Thus it appears highly improbable that seeds transmit the disease.

It should not be inferred that a small percentage of seed transmission of disease is unimportant economically. It is difficult to estimate the importance in the field of a few infected plants. There may or may not be a spread of such infection until large areas become involved. *Phoma lingam* which causes dry rot of swedes is carried by 1.74 to 5.66 per cent of the seeds produced (Dennis 1939). Five per cent infection means the sowing of an infected seed to every seven inches of drill or about one to every group of seedlings removed at singling. In a germinator an infected seed either rots or gives rise to an infected seedling which soon dies and presumably would not become established in the field. If occasional infected seedlings grow, the chances are that they would be destroyed by thinning. However, it is possible that one such seedling might infect debris in the soil, from which it is generally considered that dry rot originates. A few such focal points of infection might account for much of the dry rot observed on turnips in the autumn.

Untreated infected and contaminated seed of tomato may account for 1 to 100 per cent of the bacterial canker found in field-grown plants (Fenner 1931). Seedling infection occurs most frequently in the seed bed. Actual infection of the seed produced on diseased plants is rather rare, occurring in 2 per cent or less of the seeds from infected fruits, and depending upon the severity of the primary infection of the plant. Contaminated seed are present in much higher percentages. Surface sterilization renders these harmless so bacterial canker can be partially controlled by seed treatment.

In spite of the ease with which virus diseases are transmitted mechanically, the incidence of seed transmission of such diseases is relatively low. As high as 66.6 per cent seed transmission of streak and mosaic of tomato has been found but such cases are rare (Berkeley and Madden 1932). Direct inoculation of healthy tomato plants with crushed embryos of seed from streak-diseased plants, presented evidence that this pathogen can be carried in the embryo. The inoculum was prepared by placing surface-sterilized seeds in moist chambers until germination was initiated, then dissecting the embryos from the seed under aseptic conditions, and crushing in a mortar with a small amount of distilled water. Further proof of seed transmission of streak and mosaic in tomato was obtained by selecting seed, on a unit basis, from diseased or healthy plants and growing these seeds under greenhouse or field conditions, watching for the appearance of disease. In the greenhouse, precautions were taken against the spread of disease by insects or by mechanical means such as cultivation, watering, and pruning. Five successive crops of tomatoes were grown from clean, healthy seed in the greenhouse without a single streak or mosaic plant. Thus, two conclusions were drawn—mosaic and streak diseases of tomatoes are seed-borne and they can be controlled by the use of clean seeds.

Although this work appears rather conclusive, not all investigators are agreed on the commercial importance of seed transmission of tomato mosaic. When every plant in an entire field of 170 acres of tomatoes in Indiana became infected with mosaic it was suspected that the trouble lay with the seeds for the acreage was known to have been set with plants grown from seeds from mosaic-infected plants (Samson 1938/39). To test this hypothesis, a total of 7,700 pounds of seed was saved from this plot. Samples of this seed were taken after it had been extracted, washed, and dried, and the presence of mosaic demonstrated by making extracts and inoculating bean and Jimson weed. A total of 9,000 seedlings was grown from these seeds to the fourth and fifth leaf stages. An additional 1,200 were grown up to the time of the first blossom clusters. No mosaic appeared on any of these seedlings. It was, therefore, concluded that seed transmission of tomato mosaic is not an important factor in the occurrence of the disease in canning tomatoes in Indiana.

Some reconciliation of the data obtained by different workers on tomato mosaic transmission may be found in a comparison between the reactions of plants raised from virus-free seed and those grown from virus-infected seed (Selman 1943). These studies revealed an apparent "delayed" seed transmission of the viruses which became evident only after the plant had started to bear fruit. This would explain the lack of disease on the 10,200 seedlings described above, none of which were grown beyond the stage of the appearance of the first blossom cluster. The delayed manifestation of the disease has been interpreted (Selman 1943) in terms of variations in suscepti-bility of plants raised from seed of different origin to the multiplication and systemic spread of the virus. This implies a physiological weakness of seedlings from mosaic-infected seed and necessitates the use of virus-free seed for the production of a virus-free tomato crop. Formal proof for such a conclusion is difficult but is, at least, con-sistent with the established fact of actual infection of the embryo by the virus.

Extensive trials with cultivated species of cucurbit seeds including cucumber, melon, squash, and pumpkin, harvested from diseased plants have shown little if any seed transmission of mosaic. A small percentage of seed transmission has been se-cured, however, in 3 out of 23 commercial packets of muskmelon seed (Kendrick

1934). Also the virus causing squash mosaic has been definitely shown to be seed-transmitted and even though the resulting percentage of infected plants is low, the presence of a few infected seedlings in a field provides an excellent focus for the spread of infection by insects or by mechanical means. The light-weight, deformed seeds of squash transmit a higher percentage of the disease than the heavier, normal seeds. It is, therefore, possible to reduce the amount of disease carried by seed by careful winnowing. The safest procedure, however, is to acquire seed stocks only from mosaic-free fields. Fifty-six per cent of plants of *Cucumis melo* from 50 lots of seeds purchased on the open market indicated seed transmission of the melon mosaic virus according to Vasudeva and Pavgi (1945).

Mosaic disease of bean, cowpea, soybean, and asparagus bean also may be and commonly are spread by infected seeds (Snyder 1942). Bean varieties differ in their resistance to the disease (Smith and Hewitt 1938). Control in a susceptible variety is through the production of clean seed, obtained only by removal of diseased seedlings as they appear.

We have considered the effect of seed infection or contamination from the viewpoint of germination or seedling infections. Organisms on or in seeds may affect their food value. A case in point is that of *Aspergillus* or *Actinomyces* in cacao beans (Bunting 1932). The presence of this mold impairs the flavor of cocoa and chocolate, increases the acidity of the cocoa butter obtained, and decreases the bulk by disintegrating the cotyledons. *Aspergillus* on cacao beans is usually obvious to the unaided eye. *Actinomyces* infection is not so evident but its presence is announced by an objectional musty odor.

Control of Seed-Borne Diseases:—

There are several phases to the control of seed-borne parasites which cause disease. Inspection of seed stock which is sent from one country to another or one region in a country to another, and discard or treatment of such stock is of prime importance. To be effective this procedure necessitates the use of personnel trained in the isolation and identification of the pathogens. A recognition by seed analysts and seed dealers of the importance of the problem and the development by them of facilities and methods for disinfection would go far toward solving the problem. In seed testing laboratories already in operation routine tests could be made to include those for the presence of disease-producing organisms. This is being done in some laboratories at the present time (Porter 1939). Detection of the presence of pathogens is accomplished by placing seeds on top of moist blotters with space between them so that the rapid spread of fungi from infected to non-infected seeds is prevented. Identification is then made and seed disinfectants are employed to get a measure of possible control. Seed germination in sand or soil in the laboratory has been found to be indicative of what may be expected in the field. With the knowledge furnished by these tests the farmer or the grower can apply the effective treatment to his seeds before planting.

In this connection it might be well to consider some of the methods which have been used to disinfect seeds. Obviously the success of any method is dependent upon whether the pathogen carried on or in the seed is killed. However, the effect of the treatment upon the seed itself, *i.e.*, upon its germination and keeping quality, is of prime importance. The first of these effects, that of the treatment upon the disease organism, about which many reports have been written, will not be considered in this discussion except as it influences the physiological condition of the seed itself or the resulting seedling. The effect of the different pathogens and of disinfecting methods upon the seed itself and upon resulting yields when such seeds are planted will be considered in some detail.

Organisms which penetrate the seed coats before maturity or which are borne on the surface of the seed but send out penetrating hyphae into the seed when moisture is supplied and other germination conditions are furnished, are responsible for rotting or failure to germinate in many instances. *Helminthosporium sativum* and *Gibberella saubinetii* which are commonly associated with barley seed cause decreased germination of some samples (Porter 1936). The poor germination of certain lots of both perennial and Italian ryegrass has been attributed to a fungal infection, probably an unidentified parasite (Hyde 1932, 1938). Many other organisms either cause deterioration of the seed and thus prevent germination altogether or attack the very young seedlings as they emerge from the seed and prevent further growth so that no plants appear above the soil surface.

Any type of seed disinfection which would destroy such organisms should be of great benefit to seed germination and seedling stand. It is not enough, however, that a disinfection process destroy the pathogen. It must do this without harm to the seed. Thus it becomes necessary to study the effect of the treatment upon the seed. A process is considered satisfactory if it eliminates or materially reduces the injury from the pathogen without a deleterious effect upon the seed. If disease control and stimulation of germination and increased yields can be secured by one treatment an ideal condition is attained.

Washing seeds.—The simplest treatment to rid seeds of surface-borne organisms is washing. This has been applied successfully on the Pacific Coast to threshed wheat which contained a mixture of whole smut balls and smut dust (Bates and Bodnar 1929). Five thousand tons of smutty wheat were washed and the smut satisfactorily removed. The slight impairment of germination quality which resulted was not significant. Dry scouring could not be substituted for washing for the grains were injured so that they were not suitable for seed. Large washers in use in flour mills for removing smut from wheat were used in these tests.

Heat treatment.—Steeping in hot water has been employed rather extensively. Treatment of rye grass seed carrying the blind disease with water at 50° C. for 15 minutes following preimmersion for four hours in tepid water, or at 50° C. for 30 minutes without preimmersion gave full control of the fungus and caused little or no reduction in germination if the seeds were dried immediately after treatment (Calvert and Muskett 1944). The superiority of moist heat supplied by a vapor-heat machine over hot water for seed treatment has been demonstrated by results of several hundred tests (McWhorter and Miller 1944; Miller and McWhorter 1948). Peas, beets, cabbage, and several grasses withstood temperatures of 140° to 150° F. for 40 to 90 minutes without significant retardation or reduction of germination, while pathogens belonging to the genera *Macrosporium, Fusarium,* and *Sclerotinia* were killed at much lower temperatures in shorter times. *Phoma* was usually killed and bacterial infestation was reduced by vapor heat. It has been pointed out that vapor heat treatment is more practical than hot water because: (A) a critical temperature control is unnecessary to insure disinfection and prevent injury to the seed; (B) treatment can readily be applied to tons of seed at a time; (C) seeds are only slightly dampened and the excess water is removed by the same machine without rehandling the seeds; and (D) vapor heat can be applied to seeds on moving belts suitable for commercial use.

A new short wet method of seed disinfection has been reported rather recently (Muskett 1944). The quantity of liquid used is limited to about 4 per cent calculated on the original weight of the seeds, so that the treated seeds dry quickly and can be placed in bags without danger of injury. Thorough wetting of the seeds is accomplished by including an effective wetting agent with the disinfectant. This is known as the slurry method. Chester (1948) pointed out that the combination of vapor heat, which treats the seeds inside, with dust or slurry treatment assures complete protection of the seeds against attack.

Dry instead of moist heat has been used successfully in seed disease control of cotton (Lipscomb and Corley 1923). *Colletotrichum gossypii* Southw., which causes anthracnose of cotton, penetrates the seed coat and is immune to chemical treatment. The hot water method cannot be used, for the thermal death point of the seed is too near that of the fungus. Dry seeds will withstand the temperature of boiling water for hours provided they are heated in a vacuum or an inert atmosphere such as nitrogen to prevent oxidation of the fats and proteins in the seed. Satisfactory disease control was thus obtained on highly infected seed.

Dry heat but at slightly lower temperatures can be applied to cotton seeds for control of anthracnose without the necessity of heating in the absence of oxygen (Lehman 1925). To prevent injury to the seed, however, they must be "conditioned" at 50° C. for 36 hours or at 60° C. for 18 to 24 hours before heating at 95° C. for eight hours or more, which gave full control of the disease. The preheating "conditions" the seed by decreasing the moisture content. When the moisture content of the seeds was as high as 3.9 per cent of the dry weight at the beginning of a 12-hour heating period at 95° C., viability was reduced. Seeds with less than 3.62 per cent moisture were not harmed. The intense heat was necessary to kill the fungus since desiccation served to prolong the life of the pathogen.

Fungicides and insecticides.—Chemicals of many different kinds have been used extensively for seed treatment to control disease. Many have been effective in destroying the pathogen without any effect on the seed or its germination capacity. It appears that insect infestations of a number of seeds can be eliminated by several different chemicals considerably within the limits of safety for the seeds themselves. For example, seeds of wheat, oats, barley, corn, buckwheat, rye, sunflower, timothy, clover, alfalfa, cowpeas, beans, and lima beans were not injured by fumigation with tertiary butyl chloride, isopropyl formate, ethylene dichloride, or trichloroethylene in twice the concentration necessary to kill rice weevils (Young 1929). Although the margin of safety for chemical treatment of seeds for control of fungus diseases is not so great, still many successful treatments have been perfected, in which the pathogen has been destroyed and the seed unaffected. It is very difficult, however, to make any generalizations from these results. The kind of organism, the type of the seed, and the nature of the chemical are all of primary importance.

Copper and mercury compounds and formaldehyde have been used widely as seed fungicides. Copper sulfate and cuprous oxide have been found to reduce or retard the germination of cabbage, cucumber, and peas but to increase or accelerate the germination of beet, eggplant, pepper, and spinach (Foster 1947). Injury in the first three seeds was thought to be due to the sulfhydryl groups present in them. The copper fungicides penetrated the seed coats and destroyed these sulfhydryl groups. Seeds uninjured by the copper compounds do not possess sulfhydryl groups. More recently certain organic fungicides containing no mercury showing great promise have been developed. Tetrachloro-para-benzoquinone (Spergon), ferric dimethyldithiocarbamate (Fermate), and tetramethyl-thiuram-disulfide (Thiosan) have been found to give adequate protection of seed from decay by *Pythium ultimum* in greenhouse and field tests of vegetable seed and may replace the copper and mercury compounds which have been used for this purpose (McNew 1943). In vegetable seed-treatment trials in Washington, Arasan, Spergon, and Semesan were used without injury to the seed by dusting an excess of the material on the seed and screening off the surplus, but Cuprocide applied in this way sometimes reduced germination (Gould 1944). Some variation was found in the efficacy of the different materials, depending upon the variety of seed tested. Some organic compounds containing mercury, such as Semesan, Uspulun, and Ceresan have been in use for some time. Information on the specific effects of these substances on different varieties of seed has accumulated until many data are now available. Seeds of lettuce, cantaloupe, and peas may be sterilized without seed injury by soaking for two hours in a saturated solution of Semesan and then passing through a 5 per cent solution of bromine water (Stephenson 1942). This procedure killed seeds of Kentucky blue grass. Ceresan was also fatal to grass seeds. Treatment with calcium hypochlorite was without injury but failed to sterilize grass seed. Pretreatment with 95 per cent alcohol for one minute followed by a 10 per cent filtered solution of calcium hypochlorite for 30 minutes resulted in adequate sterilization. The alcohol acted as a wetting agent. New Improved Ceresan dust has been used advantageously on tomato seeds (Davis and Haenseler 1944).

Silver nitrate solutions are known to have germicidal value in seed disinfection. All the external spores and bacteria on wheat and barley grains are killed by soaking in a 5 per cent solution of silver nitrate for 18 to 24 hours, and then washing thoroughly in a weak solution of sodium chloride to precipitate the silver and prevent its entrance into the seed and injury to the embryo (Schroeder 1910). This can be used only if the seed coats are intact.

Formaldehyde was one of the first chemicals used rather generally for disinfection of seeds. The resulting adequate control of disease has never been questioned but unfortunately numerous cases of impairment of seed quality have been reported from its use. One recommended method for grain disinfection consists of a dip of ten minutes in a solution made by adding one part of commercial formaldehyde solution to 320 parts of water, followed by a ten-minute drain. Instructions for this treatment have recommended that the treated seed be dried thoroughly before storing. Frequently it has been advised that instead of storing, the seed should be planted immediately following disinfection, thus indicating that storage might be more harmful than formaldehyde treatment. It has been assumed that moist storage has caused the injury and hence the admonition to dry treated seeds thoroughly before storing. It was not until 1920 that the harmful effect of drying after formaldehyde treatment was established (Hurd 1920). Wheat seeds were entirely unharmed by a 0.1 per cent solution (1 to 40) and if kept moist they could be held indefinitely without injury unless infected by molds. If treated seeds were allowed to dry and were stored without thorough aeration, germination capacity was seriously impaired. Injury was attributed to the deposit on the seed of paraformaldehyde which formed as the formaldehyde solution evaporated. This volatile substance gave off formaldehyde gas which penetrated the seed coats and probably went into solution in the testa and diffused to the embryo. The degree of injury in storage was thus due to dryness permitting the formation of paraformaldehyde and lack of aeration to dispose of the harmful gas. In atmospheres more moist than 70 per cent relative humidity the seeds remained fully viable. As the humidity was reduced there was severe injury which reached a maximum in intermediate humidities, and declined gradually as the atmosphere became more dry, disappearing almost entirely in an absolutely dry chamber. The paraformaldehyde formation increased as humidity decreased so the amount of seed injury was not directly related to the quantity of this substance on the seed coats. Untreated seeds were found to be less injured by formaldehyde gas in dry chambers. These data have been interpreted to mean that formaldehyde does not enter the seed as a gas or in solid polymeric form, but in solution in the seed coats. Therefore for severe injury as a result of drying after formaldehyde treatment there must be an optimum atmospheric humidity which permits, first, the evaporation of formaldehyde solution and the formation of paraformaldehyde, and, second, the solution of formaldehyde gas in the seed coats. Post-treatment seed injury can be reduced to a minimum by spreading the seed thus allowing rapid evaporation of formaldehyde solution and escape of formaldehyde gas from the seed mass, or can be prevented entirely by the simple method of washing the seed immediately after treatment.

This report was made in 1920. A second report on the prevention of formaldehyde injury made that same year was based on the condition of the seeds at the time the formaldehyde solution was applied (Braun 1920). Here the emphasis was on pre-disinfection treatment rather than post-disinfection treatment. In the course of experiments on the blackchaff disease of wheat, it was found that both formalin and copper sulfate injury could be reduced to a minimum or overcome entirely by allowing the seeds to absorb water for six hours before disinfection. Even more favorable effects were evidenced when the seeds to be disinfected were treated by the "presoak" method which consisted of soaking in water for ten minutes and then covering for six hours. Similar results were obtained from nine widely-grown wheat varieties and barley, oats, and maize. The success of the method was attributed to two factors: (A) the microorganisms are more susceptible to harmful chemicals when they are resuming vegetative activity than when they are in the resting stage; and (B) a solvent has a diluting effect on any solute diffusing into it from a stronger solution. The pathogens usually have a shorter germination period than the seeds and thus are susceptible to injury from the disinfectants before the seeds are. The presoak period should never be long enough to bring about germination of the seeds. The saturation of the seed cells and cell walls with water during the presoak period diluted the disinfectant beyond the point of injury as it entered the seed. Actual stimulation of germination in presoaked seeds was claimed. This was the result of a shortened germination period and hence a minimizing of the danger of infection by soil organisms in this susceptible period and a possible stimulating effect of a toxic agent in minimum doses. As a commercial practice screened wheat seeds should be soaked with water for ten minutes at about 6 a.m., drained, covered, and left until noon, then soaked with formalin, 1 to 400 for ten minutes, drained, covered, and left until 6 p.m., when they should be spread out to dry overnight and be ready for planting the next morning. It should be noted that storage is not recommended.

The evidence of formaldehyde injury to seeds led to a study of some of its physiological effects on the wheat grain (Atwood 1922). It has been shown that the chemical penetrates the coats but slowly. Its presence in the seed affects diastatic action and hence reduces starch digestion and limits the availability of carbohydrate to the young seedlings. Depression of respiration and catalase activity have also been noted.

Phytohormone effects.—Certain other tests made on treated grain have indicated a formaldehyde inactivation of heteroauxin (Anon. 1938). This discovery led to the incorporation of synthetic phytohormones in the formaldehyde dressing to prevent injury. Some degree of success has been attained (Grace 1938). Reduction in germination and early growth resulting from formaldehyde treatment could be largely overcome by adding 1-naphthylacetic acid or 3-indolylacetic acid in concentrations of 0.01 to 5 p.p.m. Similar effects of hormones were observed after copper sulfate and hot water treatment of seeds. The most marked response from the addition of hormones was increased root development. This was taken to substantiate the suggestion that formaldehyde inactivated the seeds' natural hormone supply, but it was thought more likely that a precursor or accessory factor of normal growth-promoting substance was affected. The enzyme system may be involved. Although these growth substance effects seemed conclusive it has not always been possible to obtain such definite benefits as shown by later reports of the same investigator (Grace 1939, 1940) especially in comparison with untreated seeds. The germination medium and temperature may be factors.

One other report on the effects of phytohormones in this connection has appeared in the literature (Baylis et al. 1943). This was in regard to seed treatment of peas to control pre-emergence damping off, where it was found that the presence of a growth-promoting substance in a mercurial preparation gave no increased beneficial effect as regarded emergence, vigor of growth, or reduced liability to phytocidal damage. Other tests with alpha-naphthaleneacetamide have demonstrated its ineffectiveness when used alone as a fungicide (Crosier and Heit 1941). Clearly, much more work is needed in this field.

Injury to seeds or their germination capacity by fungicides depends upon the quantity of chemical used in proportion to the quantity of seeds, the concentration of the chemical, and length of time the seeds are exposed to the chemical as well as the variety, coat characters, and physiological condition of the seeds themselves. Many investigators have added to our knowledge of these factors (Miller and Grogan 1942; Hitchcock and Carleton 1893; Pont 1934; and others).

Treatment Effects on Seeds and Germination:—Most of the work has presented evidence for a control of organisms without effect on the seed or an actual deleterious effect on the seed or its germination. Some have claimed a control of organisms coupled with a beneficial effect on these seed. As early as 1893 increased yield was reported from wheat and oat plants produced from seed which had been treated with solutions of copper sulfate or potassium sulfide or with water at a temperature of 132° to 140° F. (Kellerman 1893). This increase in yield was greater than would be accounted for by replacing smutted with sound grain. Experiments with cereals in 1943 with formaldehyde or New Improved Ceresan also yielded evidence that even in the absence of smuts, seed treatment may be profitable (Crosier 1944b). Treatment of pea seeds was found beneficial whether good or bad stock was used (McNew 1944). The greatest benefit came from treating good seed. Seed treatment here is regarded as crop insurance.

For the most part, however, increased germination or yield or both obtained from seed treatment are in comparison with untreated infected seed rather than untreated sound seed. Seed treatment with copper carbonate dust, a 1 to 40 solution of copper sulfate, or a 1 to 100 solution of Uspulun, controlled fungus growth and in some cases apparently stimulated the germination of rice seed submerged in water in Petri dishes (Jones 1926). Fungicide treatments also gave better stands of rice plants in the field but it was recognized that other factors were involved. Of several different treatments of seeds to control the stripe disease of barley, Uspulun resulted in the highest percentage of germination and highest yield, while reducing the stripe disease to a slight trace (Leukel *et al.* 1926). Semesan and Bayer compound were almost as good as Uspulun. In spite of the fact that Germisan gave perfect control of the disease, it did not improve germination or materially increase the yield of grain. Further work on barley (Christensen and Stakman 1935) has shown that treating seeds infected with *Fusarium* spp. and *Helminthosporium* spp. with Ceresan not only increased the stand but produced more vigorous seedlings. The improvement was approximately proportional to the degree of infection of the treated seeds, and did not represent stimulation since clean, healthy seed were superior to infected seed treated with Ceresan. Barley seeds heavily infected with any of a large group of fungi and bacteria are apt to be shrivelled, discolored, and of an inferior variety. Significant increases in yield have been secured by organic mercury dust applications to seeds of oats, barley, flax, and corn (Porter 1935), and by hot water treatment of oats (Arthur 1891). The use of Spergon as a seed protectant increased the yield of canning peas by reducing the incidence of root rot and thus increasing the stand. Eighteen per cent more green shelled peas have been obtained per acre from treated than from untreated seeds.

Recent development of a method of pelleting onion seed with organic sulfur dusts has replaced the older formaldehyde treatment for control of the fungus causing smut (Newhall 1945). Without such control the seedling stand and the bulb yield are much reduced.

A popular review of the history of seed treatments from before the time of Tillet in 1775 to the most modern slurry or aqueous suspension method of treating corn seeds, and the special machines for its use has been made by Miles (1946).

Damping-off.—Damping-off organisms frequently cause considerable loss among seedlings after they have pushed their way through the soil. The causal agents are present in the soil and attack and rot the stem of the young plants. Certain of these pathogens infect the seedling as it breaks through the seed coats and before it reaches the surface of the soil. Such pre-emergence damping-off has been demonstrated to be seed-borne. Pea seedlings are among those peculiarly susceptible to this disease. Mycological examination of pea seedlings which failed to emerge show that they often became infected at a very early stage, even before germination had occurred (Baylis 1941a). Species of *Pythium* and *Fusarium* were especially pathogenic. Some control was obtained by dressing the seed with red cuprous oxide or an organic mercurial fungicide in experiments carried out during the early growing period for four consecutive years (Baylis *et al.* 1943). Further evidence of protection against pre-emergence damping-off by seed treatment with fungicides has been furnished for certain forage legumes

(Allison and Torrie 1944). However, no control of post-emergence damping-off was secured by such procedures and doubt was cast on the advisability of the general adoption of seed treatment of forage legumes in Wisconsin.

During the last two decades the seed laboratory has handled many species of slow growing seeds including horticultural forest seeds and seeds of wild plants. In many cases these seeds had to be kept for weeks or months at a low temperature in a moist medium for after-ripening. In the case of seeds with fleshy fruits, the fruits were removed and the seeds thoroughly washed to free them of all organic matter and after-ripened in granulated peat. After this treatment the seeds were germinated in a soil consisting of one-third each of granulated peat moss, building sand, and steam sterilized sod compost. With this treatment it was rare to have any trouble with mold or damping-off if the seeds were viable at the start. This treatment also worked well with slow germinating seeds from dry fruits with molds appearing rarely on any seeds except the dead ones.

Considering the number of agricultural stations and big industries now interested in effective seed and soil fungicides and fumigants, it is safe to prophesy that great advances are soon due in this phase of agriculture. Better methods of applying chemicals already in use will be found and new, more effective chemicals will be developed. Some of the latter will be for the control of specific pests while others will be effective with many seed- and soil-borne pests.

Factors Affecting Control of Seed-Borne Diseases by Disinfection:— From the foregoing discussion it is evident that the published literature is filled with various and often conflicting reports of fumigation injury to seeds and control of disease. This may be due to any of several causes among which are: (A) a single experiment with many uncontrolled factors and insufficient data prevents the drawing of valid conclusions; (B) improper dosage; (C) improper ventilation after fumigation; and (D) unfavorable germination conditions. In an effort to obtain reliable data to cover these points, 58 varieties of seeds have been subjected to eight different series of tests making a total of 464 experiments (de Ong 1919). The effect on germinating power of all the grains and vetches was similar and so small as to be insignificant. Beans showed some variation with different treatments, but were not injured as easily as reported by other workers. It was emphasized that if individual tests were considered some might be selected to yield data indicating that treatments were dangerous but the general conclusion was drawn that sterilization techniques are safe practices at dosages usually given when proper precautions are taken.

The quality of the seed used also bears a relation to the amount of injury sustained by the seed and to the efficacy of the sterilization treatment as well as to the actual capacity to transmit the disease. Soybean seeds stored with a moisture content of 6.51 per cent produce good seedling stands without any treatment but seeds stored with 21.2 per cent moisture must be disinfected if good germination is to be obtained (Tervet 1945). Frost injury of seeds and temperature of storage also affected the percentage infection with microorganisms. Using 22 different kinds of vegetable seeds and recommended dust treatments, seed lots of low viability have been found to benefit more by treatment than seeds of high viability (Tisdale et al. 1945). Also seed treatments resulted in largest increases in seedling production when the soil temperature was comparatively low and the soil moisture high. The amount of undecomposed organic matter in the soil is also important. Good tomato seeds with a germination capacity of 98 to 99 per cent, for example, have been found to withstand treatment with 2 per cent formaldehyde for ten minutes while the safe limit of treatment of seeds with a germination capacity of only 80 per cent was 1 per cent for five minutes (Jozefowicz 1930). These figures represent effects when the seeds were sown wet. Both seed lots were less resistant if they were dried after formaldehyde treatment. Spergon improved the seedling stand from poor quality pea seed, but had little effect on good quality seed (Hutton 1944). Formalin injured all grades of wheat seeds, but the amount of injury was related to the quality of the seed, the inferior shrivelled grains being more susceptible to harmful effects (Mead 1939). As a result it was advised that an organic mercury dust should be substituted for formalin in the treatment of shrivelled seeds.

Recent work has shown that inferior seed of oats, i.e., those which germinated slowly and gave smaller seedlings, produced most smutted plants (Tervet 1944), and that a higher percentage of squash-mosaic virus was transmitted by light-weight and deformed seeds (Middleton 1944).

It goes almost without saying that soil conditions at the time of planting and shortly thereafter affect the response of seeds to treatment for disease. Seeds of vegetables sown early were benefited by treatment with organic mercury preparations but the same treatments were without effect in later sowings, when the soil was warmer and germination more rapid (Clayton 1928). The amount of soil moisture at the time of planting is thought to determine the effectiveness of dust applications to seed for control of the stripe disease of barley (Leukel et al. 1926). Pea and lima bean seedling stands depend to a great extent on the amount of moisture in the soil (Forsberg et al. 1944; McNew 1944; Cunningham 1944). Soil temperature and texture also have an influence on the results secured.

Antibiotic Organisms:—Microorganisms in the soil have been studied in relation to seed or seedling injury from pathogens carried by the seed, with a view to possible antibiotic effects in reducing injury. Three papers appearing in the years 1936, 1937, and 1938 have dealt with this subject. In the first of them (Christensen 1936), it was stated that seedling injury arising from diseased barley seed was not lowered by the microorganisms in the soil. In the second (Novogrudski et al. 1937) which deals with the effect of treating diseased flax seed with certain soil-inhibiting bacteria, it was reported that Bacillus fluorescens and B. mesentericus added to diseased seed of one variety of flax reduced the severity of disease on seedlings produced but had no effect on another flax variety. B. megaterium reduced disease in both varieties while B. mycoides generally increased the incidence of disease. The third report (Henry and Campbell 1938) describes the inactivation of the fungi, *Polyspora lini* and *Colletotrichum lini*, both affecting flax, when infected seeds are sown in natural soil. This is attributed to the antibiotic action of the microorganisms of the soil since similar seed produces high infections in sterilized soil. Further it is stated that infection may be reduced as much by this method as by certain sterilization techniques. Some seed-borne pathogens are not so affected as evidenced by smut fungi. It was recognized that steam sterilization of the soil brought about chemical and physical changes in the soil but the best explanation for the reduction in disease noted was thought to be biological.

More recently antibiotics have been used to treat infected seeds (Henry *et al.* 1951; Smith 1950; Wallen *et al.* 1950). Streptomycin has been effective in the control of bacterial blight of beans and covered smut of oats, and actidione has reduced infectivity of pathogenic fungi on pea seeds as well as covered smut of oats.

A biological test for the presence of fungicides on seeds has been developed based on the inhibition of growth of some fungi on agar near treated seeds (Mead 1945). It is claimed that the test is sensitive and reliable in determining the disinfectant coverage on a seed sample, and that it might be adapted for the evaluation of fungicides. More recently Burchfield and McNew (1948) have reported a colorimetric method for analyzing seed for dosage of 2,3-dichloro-1,4-naphthoquinone. After washing the chemical from the seed with acetone it was treated with 10 per cent aqueous dimethylamine to produce a red color. Since the intensity of the color was directly proportional to the amount of dichloronaphthoquinone, an accurate determination could be made by measuring the amount of light transmitted.

Effect of Seed Treatments on Viability in Storage:—The residual effects of the sterilizing agent used have been discussed for formaldehyde, in which case they were directly related to seed storage after treatment. This brings up the question of the length of life of seeds in storage after various treatments. As a matter of expediency some treatments may be applied by the seedsmen to large quantities of seed with a fair degree of success. The advantages of this method over individual treatment by different people of small seed lots are obvious. Before large-scale seed treatment can be done successfully, however, it is necessary to know for each variety of seed and for each disinfectant used the results of storage under various conditions. As early as 1893 it was reported that immersion of corn, oats, and wheat seeds in 0.5 per cent solution of potassium sulfide for 8 or 24 hours resulted in prompt germination when the seeds were planted immediately after treatment but they could not be stored without deterioration (Kellerman 1893). However, these same seeds could be stored safely after sterilization with water at 132° F. for 15 minutes. Tests were made after 5.33, 13.25, and 17.75 months of storage.

Because of the general practice of dusting grains, especially wheat, with organic mercury compounds some time prior to the sowing date, viability in storage has been investigated (Baylis 1941*b*; Brett and Weston 1941).

Tests have been made from 1 to 12 months after treatment with recommended and excess dosages of the chemicals. The moisture content of the seed at the time of treatment and during the storage period is of prime importance. If the seed is too moist when treated, a large amount of the dust adheres to the surface causing injury. If the water content is high during the storage period, deterioration is rapid in untreated seeds and is accelerated in treated seeds. Whether the storage container is open or sealed also bears a relation to keeping quality. Dusting injury is apparent in wheat containing 16.7 per cent moisture after 12 months of storage in a closed container. No evidence of deterioration was obtained after one, two, or six months under these conditions. Untreated seeds with lower moisture contents can be stored successfully for more than a year in sealed containers but dusted seeds retain vitality longest in open storage. Initial seed viability and fluctuation of storage temperature are also to be considered in reduction of germination capacity of both treated and untreated seeds. Dusting grains with ethyl mercury phosphate was without deleterious effects when storage was in closed containers at 20° C. but proved harmful at 30° C. (Wark 1942). A residue of ethyl mercury phosphate can be left safely on the surface of tomato seeds which are stored for as long as two years in open or sealed jars (Vaughan 1944). The behavior of treated and untreated seeds was essentially the same regardless of storage conditions. Colhoun (1945) made a study of the dusting, short wet, and fixation methods of seed disinfection in relation to the storage of flax seeds. Seeds containing not more than 10 per cent moisture disinfected with dry fungicide were stored successfully for periods up to 18 months. Short wet and fixation treatments (using a powder and separated milk) injured the seeds during subsequent storage. Higher moisture contents (up to 13.2 per cent) of the seeds before treatment increased the injury.

It should be recognized that the pathogens on the unsterilized seeds in storage, especially under conditions of high humidity and high temperature, may, themselves, bring about deterioration so that the longevity of untreated lots would depend to a great extent upon the severity of infection and upon the pathogenicity of the associated organisms. Sound healthy seed would undoubtedly remain viable longer under all conditions than diseased seed. Some insight into the biochemical effects on wheat grain of bacteria and fungi have been described (Agronomov et al. 1934). Increased enzyme activity, changes in chemical constitution of the grain, and actual loss of nutritive properties under moist conditions were reported.

Life Span of Pathogens:—Still another factor to be considered in the control of seed-transmitted diseases is the longevity of the pathogens themselves. *Helminthosporium turcicum* in the seed and glumes of Sudan grass may remain viable, though with somewhat reduced germination, for at least two winters (Chilton 1940). Colhoun and Muskett (1948) tested four organisms on 21 samples of flax seeds contaminated with only one parasite per sample. They found that the longevity of the fungi varied within the following limits: *Colletotrichum linicola,* 26-69 months; *Polyspora lini,* 16-55 months, *Botrytis cinerea,* 16-40 months; and *Phoma* sp.,

27-43 months. They suggested that the time required for the death of the fungi was related to the manner in which it was carried by the seed, as well as the degree of contamination, and concluded that flax disease fungi could not be controlled by seed storage, since the time required for their inactivation was much longer than that used in practice for flax seed storage, and since the germination capacity of the seeds is seriously reduced by the time the organisms are dead.

A comparison of tomato mosaic in plants produced from seed planted soon after extraction from the fruit and from seed stored 3 to 12 months before planting show a much smaller per cent of infection in the latter (Doolittle and Beecher 1937). Using old seeds for plantings would thus reduce mosaic infection while producing several generations of plants in close succession, as done in breeding work, would tend to increase seed transmission of the virus. Squash-mosaic virus, on the other hand, remains fully viable on seeds three years old (Middleton 1944), while the yellow ring-spot virus is still active on tobacco seed stored for five and one-half years (Valleau 1939). In connection with the latter, it was pointed out that the virus is inactivated quickly by drying or by standing for short periods *in vitro*, but retains its infectivity for long periods in association with living plant cells. It was also stated that it is not known whether the virus would survive after the infected seed has lost its germination capacity.

Residual Effects:—We have spoken of the residual effects of the disinfectant on the seed itself, but, in legumes whose growth depends upon inoculation of the roots with nodule bacteria, a failure to remove all of the chemical held on the seed surface may result in the production of a sterile zone around the seed and subsequent prevention of inoculation. This has been found rather serious when mercurial chloride is used as the disinfecting agent (Anderson and Walker 1931). The toxic effects were measured by the extent of a sterile zone formation around treated seeds on agar plate cultures of *Rhizobium* and by effect on germination, and were especially noted for large seeds such as soybeans. Smaller, horny-coated seeds such as clover were not affected. Anderson and Walker claimed that hydrogen peroxide could be used just as effectively for sterilization as mercuric chloride and had no effect on surrounding organisms. Zimmerman and Crocker (1933, 1934) found that greenhouse roses were injured when they were grown in soil which had been treated with $HgCl_2$ solution to kill earthworms. This injurious residual effect was brought about by the reduction of the chloride to metallic mercury by the organic matter of the soil. The metallic mercury possessed sufficient vapor pressure to move through the air and injure roses in untreated benches of the same greenhouse.

On the other hand, Kernkamp (1948) found that the mercurial, Spergon, when applied with commercial Nitragin did not influence nodulation of soybean plants when the seeds were planted in soil that already contained the bacteria. However, Spergon did reduce nodulation somewhat when inoculated seed were planted in soil that contained a small number of nodule bacteria, though this reduction was not significant statistically. Preliminary tests also indicated that New Improved Ceresan, or Semesan Jr., had no effect on nodulation or yield.

In conclusion, then, it may be said that many diseases are seed-borne and that their transmission in this manner represents a considerable economic loss, both as to destruction of the seed itself and to the destruction or decreased yield of the seedlings produced. The control of such diseases may be effected by selection of sound seed from healthy plants, sterilization of infected seeds, crop rotation, the use of old seeds for planting, or the development of disease-resistant strains.

References:—

Agronomov, E. A., M. S. Dunin, A. A. Bundel, A. N. Goryatchick & N. A. Korenev, 1934: Biochemistry and microbiology of stored wheat grain infected by *Fusarium* (Food Supplies Tech. Publ. office Leningrad, Separate, 96 pp.; *abstr. in* Chem. Abstr. 29:6960, 1935).

Allison, J. L., & J. H. Torrie, 1944: Effect of several seed protectants on germination and stands of various forage legumes (Phytopath. 34:799-804).

Anderson, D. A., & R. H. Walker, 1931: Residual effects of some germicides used in sterilizing legume seeds (Proc. Iowa Acad. Sci. 38:321-325).

Andrus, C. F., 1938: Seed transmission of *Macrophomina phaseoli* (Phytopath. 28: 620-634).

Arthur, J. C., 1891: Loose smut of oats (Indiana Agric. Exp. Sta. Bull. 35, Vol. 2:79-107).

Atwood, W. M., 1922: Physiological studies of effects of formaldehyde on wheat (Bot. Gaz. 74:233-263).

Bates, E. N., & G. P. Bodnar, 1929: Smut on Pacific Coast wheat can profitably be removed by washing (U.S.D.A. Yearbook 1928:542-543).

Baylis, G. T. S., 1941a: Fungi which cause pre-emergence injury to garden peas (Ann. Appl. Biol. 28:210-218).

————, 1941b: Viability of dusted wheat after storage (New Zealand Jour. Sci. & Tech., Sec. A, 23:126A-130A).

Baylis, G. T. S., R. S. Deshpande & I. F. Storey, 1943: Effect of seed treatment on emergence of peas (Ann. Appl. Biol. 30:19-26).

Berkeley, G H., & G. O. Madden, 1932: Transmission of streak and mosaic diseases of tomato through seed (Sci. Agric. 13:194-197).

Braun, H., 1920: Presoak method of seed treatment: A means of preventing seed injury due to chemical disinfectants and of increasing germicidal efficiency (Jour. Agric. Res. 19:363-392).

Brett, C. C., 1939: The production, handling, testing and diseases of seeds (Ann. Appl. Biol. 26:616-627).

Brett, C. C., & W. A. R. Dillon Weston, 1941: Seed disinfection. IV. Loss of vitality during storage of grain treated with organo-mercury seed disinfectants (Jour. Agric. Sci. 31:500-517).

Bunting, R. H., 1932: Actinomyces in cacao beans (Ann. Appl. Biol. 19:515-517).

Burchfield, H. P., & G. L. McNew, 1948: The colorimetric determination of 2,3-dichloro-1,4-naphthoquinone on seed (Phytopath. 38:665-669).

Calvert, E. L., & A. E. Muskett, 1944: Blind seed disease of rye-grass (Nature 153: 287-288).

Chester, K. S., 1948: Vapor-heat treats seed inside. New method when followed by dust or slurry treatment assures complete seed protection (Southern Seedsman 11(4):28, 32, 36).

Chilton, S. J. P., 1940: The occurrence of *Helminthosporium turcicum* in the seed and glumes of Sudan grass (Phytopath. 30:533-536).

————, 1942: Some pathogenic fungi occurring in the seed of red and subterranean clover (Phytopath. 32:738-739).

Christensen, J. J., 1936: Associations of microorganisms in relation to seedling injury arising from infected seed (Phytopath. 26:1091-1105).

Christensen, J. J., & E. C. Stakman, 1935: Relation of *Fusarium* and *Helminthosporium* in barley seed to seedling blight and yield (Phytopath. 25:309-327).

Clayton, E. E., 1928: Increasing stands from vegetable seeds by seed treatment (New York [Geneva] Agric. Exp. Sta. Bull. 554, 16 pp.).

Colhoun, J., 1945: The prevention of seed-borne diseases of flax. III. The dusting, short wet and fixation methods of seed disinfection in relation to the storage of the seed (Ann. Appl. Biol. 32:34-37).

Colhoun, J., & A. E. Muskett, 1948: A study of the longevity of the seed-borne parasites of flax in relation to the storage of the seed (Ann. Appl. Biol. 35:429-434).

Crosier, W. F., 1936: Prevalence and significance of fungous associates of pea seeds (Proc. Assoc. Off. Seed Anal. N. Amer. 28:101-107).

————, 1944a: *Diplodia Gossypina* and other fungi in cotton seed (Assoc. Off. Seed Anal. News Letter 18(2):13-15).

————, 1944b: Seed treatment of cereals in 1943 (Farm Res. 10(2):12).

Crosier, W. F., & C. E. Heit, 1941: Response of germinants from beans, corn and peas to seed treatments with hormones and mercurials (Proc. Assoc. Off. Seed Anal. N. Amer. 32(1940):88-92).

Crosier, W. F., & D. Weimer, 1940: Some fungi associated with grass seed (Proc. Assoc. Off. Seed Anal. N. Amer. 31(1939):120-124).

Cunningham, H. S., 1944: Lima bean seed treatment on Long Island (Phytopath. 34:790-798).

Davis, B. H., & C. M. Haenseler, 1944: Tomato seed treatment with New Improved Ceresan dust (Phytopath. 34:847-848).

Dennis, R. W. G., 1939: Notes on seed transmission of *Phoma Lingam* in relation to dry rot of swedes in Scotland (Ann. Appl. Biol. 26:627-630).

de Ong, E. R., 1919: Effect of excessive sterilization measures on the germination of seeds (Jour. Econ. Ent. 12:343-345).

Doolittle, S. P., & F. S. Beecher, 1937: Seed transmission of tomato mosaic following the planting of freshly extracted seed (Phytopath. 27:800-801).

Doyer, L. C., 1938: Manual for the determination of seed-borne diseases (59 pp., Internat. Seed Test. Assoc., H. Veenman & Zonen, Wageningen, Holland; *rev. in* Rev. Appl. Mycol. 18:265, 1939).

Edwards, E. T., 1941: Internal grain infection in maize due to *Gibberella Fujikuroi* and *Gibberella Fujikuroi* var. *sublutinans* (Austral. Inst. Agric. Sci. 7:74-82).

Fenner, L. M., 1931: Bacterial canker of tomato and its distribution with the seed from infected fruit (Jour. Econ. Ent. 24:544-547).

Forsberg, J. L., E. Olson & A. M. Binkley, 1944: Experiments with pea seed treatments in Colorado (Phytopath. 34:753-759).

Foster, A. A., 1947: Acceleration and retardation of germination of some vegetable seeds resulting from treatment with copper fungicides (Phytopath. 37:390-398).

Gould, C. J., 1944: Vegetable seed-treatment trials in western Washington in 1944 (Phytopath. 34:935).

Grace, N. H., 1938: Effect of phytohormones on seeds damaged by formaldehyde and other disinfectants (Canad. Jour. Res. Sec. C. 16:313-329).

————, 1939: Effects of plant and animal hormones on seeds damaged by formaldehyde (Canad. Jour. Res. Sec. C. 17:445-451).

————, 1940: Effects of two preparations of naphthylacetic acid on the germination and early growth of wheat seed damaged by formaldehyde (Canad. Jour. Res. Sec. C. 18:215-218).

Henry, A. W., & J. A. Campbell, 1938: Inactivation of seed-borne plant pathogens in the soil (Canad. Jour. Res. Sec. C. 16:331-338).

Henry, A. W., E. A. Peterson, R. L. Millar, and J. S. Horricks, 1951: Control of covered smut of oats by seed treatment with an antibiotic (Science 113:390).

Hitchcock, A. S., & M. A. Carleton, 1893: The effect of fungicides upon the germination of corn (Kansas Agric. Exp. Sta. Bull. 41:63-79).

Hurd, A. M., 1920: Injury to seed wheat resulting from drying after disinfection with formaldehyde (Jour. Agric. Res. 20:209-244).

Hutton, E. M., 1944: The field emergence and yield of garden peas as affected by treatment of the seed with fungicidal dusts (Austral. Counc. Sci. & Indus. Jour. 17:71-74).

Hyde, E. O., 1932: Germinating capacity of perennial rye-grass seed (New Zeal. Jour. Agric. 44:316-319).

——, 1938: Germinating capacity of Italian rye-grass seed (New Zeal. Jour. Agric. 56:357).

Jones, F. R., 1938: A seed-borne disease of sweet clover (Phytopath. 28:661-662).

Jones, J. W., 1926: Germination of rice seed as affected by temperature, fungicides and age (Amer. Soc. Agron. Jour. 18:576-592).

Jozefowicz, M., 1930: The effect of certain treatments on the germination of tomato seeds (Ann. Appl. Biol. 17:504-513).

Kellerman, W. A., 1893: Experiments in germination of treated seed (Ohio Agric. Exp. Sta. Tech. Ser., Bull. 1:201-205).

Kendrick, J. B., 1934: Cucurbit mosaic transmitted by muskmelon seed (Phytopath. 24:820-823).

Kernkamp, M. F., 1948: Chemical treatment of soybean seed in relation to nodulation by nodule bacteria (Phytopath. 38:955-959).

Lehman, S. G., 1925: Studies on treatment of cotton seed (North Carolina Agric. Exp. Sta. Tech. Bull. 26, 71 pp.).

Leukel, R. W., 1926: The present status of seed treatment, with special reference to cereals (Bot. Rev. 2:498-527).

——, 1948: Recent developments in seed treatment (Bot. Rev. 14:235-269).

Leukel, R. W., J. G. Dickson & A. G. Johnson, 1926: Seed treatment experiments for controlling stripe disease of barley (Phytopath. 16:565-576).

Lipscomb, G. F., & G. L. Corley, 1923: On the vitality of cotton seed (Science 57:741-742).

McNew, G. L., 1943: Relative effectiveness of organic and inorganic fungicides as seed protectants (Phytopath. 33:9).

——, 1944: Pea seed treatments as crop insurance (Canner 98(20):20-22, 46, 48, 50; abstr. in Exp. Sta. Rec. 91:427, 1944).

McWhorter, F. P., & P. W. Miller, 1944: The application of vapor heat as a practical means of disinfecting seeds (Phytopath. 34:935-936).

Mead, H. W., 1939: Shrivelling of wheat kernels by stem rust and its effect on seed value (Sci. Agric. 19:481-493).

——, 1945: A biological method of detecting the presence of fungicides on seeds (Sci. Agric. 25:458-460).

Middleton, J. T., 1944: Seed transmission of squash-mosaic virus (Phytopath. 34:405-410).

Miles, G. F., 1946: 300 years of chemical seed treatment (Agric. Chem. 1(7):22-25, 46).

Miller, J. H., & R. Grogan, 1942: Injury to tomato seed in disinfection (Phytopath. 32:524-528).

Miller, P. W., & F. P. McWhorter, 1948: The use of vapor-heat as a practical means of disinfecting seeds (Phytopath. 38:89-101).

Muskett, A. E., 1944: The short wet method of seed disinfection (Ann. Appl. Biol. 31:218-221).

Neergaard, P., 1940: Seed-borne fungous diseases of horticultural plants (Proc. Internat. Seed Test. Assoc. 12:47-71).

Newhall, A. G., 1945: Pelleting onion seed with fungicides (Farm Res. 11(1):18, 20).

Novogrudski, D., E. Berezova, M. Nakhimovskaya & M. Perviakova, 1937: The influence of bacterization of flax seed on the susceptibility of seedlings to infection with parasitic fungi (Rev. Appl. Mycol. 16:676).

Orton, C. R., 1931: Seed-borne parasites. A bibliography (West Virginia Agric. Exp. Sta. Bull. 245:1-47).

Pont, J. W., 1934: Physiological studies with seed of *Andropogon sorghum* Brot. (Botanist, Dept. Agric. Union S. Africa, 64 pp., publ. by N. V. Swets & Zeitlinger, Amsterdam).

Porter, R. H., leader, 1935: Effect of organic mercury dusts on seeds of oats, barley, flax and corn (Iowa Agric. Exp. Sta. Rept. 1934/35:83-84).

————, 1936: Effect of seed-borne pathogens and of seed disinfectants on the germination of barley seed (Proc. Assoc. Off. Seed Anal. N. Amer. 27(1935):94-99).

————, 1939: Detection and classification of seed-borne organisms, their effect on germination and their control by seed disinfection in laboratory and field (Proc. Assoc. Off. Seed Anal. N. Amer. 30(1938):195-213).

Rudolph, B. A., 1944: The unimportance of tomato seed in the dissemination of *Verticillium* wilt in California (Phytopath. 34:622-630).

Rudolph, B. A., & G. J. Harrison, 1944: The unimportance of cotton seed in the dissemination of *Verticillium* wilt in California (Phytopath. 34:849-860).

Samson, R. W., 1938/39: Seed transmission of tomato mosaic (Indiana Agric. Exp. Sta. Ann. Rept. of Director 52:54-55).

Schroeder, H., 1910: The resistance of wheat and barley grains to poisons, with special reference to seed sterilization (Centralbl. Bakt. 2 Abt. 28:492-505; *abstr. in* Exp. Sta. Rec. 24:532, 1911).

Selman, I. W., 1943: The appearance and spread of mosaic infection in the tomato crop and the relation to seed transmission of the virus (Ann. Appl. Biol. 30:331-338).

Smith, F. L., & W. B. Hewitt, 1938: Varietal susceptibility to common bean mosaic and transmission through seed (Calif. Agric. Exp. Sta. Bull. 621:1-18).

Smith, W. L., 1950: Seed treatment with streptomycin for the control of bacterial blight of beans (Rev. Appl. Myc. 29:600).

Snyder, W. C., 1942: A seed-borne mosaic of asparagus bean, *Vigna sesquipedalis* (Phytopath. 32:518-523).

Stephenson, R. B., 1942: Sterilization technique for grass seeds (Plant Physiol. 17: 324-325).

Tervet, I. W., 1944: The relation of seed quality to the development of smut in oats (Phytopath. 34:106-115).

————, 1945: The influence of fungi on storage, on seed viability, and seedling vigor of soybeans (Phytopath. 35:3-15).

Tisdale, W. B., A. N. Brooks & G. R. Townsend, 1945: Dust treatments for vegetable seed (Florida Agric. Exp. Sta. Bull. 413, 32 pp.).

Valleau, W. D., 1935: Seed transmission of *Helminthosporium* of corn (Phytopath. 25:1109-1112).

————, 1939: Symptoms of yellow ring spot and longevity of the virus in tobacco seed (Phytopath. 29:549-551).

Vasudeva, R. S., & M. S. Pavgi, 1945: Seed transmission of melon mosaic virus (Current Sci. 14:271-272).

Vaughan, E. K., 1944: The use of ethyl mercury phosphate for treating tomato seed in New Jersey (Phytopath. 34:175-184).

Wallen, V. R., M. D. Sutton & A. J. Skolko, 1950: The effect of actidione on the growth of pathogenic fungi and on the germination of pea seed (Phytopath. 40:156-160).

Wark, D. C., 1942: The influence of storage in contact with certain seed-pickling dusts on the germination of grain (Austral. Inst. Agric. Sci. Jour. 8:22-25).

Young, H. D., 1929: Effect of various fumigants on the germination of seeds (Jour. Agric. Res. 39:925-927).

Zimmerman, P. W., & W. Crocker, 1933: The injurious effect of mercury vapor from bichloride of mercury in soil of rose houses (Flor. Exch. 81(21):13; *also in* Boyce Thompson Inst. Prof. Pap. 1:222-225, 1933).

————, ————, 1934: Plant injury by vapors of mercury and compounds of mercury (Contrib. Boyce Thompson Inst. 6:167-187).

Anon., 1938: Investigations under the direction of Dr. K. W. Neatby (Natl. Res. Counc. Canada Ann. Rept. 20(1936/37):85).

INDICES

Subject Index

Author Index

Aamodt, O. S., 15, 16, 90
Åberg, E., 211
Able, C. F., 71
Abolina, G., 207
Ackerson, C. W., 200
Adams, J., 131
Adrian, J., 55
Afanasiev, M., 126, 132, 133, 163
Agronomov, E. A., 244
Agulhon, H., 110
Ahmad, B., 196
Aikman, J. M., 133
Akamine, E. K., 119
Albaum, H. G., 68
Alberts, H. W., 65
Albrecht, H. R., 9, 19
Albrecht, W. A., 41
Alcock, A. W., 56
Allard, H. A., 207
Allard, R. W., 103
Allen, R. L., 205
Allen, T. C., 11
Allison, J. L., 241
Althaus, H. C., 105
Altschul, A. M., 43, 148, 152, 160, 179, 197
Alvarez, L. A., 199
Andersen, A. M., 119, 214
Anderson, D. A., 245
Anderson, J. A., 32, 190, 193, 195
Andrews, F. R., 152
Andrews, F. S., 9
Andrews, F. W., 119
Andrews, J. S., 203
Andronescu, D. I., 217
Andrus, C. F., 231
Arthur, J. C., 95, 240
Arthur, J. M., 17
Asenjo, C. F., 190, 192
Ashby, E., 212
Atkins, W. R. G., 63
Atwood, W. M., 123, 238
Auscherman, L. E., 227
Avery, G. S., Jr., 51, 52, 192, 217
Axtman, G., 219

Babcock, S. M., 72
Babichev, I. A., 193, 202
Bach, D., 84
Bahl, A. N., 196
Bahme, R. B., 97
Bailey, C. H., 37, 52, 74, 75, 76, 77, 78, 160, 171, 203
Bailey, W. M., 68

Bakke, A. L., 75
Balcazar, M. R., 200
Baldwin, H. I., 132, 133
Ball, C. D., 50
Balls, A. K., 187, 199
Bamann, E., 192, 197
Barton, A. W., 67
Barton, L. V., 59, 68, 79, 82, 88, 90, 91, 102, 103, 104, 105, 114, 118, 119, 120, 124, 125, 132, 134, 141, 142, 143, 146, 147, 148, 150
Barton-Wright, E. C., 52, 53
Bates, E. N., 235
Baylis, G. T. S., 239, 240, 243
Bayliss, W. M., 184
Beadle, G. W., 34, 185
Beaumont, J. H., 76, 77
Beckford, O. C., 188
Becquerel, P., 109, 140
Beecher, F. S., 245
Bell, G. D. H., 208, 209, 211, 213
Benecke, W., 33
Benedict, H. M., 20, 108, 119
Bennett, N., 137
Berezova, E., 248
Berger, J., 51, 52, 54
Bergmann, M., 191, 194
Berkeley, G. H., 233
Bernard, M. N., 96
Bernton, H. S., 41
Bertagni, P., 53
Bethke, R. M., 56
Beumer, H., 50
Bevilotti, V., 110
Bhargava, P. N., 49
Bibbey, R. O., 143
Bigé, 50
Binkley, A. M., 247
Bird, J. N., 8
Bishop, J. C., 57
Blakeslee, A. F., 12, 216, 221, 222, 223, 229
Block, K., 160
Block, R. J., 35
Blue, W. G., 41
Bodnar, G. P., 235
Bolas, B. D., 206
Bolling, D., 35
Bolsunov, I., 66
Bond, L., 105
Bonner, D., 34, 185, 219
Bonner, J., 51, 219

Bonnet, R., 183
Bonnier, G., 81, 179, 180, 181
Borchers, R., 193
Borodina, I. N., 10
Botha, P. J., 97
Bottelier, H. P., 192
Bournot, K., 198
Bowman, D. E., 187
Boyles, B. B., 9
Bradley, A., 203
Braun, H., 67, 238
Brett, C. C., 231, 243
Brewbaker, H. E., 11
Briggs, H. M., 35
Brink, R. A., 1, 2, 8, 18, 19, 33, 218, 222, 224
Brittingham, W. H., 15
Brooks, A. N., 249
Broome, F. K., 57
Brown, A. H., 83
Brown, A. J., 63
Brown, C. E., 203
Brown, E., 115, 118
Brown, E. O., 88
Brown, J. W., 79, 82, 103, 165, 178
Brown, R., 38, 63, 73, 97, 98, 174, 175, 218
Bruman, A. J., 204, 212
Brun, J., 106
Brunner, G., 166
Buchinger, A., 64
Buchner, E., 184
Buckner, G. D., 219
Bukharina, E. V., 202
Bundel, A. A., 56, 202, 246
Bunting, R. H., 234
Burchfield, H. P., 243
Burgeff, H., 166
Burgess, C. H., 120
Burke, T. W. L., 65
Burkholder, P. R., 52, 53, 167, 219
Burlison, W. L., 100
Burton, G. W., 10, 11
Busse, W. F., 109, 124
Bytschikhina, E. A., 120

Caffrey, M., 204
Cailleau, R., 53
Cajlachjan, M. C., 207
Caldecott, R. S., 108
Calder, R. A., 6
Caldwell, M. L., 187
Calvert, E. L., 235
Calvery, H. O., 190